# PSYCHOTHERAPY RESEARCH

## Methodological and Efficacy Issues

## APA Commission on Psychotherapies

## MEMBERS AND CONTRIBUTORS

# Preface

The Commission has attempted to evaluate controlled research dealing with the issue of effectiveness of psychotherapy. The final report represents the work of many individuals with different biases, attenuated by open and scholarly interactions. While the report does not solve the many difficulties inherent in evaluating the efficacy of psychotherapy, it may enable the reader to experience the dilemmas associated with the task. This is the rationale for presenting a lengthy, detailed discussion of methodological issues.

One very important problem is that reported research often is not fully representative of the current state of clinical practice. Therefore, we have tried to place the conclusions derived from the research data within the context of contemporary clinical experience.

Toksoz B. Karasu, M.D.

# Introduction

For many decades psychotherapy was practiced without any systematic attempt to justify it as an effective form of treatment for mental and emotional problems. Among psychotherapists there was the general belief that what they were doing was usually effective, and support for this belief was provided predominantly through reports of individual cases. Occasional doubts concerning efficacy often led to the emergence of "new" psychotherapies, which in turn were justified by anecdotal reports in the literature.

This unquestioning acceptance of psychotherapy as an effective treatment modality was challenged in the early 1950s by Eysenck. His evaluation of the limited data available at that time led him to the conclusion that outcomes resulting from this form of therapy were no better than could be expected by providing no treatment at all. Since that time, the issue of the effectiveness of psychotherapy has been examined with increasing sophistication. Numerous reviews of the literature using box-score methodologies and meta-analyses have not, however, fully resolved the question of efficacy. Nevertheless, the researcher has been increasingly pressured by demands from local, state, and federal governmental agencies to provide evidence of the efficacy and safety of mental health care practices for the purpose of determining their eligibility for public funding.

The present report examines the issue of the effectiveness of psychotherapy from a methodological and historical perspective on the basis of controlled studies. Its findings reveal that psychotherapy appears efficacious more often than not, but that the conditions under which it works are not well understood. Even with the greater sophistication of research techniques and designs, there is still some discrepancy between clinical practice and beliefs and what has been demonstrated in controlled studies. Greater progress in therapeutic effectiveness may have been made than has been documented. This report emphasizes the need for creative new approaches to the problem of evaluating the effectiveness of psychotherapy.

We are particularly grateful to Melvin Sabshin, M.D., for his encouragement and support. As Medical Director of the APA, his continued commitment to intellectual progress in this field made an indelible mark on this report.

We would also like to extend our appreciation to Marie Ascoli, Marie Barbetta, Louise Notarangelo, and Rita Segarra for their careful preparation of the manuscript. In addition, we would like to thank Katherine Wild for her meticulous proof-reading of the report in all its various stages, and David Andrews for his editorial contribution.

# Contents

# List of Tables

# CHAPTER 1

# Problems of Definition and Description

Is psychotherapy effective? In 1969 Strupp and Bergin proposed replacing this traditional question with the more scientific "What specific therapeutic interventions produce changes in specific patients under specific conditions?" (p. 20). But in order to provide even approximate answers to this latter question, precise definitions and descriptions, of all the various elements that enter into psychotherapy, are necessary. Therapy outcomes depend on the characteristics of both patients and their therapists as well as on the characteristics of the treatments these therapists provide. The following section addresses the issues involved in providing such adequate definitions and descriptions.

## Populations

A critical issue encountered in research on psychotherapy concerns an adequate description of the population selected for investigation. Patients coming to psychotherapy, far from being relatively homogeneous, are quite heterogeneous on almost every measure one could devise (Kiesler 1966). They differ on a whole host of dimensions, including intelligence, age, and the nature, duration, and severity of their problems, as well as their degree of motivation for therapy. And these differences make them differentially receptive to different forms of therapy (Strupp and Bergin 1969).

It has been argued by some (Kazdin and Wilson 1978, Marks 1969) that, in carrying out research, homogeneity of patient samples is desirable, for several reasons. First, little is gained by subjecting a diverse group of patients (representing a mixture of syndromes) to a treatment when only some may be expected to respond to it. In fact, patients not responding might very well mask an effect on the one syndrome that is improving. Once a given form of treatment and the type(s) of patient(s) likely to respond to it are relatively well established, outcome study results are less ambiguous and more clearly interpretable if patient samples are selected that are relatively homogeneous (Fiske et al. 1970, Horowitz 1976). This strategy

1

is most likely to lead to studies demonstrating differentiated successful treatment (Bordin 1974).

A second reason for choosing an explicitly defined, relatively homogeneous sample is that meaningful comparisons may then be made across studies (Paul 1967). Also, generalizations to other samples will be relatively unambiguous (Klein et al. 1980).

In assembling a homogeneous sample of patients, particularly if the disorder being considered is uncommon, one important difficulty may arise: In any one setting only a few patients may be suitable for the sample. In practice this means that, because the process of selecting patients could be quite lengthy, collaborating with other investigators might be the best strategy.

However, in some situations using homogeneous samples might not be so advantageous. For a relatively new, untried treatment, psychosocial or psychopharmacological, a random sample of patients (with a wide range of symptoms) might better highlight the treatment's efficacy. Conceivably, patients representing several different disorders might all respond to a new type of treatment. This finding would be masked if the treated group was homogeneous in their psychopathology. Moreover, the sample's homogeneity would limit generalizations to other groups. Meltzoff and Kornreich 1970 express this point very well:

> Homogeneity can be expected to reduce error variance at the expense of generality. For example, the sample can consist of only employed, middle-class, college educated, male-obsessive-compulsives aged thirty to thirty-five seen for fifty-minute sessions twice a week by male, psychoanalytically oriented therapists with at least ten years of experience. This automatically takes care of eleven variables and tells us with whom we are dealing, but it limits generalizations that can be made to the populations of patients and therapists from which the samples were drawn [pp. 26–27].

These authors believe that if effects of psychotherapy are not general and strong enough to cut across patient, therapist, and technique lines, then no general claims should be made about efficacy.

This contention does not negate the fact that recent years have brought an increasing interest in detailed specification of the characteristics of not only the patients, but of therapists and treatment conditions as well (Bergin and Strupp 1972, Kazdin and Wilson 1978). But until recently no standard reference measures existed that could be used to define a given clinical group (Garfield 1978b), and the utility of diagnostic schemes used in the past has been very limited for research (Frank 1966, Strupp 1978). This is because clinical diagnoses are often based on vague, overlapping criteria that place a patient's diagnostic label in doubt (Frank 1966).

In 1972, Feigner et al. sought to remedy this situation by providing diagnostic criteria for fourteen psychiatric illnesses. This approach aimed to provide a framework for comparing data gathered in different centers and to promote communication among investigators. These criteria, modified and expanded expressly for research purposes by Spitzer, Endicott, and Robins (1978), became the Research Diagnostic Criteria (RDC). Their design enabled research investigators to apply a consistent and standardized set of criteria for the description or selection of relatively homogeneous samples of subjects with functional psychiatric illnesses. Many of the terms and criteria found in RDC have become incorporated in *DSM-III*, the revised nomenclature of the American Psychiatric Association.

Even with standardized diagnostic schemas, though, having two or more clinicians diagnose the disorder is clearly desirable; at least until such time as it has been demonstrated that there is a high degree of agreement among these clinicians. Also, although researchers are fundamentally in agreement that the criteria provided by *DSM-III* represent an improvement over previous idiosyncratic schemas, it is desirable to employ multiple measures relating to diagnostic issues, particularly in studies in which diagnosis is a significant variable. Diagnosis could, for example, be augmented by additional criteria based on scores obtained in standardized rating scales; that is, those measuring symptoms or personality traits (Garfield 1978b).

We are still clearly in need of better methods of assessing the totality of a patient's functioning in terms of both strengths and weaknesses (Strupp 1978). One recent attempt to develop measures of strengths as well as of dynamic factors is made in the report on Sequential Diagnostic Evaluation by Plutchik et al. This report included scales for measuring ego strength, ego function, ego defenses, and coping styles. Another illustration of this issue may be found in the paper by Karasu and Skodol (1980). They demonstrated that three patients who had the same *DSM-III* diagnosis differed markedly on various psychodynamic variables such as conflicts and ego functioning.

## Therapists

Another research concern is the appropriate definition or description of the therapist. This is important since the individual differences found in patient populations also exist among therapists. Like patients, therapists differ on a multitude of dimensions including age, sex, cultural experience, psychological sophistication, and social values (Strupp 1978). They also differ among themselves on such factors as professional discipline, training, professional experience, belief in the efficacy of treatment, personal therapy, interests, and personality (Fiske et al. 1970, Meltzoff and Kornreich 1970, Sundland 1977).

It is difficult to understand, at least since Kiesler (1966) presumably laid to rest the "therapist uniformity assumption," how therapists can be considered interchangeable units. Yet it is the rare study that even provides information on the competence of the therapists (Luborsky et al. 1975) or that defines the therapist sample in any greater detail than "experienced," "senior clinician," or "inexperienced" therapist. As May (1974) pointed out, even the definition of experience may be a good deal more complex than it first appears. "Counting patients previously treated or hours of patient contact will not satisfy those who insist on a judgment of skill. But how reliable and valid are judgments of skill? . . . Skill in doing what?" (p. 129).

Although therapist and therapy variables cannot be completely separated since the personality, training, and experience of a therapist pervades any technique he or she may choose to use (Frank 1966), clearly the identification and control of therapist variables will reduce ambiguity of results and facilitate replication of findings. Unfortunately, in spite of the early efforts of investigators such as Parloff (1956), Holt and Luborsky (1958), and Whitehorn and Betz (1954, 1957, 1960) and later research by Parloff, Waskow, and Wolfe (1978), it is still not clear what therapist variable or combination of variables affects outcome of treatment. Parloff et al. (1978) suggest that this state of affairs may be due in part to the selection for study of overly simplistic global therapist variables such as personality, mental health, and experience. However, as Razin's (1977) comprehensive review of research on the *A–B* variable indicates, even exhaustive investigation of this single, clearly defined variable provides little support for any correlation between it and the outcome of therapy. Briefly, what Razin (1977) concluded is that there is a consistent constellation of personality differences between *A* therapists (those most successful with schizophrenia) and *B* therapists (those least successful with patients given this diagnosis). However, while these differences are replicable and possibly valuable for theory and research in personality, *"the* A–B *variable is not a powerful predictor of any important process or outcome parameters in real, ongoing therapy"* (Razin 1977, p. 320).

It is evident, therefore, that it is difficult to isolate relevant therapist variables and to determine their impact. Specified therapist variables are always in danger of being confounded with other uncontrolled variables, with unspecified patient characteristics, and with the therapist's idiosyncratic interpretation of treatment techniques (Parloff et al. 1978). Nevertheless, it is still incumbent upon any researcher in the area of psychotherapy to specify with the greatest accuracy the characteristics of his or her sample of therapists. Only then will it be possible to accurately identify the role of therapist variables in influencing the outcome of psychotherapy.

## Therapy

As pointed out previously, it is difficult to separate the treatment from the psychotherapist who provides the treatment. There is an obvious interaction between the two (Fiske et al. 1970, Frank 1966, Strupp 1978). Nevertheless, in any study of psychotherapeutic effectiveness, it is essential that an attempt be made to describe comprehensively the psychotherapeutic methods to which therapeutic changes are being attributed (Fiske et al. 1970, Strupp 1973, Strupp 1978, Strupp and Bergin 1969).

Bergin (1967) has reported that it has been conservatively estimated that there are at least thirty-six identifiable systems of therapy. Parloff (cited in Karasu 1977) has listed by name more than 140 presumed forms of currently practiced psychotherapy. Garfield (1978) estimates that over 100 types of psychotherapy exist. Other investigators prefer to focus on the common factors in therapies (Frank 1974, Garfield 1974, Marmor 1974, Masserman 1978). However, there can be little doubt that psychotherapy as currently practiced does not refer to a uniform, homogeneous process (Kiesler 1966, Strupp 1978). Further, although it might seem to be belaboring the issue, general categories of therapy such as behavior therapy and dynamic psychotherapy obviously include different techniques. Yet these global entities have been compared empirically (Sloane et al. 1975) and in reviews of outcome (Luborsky et al. 1975) as if one could make a general conclusion about "behavior therapy" or "psychotherapy" per se.

Another facet of the "therapy uniformity myth" (Kiesler 1966) concerns the fact that there is no uniformity in routine treatment even within a given treatment center. Routine treatment varies from setting to setting and from one investigation to another. Therefore, in order to properly evaluate the outcome of comparative research, detailed information must be provided on the specific techniques employed and the length of time they operate (Kazdin and Wilson 1978).

One of the major difficulties in psychotherapy research is, therefore, that of adequately specifying and describing what actually occurs during treatment. However, relying on the therapist's description of his or her treatment without further documentation does not provide sufficient definition of the treatment factor. When established treatment procedures are being considered, this problem becomes even more complex, because most experienced psychotherapists have developed their techniques in more or less idiosyncratic ways (Paul 1976). In addition, therapists who are part of a strong theoretical tradition develop ways of discussing their therapeutic efforts that may not directly translate what they actually do in their therapeutic encounters (Bordin 1974).

Several factors enter into an adequate definition of the treatment variable. Fiske et al. (1970) have enumerated some of the more general components. For example, a complete description would include the theory underlying the treatment, the rationale for its presumed effects, and how it differs from other theories. Recognizing that this ideal statement probably cannot be realized in most instances, Fiske et al. still maintain that an attempt should be made to portray the therapy in its ideal form and then to indicate to what extent this ideal was approximated; that is, describe the treatment as it actually was. The goals of treatment (for example, symptom resolution or personality reconstruction) as well as the methods used to achieve these goals should be specified, as should the components of the treatment process. Examples of such components needing

specification might be transference, interpretations, therapeutic alliance, working through, imagery, homework assignments, and so on.

As pointed out previously, however, the therapist's description of therapy is insufficient by itself. The description must be
supplemented by other specifications. These specifications are
necessary so that it can be determined whether or not a technique has been properly conducted. For example, supervisors'
reports may be included to correct for biases in the therapists'
observations, but supervisors themselves may be subject to
theory-dictated observational biases. Independent observers
may provide descriptions based on audio- or videotapes of
selected therapy sessions or portions of sessions. However, the
problem of defining treatment still is not completely solved
inasmuch as, even with videotaping, only a relatively limited
aspect of the therapist's behavior is selected for observation
(Bordin 1974). In addition, the process of analyzing tapes is
time consuming and costly. Nevertheless, these independent
observations are indispensable to an adequate definition of the
actual therapeutic process. Other aspects of treatment that
should be specified include total calendar time, number and
duration of sessions, fees charged, and the orientation of the
therapist (Fiske et al. 1970).

These, then, represent some of the basic requirements for an
adequate description of the treatment variable. Without detailed and precise specifications of the treatment components,
this criterion cannot be met (Kazdin and Wilson 1978).

# CHAPTER 2

# Nature of Control Groups

Once the population under investigation has been defined, it is then necessary to specify what control or comparison groups are appropriate and how the total sample is to be drawn. During the time period represented by a psychotherapeutic intervention, patients are experiencing many other influences, and any change may be due to any or all these influences. Studies purporting to demonstrate that a particular treatment has produced changes must permit the inference that, had the treatment not been introduced, the observed changes would not have taken place. This means that *controls must be introduced to rule out plausible alternative hypotheses.* For example, an investigator might find that a group of depressed patients that have participated in a course of short-term psychotherapy shows a significant reduction in their symptomatology. Without a control group, however, the investigator cannot rule out that such alternative factors as spontaneous remission or merely the passage of time are responsible for the improvement rather than the psychotherapy.

It should be stated at the outset that there is no single control group that would be appropriate for the testing of all hypotheses. There are a number of options, and selection should be based on the advantages and limitations of each, on the particular question to which the research is directed, and on the feasibility of the use of the various types of controls in a given research setting (Meltzoff and Kornreich 1970).

## Untreated Controls

The most straightforward strategy for controlling for extraneous factors that could account for experimental findings is to use an untreated control group. Methodologically, a group receiving no treatment serves to control for factors likely to jeopardize internal validity, such as history, maturation, the effects of repeated testing, and statistical regression (Campbell and Stanley 1963).

In actual fact, however, the term *untreated controls* is probably a misnomer, particularly in psychotherapy research (Frank 1966, Imber et al. 1966). This is because of the serious ethical and practical obstacles that would be encountered were an attempt made to utilize a genuine "untreated" control group. For example, if patients selected for the untreated group were truly comparable to those in the experimental group in terms of symptomatology and diagnosis, could a conscientious investigator refuse them treatment? Also, on the practical side, it is difficult to conceive of many patients in enough discomfort to have sought treatment not looking elsewhere if they are refused therapy in one setting.

It thus seems evident that a true no-treatment control group is virtually impossible to set up and maintain, except possibly in a carefully restricted institutional setting. With a "captive" hospitalized population the problem of retaining no-treatment patients in a study is less crucial. However, a group of non-hospitalized patients who seek treatment and do not receive it because of an experimental design is likely to seek treatment elsewhere and thereby suffer significant attrition (Bergin 1971, Endicott 1971, Fiske et al. 1970, Gottman and Markman 1978, Strupp and Bergin 1969). A further complication is that this attrition may render the remaining patients a highly select group (Kazdin and Wilson 1978).

As a way of dealing with independent help-seeking among the untreated patients, Strupp and Bergin (1969) propose a sampling in both the treated patients and the controls of those events occurring outside the treatment situation that could presumably be called therapeutic. This strategy illustrates the principle that if you cannot control or manipulate a variable considered relevant, then it is advisable to measure it (Plutchik 1968). Endicott (1969) has pointed out, however, that while this procedure has much to recommend it, implementing the procedure and interpreting the results would both be extremely difficult.

## Dropout or Waiting-List Controls

Another way of circumventing the problems posed by attempts to use no-treatment controls that has been proposed by a number of investigators is the somewhat modified procedure of utilizing "dropout" patients or "waiting-list" patients. Actually, however, these are not particularly adequate controls.

Dropouts, sometimes called *terminator controls,* are defined as those individuals who requested treatment, but who, for one reason or another, did not keep any appointment or terminated very early during treatment, usually without the approval of the therapist (Imber et al. 1966). While they may be considered an essentially untreated group, a group composed of dropouts has serious disadvantages. Not only do they drop out of treatment for different reasons and at different times, but they are also different kinds of people with potentially different eventual outcomes (Baekeland and Lundwall 1975). The flaw involved in using these patients as controls lies in the fact that some unknown selection factor is operative in their termination and that, therefore, they represent a self-selected sample whose motivation for help is obviously different from patients accepting and receiving treatment (Gottman and Markman 1978, Imber et al. 1966, Meltzoff and Kornreich 1970). Furthermore, this solution does not deal with the randomization issue.

Waiting-list controls have several advantages over those previously discussed. First, because most treatment centers are unable to offer therapy immediately, except possibly to acute cases, a waiting list is a natural aspect of their operation. Therefore, the investigator has the advantage of a naturally formed control group of patients, presumably not different from those currently in treatment. Second, because they have been guaranteed therapy, they are less likely to seek help elsewhere, particularly if therapy has been scheduled for a specific time in the future (Gottman and Markman 1978). Third, while using a waiting-list control group does not control for expectancy effects (that is, patients' expectations that the treatment will help them), it does provide crucial information regarding the natural history of the disorder. Such a control group is, therefore, particularly useful in the early stages of research with most clinical problems (O'Leary and Borkovec 1978).

There are, however, some problems and disadvantages with waiting-list controls that must be weighed against advantages. For example, the investigator must make certain that these patients represent an unbiased sample; that is, that they have been assigned in a systematic manner. In addition, the waiting list should be reduced systematically; that is, patients must not be differentially assigned from the list to a particular therapist or to a particular kind of treatment, nor should interesting cases be given priority in assignment (Imber et al. 1966).

A second problem with this type of control group is that, prior to being placed on the waiting list, patients are customarily screened via intake interviews and, in addition, receive psychological assessment. While this may not constitute formal psychotherapy, it is possible for patients to view these interviews as helpful for their problems, particularly if they have been given some reassurance and support (Meltzoff and Korn-reich 1970).

A third problem relates to the fact that waiting-list controls permit a comparison of treatment with no treatment for only the period during which treatment is provided (Sloane et al. 1975). No long-term comparisons between treatment and no treatment are possible because the waiting-list group eventually receives treatment. Therefore, a waiting-list control group does not completely solve the problem. Quite possibly, the control group could improve over time and/or the effects of treatment could be attenuated so that, in the long run, the two groups might not prove to be different (Kazdin and Wilson 1978).

## Attention/Placebo Controls

Another type of control group, which has been used both in drug studies and studies of psychotherapy, and one that some investigators believe may be necessary (Bergin 1971, Strupp and Bergin 1969), has been called an *attention* or *placebo group*. The term *attention* is usually used when the intervention is nonpharmacological in nature, whereas the term *placebo* is generally reserved for drug studies. Whichever it is called, this type of group serves to control for such factors as the frequency of contacts and other nonspecific factors such as expectation of improvement by the patient and faith in the value of the treatment he or she is receiving (Hampton 1973, Kazdin and Wilson 1978). Patients see a "therapist" as frequently as the group receiving treatment, but the content of their sessions is not designed to be therapeutic. At least, these sessions should be neutral in nature.

The disadvantage in the use of attention/placebo controls, of course, lies in our supposed knowledge of what is therapeutic. These patients believe they are being treated, and there is a good deal of evidence that the physical and emotional status of patients in placebo groups can change significantly (Bergin 1971, Imber et al. 1966, Rosenthall and Frank 1956). It is questionable, therefore, that these patients are receiving "no treatment."

An additional difficulty with the use of attention/placebo controls that has been discussed by O'Leary and Borkovec (1978) is that treatment and control conditions may be differentially credible to patients and therapists alike and thus generate different expectations of improvement. Kazdin and

Wilson (1978) cite a number of studies in which this was found to be the case. Whether this is a problem for a given study depends largely on the conclusions the investigator wants to draw. If his or her only interest is to show that one treatment or technique is more effective than another or no treatment, then differential credibility poses no problems. In contrast, if the investigator wishes to demonstrate why one treatment is more efficacious than another, differential credibility must be ruled out as a rival hypothesis (Kazdin and Wilcoxon 1976, Kazdin and Wilson 1978).

Endicott (1969) gives a cogent description of the difficulties that can arise with the use of attention controls. Assuming that they are seen for the same amount of time as the treatment cases, he asks:

> What does one do with the patient for 45–50 minutes once or twice a week after the initial history is obtained? Won't the patient's expectancies be disappointed if the "therapist" continues to inquire about the history hour after hour, or if he insists on talking about neutral topics? What if the patient asks for advice or begins to unburden himself emotionally to the "therapist"? Will the "therapist" change the subject? If so, how will this be evaluated? If a decision is made not to control for the quantity (i.e. duration) of the attention, and this appears to be the only practical solution, there are still a host of difficulties to be considered. "Attention" is not a unidimensional variable but may include every type of interaction of which human beings are capable, except various forms of inattention. Decisions would have to be made regarding which aspects of attention would be evaluated. For example, would attention include sympathetic or empathetic responses or would the attention-giver attempt to respond to the patient in a neutral manner? If empathy is allowed, the attention becomes "therapy" according to Rogerian definitions. On the other hand, it could be seriously argued that maintaining a neutral attitude over an extended period with a person seeking help would have an anti-therapeutic effect on many patients [p.120].

Somewhat different difficulties arise where a placebo is used in drug studies. For example, although every effort may be made to keep patients and clinicians blind as to who is receiving the inert substance and who is receiving the active drug, the occurrence of side effects may make it possible to distinguish between the two groups. In addition, a group of patients who are not improving and who are receiving a treatment that is actually inert may suffer significant attrition (Kazdin and Wilson 1978).

What may be concluded from this discussion of attention/placebo control groups? Perhaps it is more expedient to conduct comparative studies utilizing differing forms of therapy, all of which are believed to have some effectiveness, rather than to assume we know with any degree of precision what is therapeutic and what is not.

## Alternative Treatment Controls

Therefore, as another approach to the control problem, alternative treatment groups, with or without a "treatment-as-usual" condition, can be used. If, for example, the question is whether a new therapeutic approach is better than an old one, then the old one is the appropriate control (Meltzoff and Kornreich 1970).

A drug-treatment group is also a practical control group with which to compare the effects of psychotherapy. Combined with standardized instructions regarding the therapist's attitude and behavior, psychotropic medication is of established value in the symptomatic treatment of a variety of psychological disorders. In addition, it has the advantage of being a relatively inexpensive and easily replicable form of therapy (Endicott 1969).

A slightly different way of using alternative treatment groups that is particularly appropriate for relatively long-term studies of the effects of psychotherapy is to offer the control groups a form of psychotherapy that differs in an essential ingredient from that received by the experimental group (Frank 1966, Gottman and Markman 1978, Imber et al. 1966).

This design requires that the investigator make a precise statement of his or her hypotheses relative to the presence or absence of an assumed significant ingredient of treatment and the consequent change in patients. Thus testable predictions can be made concerning changes in patients as a function of some specific element or technique. Both experimental and control groups are used but, to the extent possible, neither patients nor therapists are aware of the hypothesis concerning the "active ingredient" being tested.

In the Imber et al. (1966) study, the hypothesis tested was that the patient having fewer and briefer sessions of psychotherapy (what Weissman [1979] would call "low contact") would show significantly less improvement than would patients receiving more and longer sessions over the same period. As another example, suppose an investigator were able to list all the major ingredients of a therapy program. Also suppose that he or she believed that of the 13 ingredients, ingredients 8 and 9 were the active ingredients of the therapy. The experimental group would then receive the full therapy, while the comparison group would receive all the other 13 ingredients, with ingredients 8 and 9 omitted (Gottman and Markman 1978). A major problem with this approach is that it assumes that the researcher has adequate knowledge of the probabilities that the ingredients of the treatment considered active are, in fact, therapeutically significant.

One additional and innovative type of alternative treatment control is the "PRN contact" group used by the Boston–New Haven collaborative depression study and briefly described by Weissman (1979). Treatment for patients in this group is provided only at the patient's request and not at a regularly scheduled time. This type of control group probably falls somewhere between a waiting-list group and a regularly scheduled low-contact group in terms of therapeutic interaction.

## Crossover Controls

Another type of control group is implicit in the use of a crossover design. With this method, for a given period of time one group serves as the control while the other serves as the active treatment group. At the end of this period, the roles of the two groups are reversed. At the end of the course of treatment for the group that previously served as the control group, a comparison is made between the treatment and control conditions. There are basically two drawbacks to this method of obtaining a control group. First, it is possible that the group that first receives treatment improves sufficiently so that it can no longer provide an adequate control once treatment is discontinued. Second, it is possible (though not likely) that patients in the initial control group could improve spontaneously to the point that, when they are finally given treatment, there is no room for further improvement.

## Patients-as-Own-Controls

One way to circumvent the problem of obtaining an equivalent sample of patients for a control group is to use the experimental patients as their own controls. With "own-controls" designs, changes in a patient's behavior during a waiting period are compared with changes in that same patient after treatment. However, while having the advantage of requiring a smaller total sample, this approach has at least two serious drawbacks. One is that the pretreatment waiting period is almost invariably shorter than the treatment period itself, and this lack of temporal equivalence reduces the validity of comparisons (Imber et al. 1966, Paul 1976).

A second drawback to this type of control group is that, for the design to be valid, one of two conditions must be met. Either the investigator must have comparative data on the natural history of the disorder, gathered from a large number of patients, or obtain a long period of baseline data. Only if it can be shown that behavior remains relatively stable over time and then changes rather abruptly when treatment is introduced can we be fairly certain that the intervention is responsible. This type of design has also been called a time-series experiment and is one of the quasi-experimental designs described by Campbell and Stanley (1963).

## Summary

A number of possible types of control groups have been discussed. But which is the best? The answer is that there is no single group that would be appropriate for the testing of all hypotheses. Control groups are essentially points of reference that depend largely on the purpose of the investigators (Plutchik 1973). Therefore, the best type in any given situation will be determined by both theoretical and empirical considerations. And if more than one plausible hypothesis is being tested, it is advisable to use more than one type of control group.

# CHAPTER 3

# Issues in Selection and Assignment of Patients to Groups

Let us assume that the population to be investigated has been decided upon and the type of control group or groups to be used has been established. One important issue that still remains is *how* to assign patients to the groups.

## Random Assignment

One of the most frequently used methods is random assignment. Basically, this means that patients are assigned to treatment and control groups on the basis of a method that prevents bias, such as through the use of a table of random numbers. This method of assignment assumes that *in the long run* all significant variables will be equally distributed among the groups so that any differences found at the end of the study can be attributed, within statistically definable probability limits, to treatment effects rather than to extraneous patient variables. This is a very good method so long as a sufficiently large pool of patients is available. For greater assurance that randomization has been achieved, the comparability of the groups can be checked by statistical procedures applied to the variables, such as age, sex, education, and so on, considered to be of greatest interest to the investigator (Frank 1966, Luborsky et al. 1975).

## Stratified Random Assignment

A second possible way to obtain comparable groups, particularly if the investigator has information in advance that certain characteristics of the sample such as sex or age are relevant to therapy outcome, is stratified random sampling. For example, it might be important to have an equal percent of males and females or an equal percent of individuals in certain age or socioeconomic groups. Therefore, patients are assigned randomly, but within the constrictions imposed by the variables on which you propose to stratify. The advantage of this method is that it is possible to work with smaller samples than would be necessary in the case of simple random sampling and still be assured that your samples are representative of the population, with respect to the stratified variables at least.

Frank (1966), however, points out a difficulty with this method, particularly as applied to patients in outpatient settings. Ordinarily one cannot wait for a sufficient population of patients to accumulate before starting treatment. Therefore, one must either extend the project over time or draw on the populations of several clinics. Both of these procedures present problems that potentially exist whenever an investigator requires large numbers of subjects. Extending the project over time can lead to attrition of subjects and/or research and clinical personnel as well as to financial problems. The utilization of more than one setting for the project is apt to increase the variability of the patient samples and thus lead to an increase in the number of variables on which stratification is necessary. This, in turn, is likely to counteract the gain sought by increasing the size of the sample in the first place.

## Cluster Sampling

Random assignment is, however, not always feasible. This would be the case, for example, when the investigator has no control of the distribution of his or her subjects. Under these conditions, cluster sampling is a third technique that is frequently used. It is based on the selection and comparison of groups of subjects that already exist. These could include, for example: patients on two separate wards, residents of several nursing homes, or individuals attending different senior citizen centers. When such cluster sampling is done, we assume that the members of the different groups to be compared are essentially equal initially on whatever is to be measured, such as symptoms, social isolation, distress, or medical condition. One of the groups is then arbitrarily designated as the experimental group to which the intervention is applied. The other is arbitrarily called the control group and no unusual treatments are given it. At the end of a designated period, the patients in each group are compared on the measure of interest.

This cluster sampling method is convenient and relatively easy to apply, particularly with a hospitalized or resident population, but does not, however, assure equivalence of groups. It assumes that the different intact groups that are compared are initially alike and that the "normal" procedures used at each clinic or center are essentially equivalent. These assumptions are reasonable, but often must be assessed independently.

## Matched Pairs

A fourth way to select individuals for groups, and one that Luborsky et al. (1975) consider the most powerful way of assigning patients, is matching in pairs, particularly if one member of each pair is randomized to each treatment. This method involves matching control and treatment populations, patient by patient, on certain variables believed to be relevant—such as age, sex, race, education, and family income. However, "Since each additional matching variable greatly increases the size of the population that must be screened, this approach is hopelessly impractical in outpatient studies" (Frank 1975, p. 82). Furthermore, because many potential subjects will not meet the matching criteria, such matching requires discarding a sizable percent of the total population, thereby endangering the representativeness of the samples.

## Matched Groups

A variation on this procedure of matched pairs is to assign individuals to groups in such a way as to ensure that group means for the variables in question will not be significantly different. This version of the matching procedure still presents formidable real-life difficulties. May (1974) emphasizes just how frustrating an experience matching can be as he describes the difficulties Rogers and his colleagues (1967) experienced in trying to match on six variables. In addition, May quotes the investigators on this project as stating "The matchings, though they fitted our definitions, were not always qualitatively as close or as satisfactory as we would have liked" (Rogers et al. 1967, p. 46).

Another drawback of this method is that when patients are matched on number of supposedly relevant variables, they may, in fact be mismatched on variables of equal or even greater importance. An hypothetical example of how such mismatching could lead to erroneous conclusions would be the following. Assume that an investigator wishes to assess the effects of brief psychotherapy on a group of hospitalized manic-depressive, depressed patients and on a group of schizophrenic patients. The groups are matched on sex and age. Results indicate that schizophrenics showed a significantly poorer response to the therapy than did the depressed patients. However, this finding may not be due to diagnosis per se, but may be more related to the fact that matching patients on age may mismatch them on the history of previous psychiatric hospitalizations. This could happen because schizophrenics tend to become hospitalized at an earlier age than do manic depressives. Therefore, matching on age may inadvertently compare more chronic schizophrenics with less chronic depressives, and chronicity of illness may be the crucial variable in response to this form of therapy.

Another example of how mismatching can lead to an erroneous conclusion is presented by Frank (1966). He cites that discovery that the reason the serum of schizophrenics oxidized adrenaline more rapidly than the serum of matched non-hospitalized controls was not due to schizophrenia per se, but rather to the fact that the hospitalized patients were fed a diet deficient in vitamin C (Angel et al. 1957). This unsuspected but crucial difference in situational variables totally invalidated the careful matching of patient variables in the experimental and control groups.

This section has summarized five general ways of selecting control groups: random sampling, stratified random sampling, cluster sampling, matching of pairs of subjects, and matching of group means. All these methods are based on the assumption that if the treatment and control groups are matched on relevant variables, or if these variables are randomly distributed among the groups, then all other potentially relevant variables that might account for differences among the groups would be similarly distributed. It has been shown, however, as in the study involving schizophrenic patients deficient in vitamin C, that this is not necessarily the case. As aptly put by Frank, "Often one cannot control for a variable until one thinks of it. The automatic use of controls is no substitute for thought" (1966, p. 93).

For this reason, probably the best method of attaining equivalent groups is through the use of randomization techniques, with or without the use of matching or stratification. In contrast to the haphazard process suggested by the term "randomization," this method of selecting subjects is actually a very systematic procedure that prevents the investigator from exercising direct control over the assignment of subjects and, thereby, eliminates any bias that he or she may consciously or unconsciously contribute (May 1974).

# CHAPTER 4

# Research Designs for Psychotherapy Evaluation

## Conceptual Problems

Research designs for investigating the effectiveness of a particular mode of psychotherapy or for studying the comparative efficacy of two or more therapeutic modalities cannot be classified into simple types, since they may be characterized along a great many dimensions. For example, Campbell and Stanley (1963) discuss the pretest/posttest control group design, factorial designs, and the equivalent time-samples design, among others. Meltzoff and Kornreich (1970) describe empirical, inductive, and hypothetico-deductive studies and univariate and multivariate designs as well as prospective and ex post facto studies. Fiske et al. (1970) state that there are basically two types of approaches: experimental and correlational. Horowitz (1981) describes three types of research paradigms: the contrast group design, the relational paradigm (correlational), and the descriptive approach. Plutchik (1968) describes random and matched groups designs, counterbalanced designs, and bivalent, multivalent, and parametric experiments. Kazdin and Wilson (1978) present a large number of treatment evaluation strategies, among which are constructive and dismantling strategies and comparative and process strategies. It is evident, therefore, that a number of different descriptive terms have been used to categorize the various approaches to the evaluation enterprise.

These different terms reflect the fact that research designs may be described in terms of levels of inference permitted, time period under consideration, type of sampling procedures used, number of variables considered, number of levels of each variable, and type of strategy employed. Therefore, the research design itself could be considered a variable that determines the level of inference of the results and their generality. As the design permits increasing control over possibly irrelevant or confounding variables, the number of alternative explanations to account for observed changes is reduced. While the researcher can never prove unequivocally that a particular therapeutic effort caused a particular outcome (Cronbach 1978, Gottman and Markman 1978), the reduction of alternative explanations increases his or her confidence that results are due to the specified intervention. Unequivocal conclusions about causal connections are never possible in psychotherapy research, because psychotherapy is not a simple stimulus that produces a simple response. Psychotherapy is a highly complex set of interactions between two or more individuals, extending over a period ot time. Therefore, the selection of any one piece of this complex interaction as a causal agent is extremely questionable. However, as pointed out by Fiske et al. (1970), the objective of the research design should not be the impossible one of providing controls for every possibly relevant variable, but rather to provide a framework that is replicable and that can provide at least a partial answer to an important question.

The design problem is only the first of a larger number of problems to face the investigator who wishes to conduct a research study of psychotherapy. This idea has been expressed by May (1974) in reference to what he calls "the investigator's relationship to institutional reality":

> Any reasonably intelligent person can, given time and a cookbook or two, come up with a tolerably (if not unspeakably) rigorous research design. But rigor of design can never substitute for rigor of execution! It takes considerable administrative know-how to maintain the stage so that an experiment can be executed with confidence in the results [p. 127].

In the following sections, research designs will be conceptualized as existing on five different and increasingly complex levels. At each succeeding design level, the possible confounding of variables is reduced, and the resulting level of knowledge obtained is increased. Following this will be a section devoted to process research, including a discussion of both in vivo clinical and analogue studies.

## Design Level I (The One-Shot Case Study)

This design, in which a single group of patients is studied only once after some intervention, can be considered the lowest design level, inasmuch as studies employing such a design have a total absence of control (Campbell and Stanley 1963). It is, however, the only design possible if a course of treatment or program is already ongoing.

One way of introducing a measure of control in this design

is to collect retrospective data on the patients by going to clinical records or by asking for self-report retrospective information. This approach is schematized in Figure 1. In essence, this approach attempts to argue backwards from effect to possible cause rather than to manipulate systematically independent variables in order to make probabilistic statements about cause and effect relationships. However, even under the best of conditions, many confounding factors, including the usual biases related to the unreliability of memory and denial of problems, are left uncontrolled. Conclusions, therefore, are always tenuous (Meltzoff and Kornreich 1970, Paul 1976, Plutchik 1968).

## Design Level II (The One-Group Pretest/Posttest Design)

This level design, depicted in Figure 2, involves measurement before, during, and after treatment. It is thus possible to determine with some precision the changes that occur during the period of treatment. However, there is still no control or comparison group, which prevents making adequate inferences about causation, and no follow-up is planned to determine how lasting any observed changes may be.

## Design Level III (The Extended Baseline *A–B* Design)

Level III designs, shown schematically in Figure 3, are also referred to as "intensive designs" (Chasson 1967; Glass, Wilson, and Gottman 1972). Like designs at Level II, they do not provide for a control group; they do, however, offer some degree of control. With this design, which typically uses fewer subjects than designs employing both an experimental and a control group, the patients are used as their own controls, and

**Figure 1.** The One-Shot Case Study

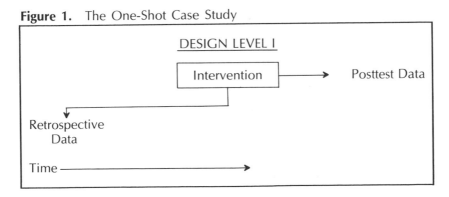

repeated measurements of a behavior or symptom to be modified are made until a stable baseline is obtained. Treatment designed to be therapeutic is then introduced and continued for a period of time. If a fairly abrupt change is noted, and behavior had been relatively constant prior to therapy, in all likelihood the change is due to the treatment variable. There is, however, at least one drawback to this design: that it will demonstrate only the effectiveness of therapies that produce rapid changes. Slow changes will not be evident.

A variation on the Extended Baseline *A–B* Design is the Extended Baseline *A–B–A* Design. The procedure here is identical to that of the *A–B* procedure, except that after the change in behavior is noted, treatment is then withheld until behavior again approaches baseline. If one wishes, one may reintroduce treatment until improvement is once more noted. By demonstrating these temporal relationships, the investigator has even greater confidence than with the *A–B* design that the therapeutic intervention was responsible for the changes observed.

Nevertheless, this approach too has drawbacks. First, it can be used to demonstrate the effectiveness of therapy only when the effect is expected to be transient and reversible. Obviously, most psychotherapists would not wish to describe their therapeutic endeavors in this manner. Therefore, if the effect of the intervention is permanent, behavior will fail to return to the baseline once the therapy has been discontinued. A second point concerns the issue of when the therapist is to discontinue treatment in order to see if the therapy was responsible for the changes. There is no unequivocal way to make this decision.

**Figure 2.**   The One-Group Pretest/Posttest Design

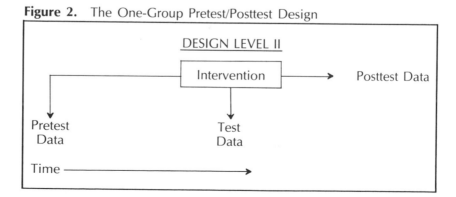

### Single-Case Design (N=1)

A further variation of the *A–B–A* methodology is the use of a single-case design. This approach, which focuses on therapeutic change in the individual patient rather than average changes across groups of patients, has been advocated by a number of investigators (Bergin and Strupp 1970, 1972; Chassan 1967; Kazdin and Wilson 1978). With this methodology, relevant hypotheses are tested separately within the data of each study patient.

The basic characteristics of the single-case design are that within the duration of the study there are several alternations between two conditions; for example, test medication and placebo and continuous assessment of responses. Ratings or evaluations are made on the patient each day or each week of treatment. Statistical analyses are then performed on the data collected in the two conditions. This method should not be confused with the usual *A–B* or *A–B–A* design in which patients are used as their own controls. With these designs, hypotheses and therapeutic changes are still tested in relation to groups of patients, whereas with the single-case method all evaluations are made separately within the data of each study patient.

As with all design strategies, the single-case method has both advantages and disadvantages. It can be especially useful in the early stages of developing hypotheses concerning clinically effective techniques of therapy. This is because it is frequently easier and less expensive to study one patient intensively rather than to recruit, maintain contact with, and test two groups of patients. A second and related advantage of the

**Figure 3.** The Extended Baseline *A–B* Design

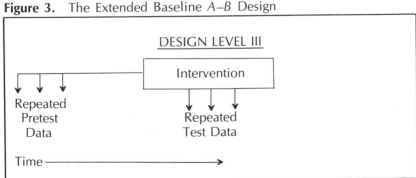

use of this intensive design is that it can be used in the evaluation of treatment for a relatively rare condition. Chassan (1967) cites the application of the use of this approach to a double-blind investigation of the treatment of a patient with narcolepsy, comparing the effectiveness of two standard and one new drug in the relief of symptoms of this disorder. The drugs were administered in random order over three days, and the procedure was repeated for a total of five such cycles over a fifteen-day period. The newer drug, adrenaline methyl, was found less effective in the patient studied than the other two medications.

The results of this study highlight one of the limitations of this methodology: The results of a single-case demonstration provide no hint of the generality of the findings to other cases. One answer to this problem that is discussed by Kazdin and Wilson (1978) is the direct replication of the same method administered by the same therapist in the same setting with more than one patient with the same problem. This solution can, however, lead to mixed results and the problem of generalization still remains.

A second difficulty with the use of single-case designs in clinical settings is that it necessitates baseline observations and the holding constant of certain conditions at certain times. These requirements can clearly come in conflict with the priority in any service-delivery setting, which is to produce clinically relevant change at the least possible cost in the shortest time possible.

Nevertheless, it has been emphasized that the limitations of single-case designs should in no way impugn their unique contribution to treatment evaluation. They allow the careful subjecting of treatment to a rigorous test on a small scale and can, therefore, serve as an appropriate screening device before techniques are subjected to larger-scale between-group investigation. Further, single-case designs can be used to augment our supply of objective information about important dimensions of therapy and, in so doing, can increase the specificity of techniques used in between-group investigations. This design would seem, therefore, to provide an important intermediate step in the overall evaluation of psychotherapeutic techniques.

Another version of the single-case design, albeit at present less systematic in conception and structure than the Level III single-case design just described, is what Horowitz (1981) has called the descriptive paradigm. Typically, this approach has simply involved case reports presented by experienced clinicians, with or without documentation available in the form of transcripts and audio or audiovisual tapes of sequences of sessions of psychotherapy. What is needed to increase the elegance and scientific value of the descriptive paradigm is a glossary of terms for the classification of observable phenomena. This glossary would, hopefully, provide a common language that would enable clinicians representing different orientations to communicate their findings in a consistent way.

## Design Level IV (The Pretest/Posttest Control Group Design)

The Level IV design, depicted in Figure 4, is what most people tend to think of as an adequately controlled study. Studies at this level involve one or more pre- and posttests and one or more assessments during the follow-up period. The use of this level of design provides considerably more precise information than is provided by lower level designs. However, its biggest advantage is that it provides a control group whose purpose is to rule out alternative explanations for research findings, such as maturation and other changes produced by the passage of time. Furthermore, the inclusion of follow-up assessment permits determining the duration of the effects noted at the end of treatment. In contrast to Level V, Level IV designs involve a relatively simple randomized or quasi-experimental trial in which state-of-the-art refinements are

**Figure 4.** The Pretest/Posttest Control Group Design

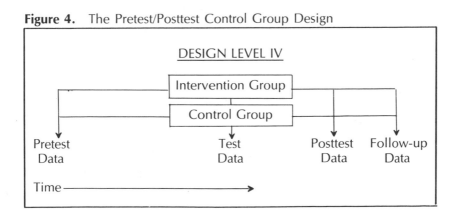

foregone, and may be the design approach to choose in order to get an inexpensive first look at a treatment of unknown utility.

Kazdin and Wilson (1978) recommend Level IV designs for what they call a "treatment package" evaluation strategy. This strategy, which is often the first approach used to evaluate a therapy technique, attempts to determine whether the technique in toto alters the problem for which it was designed; that is, there is no concern about the contribution of component parts to the effects of overall treatment. In essence, this approach, for which the appropriate comparison conditions are a treatment and/or a no-treatment control condition, can sometimes serve as a device to assess whether further research on various aspects of the technique is warranted.

The treatment package strategy for evaluating therapy has also been applied to program evaluation (Attkisson et al. 1978, Perloff and Perloff 1977). This type of research is particularly useful in such settings as community health centers, where a complex of treatment variables, including differing therapies and therapists, have been organized into a packaged program. On the one hand, it would be difficult and also somewhat artificial to separate the components of the program in order to see if the patients attending the center were benefitting from each component. On the other hand, if it were possible to do so, the elimination of those components that were nonproductive would be potentially cost efficient.

The major limitation of Level IV designs, particularly insofar as they are used to determine the outcome of interventions like individual or group therapy or other such psychosocial therapies, is that there is no precise knowledge of what actually constitutes the treatment or the special expertise of the therapists. It might be stated, for example, that a controlled study of group therapy conducted at institution $x$ demonstrated that the average level of psychosocial functioning of a group of depressed patients was improved by 28 percent when compared with a comparable group that did not receive this special treatment. But what is "group therapy" in this context? Would another clinician purporting to conduct group therapy with depressed patients get substantially the same results? Without clearer specification of the intervention and the training of the clinician, the answer to this question is simply not known.

## Design Level V (The Multivariate Design)

Designs at Level V may vary on a number of dimensions, but what they all have in common is that they are multivariate and, ideally, investigators attempt to standardize rigorously as many variables as possible, including patient, treatment, and outcome variables. For example, Level V designs might include some way of specifically defining the strategies and techniques to be used in their treatment or intervention. This process would involve preparing a detailed outline or manual describing the therapy. It would also include techniques for determining the extent to which the defined strategies were actually being used, for example, audio- and/or videotapes and/or observers. Investigations conducted at Level V would also, ideally, employ multiple measures of each variable prior to treatment, during treatment (process measures), at termination, and at follow-up. Level V designs are illustrated in Figure 5. The central advance at Level V is the opportunity to examine interactions, either within treatment, patient, or outcome factors, or across more than one domain of factors.

**Figure 5.**  Multivariate Designs

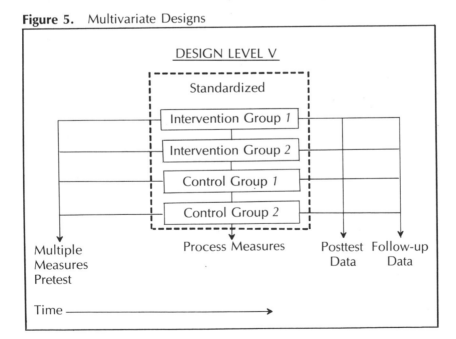

## Factorial Designs

Level V designs used to evaluate the effects of varying only one dimension of a treatment variable, for example, frequency or duration of therapy, have been called a "parametric treatment strategy" (Kazdin and Wilson 1978). When more than one dimension is varied in two or more ways (for example, diagnosis and treatment modality) and studied in all possible combinations, the study is said to have a factorial design (Edwards and Cronbach 1966). Factorial designs are illustrated schematically in Figure 6.

Factorial designs are extremely useful in research in psychotherapy for a number of reasons. First, they permit a test of significance of any interactions among the variables investigated, as well as a test of significance of the main effects. This is important because simple comparisons of treatment $X$ versus $Y$ may show little to no effect, whereas an analysis of interactive effects may be quite illuminating. For example, factorial designs may be used to assess how effective different types of treatments (for example, types $X$ and $Y$) are with patients with differing levels or types of disturbances. Thus it might be found that patients with diagnosis $A$ are not differentially affected by treatment $X$ or $Y$, whereas patients with diagnosis $B$ respond significantly better to treatment $X$.

**Figure 6.**   Factorial Designs

|  | FACTORIAL DESIGNS | |
| --- | --- | --- |
|  | Diagnosis $A$ | Diagnosis $B$ |
| Treatment $X$ |  |  |
| Treatment $Y$ |  |  |

Comparisons often gain value as the design isolates the specific types of persons and situations for which it is superior (Chassan 1969, Edwards and Cronbach 1966, Hunt 1966, Kiesler 1966, Meltzoff and Kornreich 1970).

A second reason for the usefulness of a factorially designed study is that revealing information may be obtained about the mechanisms responsible for change. By varying specific dimensions of treatment, as for example the age of the therapist in relation to the patient, it is possible to obtain information that either supports or is incompatible with mechanisms that are theoretically assumed to account for therapeutic change.

Third, factorial designs are particularly appropriate for comparative evaluations of different modes of therapy with different patient populations. With this type of design, it is feasible to study, simultaneously, the more specific effects of different therapies, types of patients, and therapists. It is, therefore, possible to shed some light on the question in which psychotherapists are most interested; namely, what therapeutic approach works best with what kind of patient (Hunt 1966, Meltzoff and Kornreich 1970).

The increasing concern with the conduct of comparative studies and the assessment of the differential effects of different techniques has not, however, always resulted in adequate outcome research. In spite of the apparent simplicity of comparing different treatments, comparative research has been beset by numerous difficulties, both methodological and conceptual. Deficiencies cited include the use of outcome criteria unique to a particular theoretical orientation, the selection of patients who are more appropriate for one of the two or more approaches being examined, the use of goals or criteria of success not uniformly appropriate for all the treatments studied, the use of therapy durations not appropriate for all approaches under consideration, the lack of careful definition of the actual processes occurring in the different therapies, the failure to avoid large overlaps in the procedures used, and the use of unsatisfactory and global outcome measures (Kazdin and Wilson 1978, Pokorny and Klett 1976, Strupp and Bergin 1969).

As pointed out by Strupp and Bergin (1969), many of these deficiencies are functions of the complexity and cost of adequately conducting comparative studies. Presumably, all of them could be overcome given large enough patient populations and adequate personnel, time, and money. However, because of the tremendous investment involved in the conduct of comparative research and in the use of Level V designs in general, it is recommended that investigations at a lower level be conducted prior to the conduct of these more complex designs (Kazdin and Wilson 1978, Paul 1976). These latter designs are more properly reserved for the investigation of the differential effects of treatments whose parameters are well specified and whose appropriate applications are known.

**31**

# List of Figures

# CHAPTER 5

# Design Strategies: Issues Related to Selection and Interaction of Variables

While there is some overlap in meaning between the terms *design methodology* and *design strategy*, we have used *design methodology* to refer to the specific arrangement of conditions used in the evaluation undertaking. *Design strategy* is used in a narrower sense to refer to the choice of variables to be studied. Up to this point we have been concerned mainly with therapeutic method as an independent variable. That is, we have discussed ways of determining whether a given treatment is better than none at all, or whether one treatment is superior to one or more other forms of therapy. The implication has been that specified techniques produce effects in a relatively straightforward manner. However, various combinations of components of treatment and various attributes of both patients and therapists can exert an influence on therapeutic outcome. In addition, the way in which interactions occur between patients and therapists during treatment can bear on the final outcome. The following section briefly addresses these issues.

## Constructive and Dismantling Strategies

When the investigator is still in the process of trying to understand which components of his or her treatment are effective, there are two strategies that are particularly useful. These have been called the *constructive* treatment strategy (Kazdin and Wilson 1978, McFall and Marston 1970) and the *dismantling* treatment strategy (Gottman and Markman 1978, Kazdin and Wilson 1978). Using the former approach, which refers to the development of a treatment package by adding components designed to enhance the effects of the therapy, the investigator usually starts with a basic treatment component that is of relatively narrow focus. He or she then adds components, either on an empirical or theoretical basis. Those components that prove effective he or she then adds to the treatment package. Kazdin and Wilson (1978) cite as an example of this constructive treatment strategy having the client actually engage in behavior modelled by the therapist after it was determined that this addition to the treatment procedure served to produce greater therapeutic change in the client than simple observation alone. An important advantage of the constructive treatment approach is, therefore, that it permits the empirical establishment of a treatment package. Most new therapies have no established body of empirically validated information. It is also important, however, that some of the components added be derived from some theoretical context so that the investigators would have some understanding of how these components relate to and interact with other components. When we have some knowledge of a nomological network, greater light is shed on the mechanisms of behavior change.

The dismantling treatment strategy proceeds by eliminating certain individual treatment components from treatment in an effort to determine whether the elements thought crucial for behavior change in fact are. Thus the results of this strategy usually go beyond the implications for conducting treatment and bear on the theoretical notions that served as a basis for the derivation of the treatment (Kazdin and Wilson 1978). This is particularly true if the various components of the treatment represent different theoretical conceptions of change.

The dismantling strategy has been used in such studies as the evaluation of systematic desensitization (Lang 1969), in the analysis of modelling programs (Bandura 1971), and of various other social skill training approaches (for example, McFall and Twentyman 1973). In the case of systematic desensitization, it has been found that certain specific components of desensitization thought to be important (the construction of a graded hierarchy of anxiety-provoking situations, for example) can be omitted without loss of efficacy. The only component that has been found to be crucial is overt or imagined rehearsal of the response to be developed. Thus, findings from studies using the dismantling strategy can have important implications about the mechanisms of behavior change by ruling out interpretations that depend on ingredients that originally were thought essential (Kazdin and Wilson 1978).

One caution about the use of systematic dismantling research is that it is important to choose those variables that are theoretically important, for example, therapist behavior or content discussed, rather than those of merely trivial interest, for example, the measured distance between patient and therapist in a therapy session. The technique's theoretical basis, which specifies the necessary conditions for behavioral change, should determine the priority of components selected for study (Kazdin and Wilson 1978).

## Patient and Therapist Variation Strategy

In addition to diagnosis and severity of maladjustment, the patient's background, demographic, motivational, and attitudinal characteristics may bear on the outcome of psychotherapy. Accordingly, the roles of such variables as age, sex, socioeconomic status, marital status, IQ, education, expectancies, and personality characteristics such as suggestibility and introversion-extraversion have all been studied (Garfield 1978, Kazdin and Wilson 1978, Meltzoff and Kornreich 1970). In addition, in some cases patients have been selected because of their differences on one or more of these specific dimensions in order to determine whether differential therapeutic outcomes are obtained as a function of these variations.

Similarly, the therapist as a variable in the outcome of psychotherapy has been widely studied. Investigations have dealt with both formal characteristics such as professional affiliation, formal training, and level of experience, as well as with more inherent characteristics and qualities such as sex, interests, various personality traits, and warmth and empathy during sessions (Kazdin and Wilson 1978, Meltzoff and Kornreich 1970, Truax and Mitchell 1971, Strupp and Bergin 1969). In addition, there has been fairly extensive research on interactional variables such as patient-therapist similarity in terms of interests and personality and therapist liking for the patient (Chartier 1971, Gunderson 1978, Luborsky 1969, Razin 1977, Strupp 1973).

Theoretically, the selection of clients and therapists according to specific dimensions increases the possibility of explaining treatment outcomes. An interaction of treatment with various characteristics of the patient or therapist implies that treatment is more or less effective depending on the variable used to classify either the patient or the therapist (Kazdin and Wilson 1978).

Problems arise, however, when investigations purporting to study the effect of the same variable produce inconsistent or contrary results. For example, Luborsky et al. (1971) report that of the eleven psychotherapy studies they reviewed in which age of the patient was the variable of interest, five found it unrelated to outcome, four found that younger patients showed greater improvement, while two of the studies found older patients had better outcomes. Inconclusive results have also been reported in the area of patient-therapist variables. Meltzoff and Kornreich (1970) state that in their review of studies purporting to offer positive support for the hypothesis of a significant relation between patient-therapist similarity and improvement, they found no convincing support of any kind. For example, one study showed a weak linear relation between personality similarity and improvement, and another a curvilinear relation between similarity and improvement.

As an illustrative example, Meltzoff and Kornreich (1970) present the following schema that portrays one possible set of outcomes from pairings of patients and therapists based on some system of personality typology:

> Personality Type A patients would suceed with any type of therapist whether similar or dissimilar in personality type, and Type B patients would fail regardless of therapist personality type. Type C patients would succeed only with similar (Type C) therapists,

| | Therapist Type A B C D | Outcome |
|---|---|---|
| | A S S S S | Succeeds with any type therapist |
| | B F F F F | Fails with all types |
| Patient Type | C F F S F | Succeeds only with similar therapist |
| | D S S S F | Fails only with similar therapist |

S = Success;          F = Failure

> and Type D patients would succeed only with dissimilar therapists. If this kind of phenomenon is operating, research that has been conducted on global or typological classifications could be expected to yield confusing positive, negative, or null results because of the particular combinations unwittingly sampled [pp. 325–326].

In summary, the lack of consistency in studies that investigate the effect on outcome of varying attributes of patients and therapists is probably due to fragmentation that occurs when one variable at a time is examined. In order to reach any definitive conclusions, it would be necessary to systematically assign all types of patients to all types of therapists and examine the relative effectiveness of each combination, while at the same time holding techniques and all other relevant variables constant. An undertaking of this magnitude would involve an inordinate amount of time, money, and personnel and its results would, in all likelihood, be difficult to interpret. This implies the need for alternative models for the conduct of research in this area. This issue will be discussed in greater detail in the section "Conclusions" in Chapter 18.

# CHAPTER 6

# Process Research

In contrast to outcome research, which is concerned with the effect of therapy on a patient at the time treatment is terminated, process research is typically viewed as the study of transactions between therapist and patient while treatment is still in progress. Some investigators, for example Bordin (1974a) and Kiesler (1971), have chosen to reject this dichotomy, believing that process and outcome studies are merely different sides of the same coin and that process measures may be viewed as interim measures of outcome. As pointed out by Kazdin and Wilson (1978), however, some studies of the processes of therapy, for example, those concerned with examining aspects of the therapist's behavior over time, are purely investigations of internal changes in treatment and do not directly address what the patient is doing. Thus not all research on the processes of therapy can be reinterpreted as outcome halted at a given point in time.

Generally speaking, however, outcome research seeks to answer questions about the effects of psychotherapy and may be conceived of as concerning *what* changes in therapy. In contrast, process research is concerned with the *how* of therapeutic change (Sargent 1961) and seeks answers to questions about the inner workings of psychotherapy, its rationale, its method and techniques (Meltzoff and Kornreich 1970). As such, process research may be divided into two broad areas: investigations that focus on the naturally occurring events in actual therapy interviews or sessions (in vivo); and those in which variables are systematically manipulated under controlled conditions outside the therapy setting. These latter are customarily referred to as analogue studies.

## In Vivo Studies

Studies of the ongoing process of psychotherapy have typically addressed themselves to such questions as: How do transactions that occur between therapist and patient affect the behavior of both over time? What occurrences in therapy are apt to reflect therapeutic progress? Are some types of therapists' responses more productive of change in patients than others? What sort of content seems most related to a patient's progress in therapy? How do patients and therapists perceive the therapy sessions, and What are the correlates of different impressions of treatment? (Howard and Orlinsky 1972; Kazdin and Wilson 1978; Orlinsky and Howard 1974, 1978; Stollak, Guerney, and Rothberg 1966). Kiesler (1973) has provided a valuable compendium of specific variables that have been used in the study of therapy process.

The method of observation chosen for studying the process of psychotherapy depends, ultimately, on the particular aspects of the process chosen for study. The most primitive forms of observation are those taken from either one's own experience or from that of fellow therapists, with or without retrospective or concurrent accounts from patients (Bordin 1974). Other investigators have attempted greater objectivity by utilizing the process of supervision. With this approach, a consultant, who presumably can maintain an objective attitude toward patient-therapist interactions, gives his or her interpretation of events transpiring during therapy (Schlessinger et al. 1966). However, only with the advent of motion pictures of psychotherapy interviews, and their verbatim transcripts, did the phenomena of psychotherapy become directly accessible to a third party (Bordin 1965). Thus today by far the most frequently used method of data collection for process studies is the collection of a full or partial recording of the events via film and/or sound recording. In spite of occasional objections that this recording may prove to be an intrusion and a disrupting influence on both patient and therapist (for example, Schlessinger et al. 1966), this approach has proved the most productive.

Methodologically, there are two fundamental difficulties in the recording of observations: (1) establishing meaningful units of observation; and (2) specifying dimensions or categories to capture "relevant" aspects of the psychotherapy experience (Strupp 1973). In dealing with the first problem, the investigator has essentially two choices. He or she can decide on arbitrary units such as time units or formal elements of speech that are easy to demarcate, communicate, and replicate, but that often lack psychological significance and are not part of the working theoretical system and vocabulary of most psychotherapists. Or, alternatively, the investigator can study psychological units such as "themes" that emerge during therapy that are maximally meaningful and critical from a theoretical standpoint.

These latter variables, however, are exceedingly difficult to demarcate. The farther the variables are from observable or countable items, the greater the risk run by the investigator of not achieving adequate reliability and replicability (Meltzoff and Kornreich 1970, Stollak et al. 1966, Strupp 1973, Strupp and Bergin 1969). For this reason, the first alternative is the one most frequently chosen. Ideally, however, the investigator endeavors to find units that can be judged with a high degree of interrater reliability on the one hand, and that are rich in theoretical meaning on the other.

The second problem encountered in the recording of observations, that of specifying categories for the description of events during psychotherapy, is the more difficult of the two and has typically been approached via content analysis. A number of content-analysis systems appear in the literature (for example, Auld and Murray 1955; Dittes 1959; Marsden 1965, 1971; Strupp 1962). Marsden (1971) has divided them into three broad procedural families that he calls models: the classical model, the pragmatic model, and the nonquantitative model. The validity for content analysis of the nonquantitative model, which involves linguistic analysis, has been questioned by linguists and content analyzers alike (Marsden 1971) and will not be discussed here. The model most widely used has been the classical model, explicated by Berelson (1952), which has been used in studies of the characteristics of patients, of therapists, of patient-therapist interactional systems, of internal psychodynamic states, and of contingent relationships between patients and therapists. This model specifies that units, for example all patient speech between two therapist statements, be coded to categories descriptive of the content itself, for example interpersonal relations. Once the units are coded, the analyst may make inferences about the internal state of the communicator, for example, that he or she feels depressed or guilty. In contrast, the pragmatic model requires that units, for example nouns, are coded to categories that describe some condition of the communicator, for example aggression. Thus, with the pragmatic model, inferences are made initially and serve as the basis for coding. This procedure is typically chosen when the behavior denoting the internal condition in question cannot be adequately specified (Marsden 1971).

A number of content-analysis systems are reported to have adequate reliability. None, however, has been utilized to any extent by other than its originator and sometimes not even by him or her. "System after system has been developed and presented in one or two demonstration studies, only to lie buried in the literature, unused even by its author" (Marsden 1965, p. 315).

A further drawback of content analysis as a method for studying the process of psychotherapy is that most investigators have preferred to develop their own categorical systems, anchoring them to their own psychotherapeutic orientation. This practice effectively precludes comparisons among data collected by therapists of different theoretical persuasions. Some systems, for example Bales's twelve-category system of interaction process analysis (1950), are not restricted to any one theoretical orientation. But these have been considered too general and overinclusive to be of much value for research in psychotherapy (Strupp 1973). It may be that no one system is capable of encompassing the relevant aspects of the therapeutic process of such theoretically disparate treatments as psychoanalysis and gestalt therapy.

## Analogue Studies

The large body of research utilizing systems of content analyses has been heavily influenced by psychoanalytic and client-centered theory. In contrast, the impetus for experimental manipulation of specified technique variables has come largely from investigators favoring behavioral approaches. This type of research, which evaluates treatment under conditions that only resemble or approximate the clinical setting, is usually referred to as *analogue* or *simplification* research.

Although there is no sharp point of demarcation between them, analogue studies of the process of psychotherapy are basically of two types: those that derive mainly from a behaviorist orientation, and those that deal with the process of psychoanalytic treatment.

In studies of the first type, phenomena originally observed in the clinical setting are abstracted and transferred to laboratory or laboratory-like situations, where greater precision can be obtained in experimental isolation, manipulation, and control (Bordin 1965, Paul 1976). The ultimate goal is to reveal empirical relationships that can be generalized to actual therapy settings (Kazdin and Wilson 1978).

There are a number of advantages to be gained through the use of this type experimental analogue. First, the control it provides more readily permits ruling out alternative explanations for findings by minimizing sources of variance that could otherwise obscure the effects of treatment. Investigators are able to use larger, more homogeneous, and more clearly specified populations. For example, the subjects, who are often college-student volunteers, can be selected for their similarities on both the target problem and demographic variables. Similarly, the training and experience of "therapists" can be systematically manipulated.

Second, the fact that patient treatment does not have the highest priority in laboratory situations permits the investigator to manipulate variables systematically in ways that are not often possible in the real therapeutic situation. With analogue research, subjects can ethically be assigned to a control condition that is not expected to effect change, specific ingredients of treatment may more readily be withheld than under clinical conditions, and subjects need not be assigned to any treatment at all. This freedom to provide or withhold specific ingredients of treatment is perhaps the greatest advantage of laboratory analogue research (Stollak 1966, Kazdin and Wilson 1978). By increasing the opportunity to test hypotheses, it greatly expands the number of questions that can be asked about therapy: "Freed of the restrictions imposed by the use of patients, the problems of invading a highly personal relationship and the ethics of doing so, the investigator can carry out more experiments in the time it takes to do one in the clinic" (Bordin 1966, p. 191).

Many different types of analogue studies have been conducted. There have been those concerned with how such variables as interviewer style (Heller, Davis, and Myers 1966), experience (McNair and Lorr 1964), and empathy (Pierce and Mosher 1967) affect the process of treatment. There is also a large literature concerned with the extent to which therapists' attempts at verbal conditioning affect the process of treatment and of various characteristics of interactional behavior (Meltzoff and Kornreich 1970).

The second type of analogue study, that deriving from an interest in developing a greater understanding of the process of psychoanalytic treatment, is typically conducted under conditions that more nearly approximate actual clinical settings. Bellak and Smith (1956), for example, conducted a study in which patients' sessions were recorded for several months. Two analysts were asked to judge the patients' behavior independently, with reference to the same set of variables. Ratings were made both quantitatively and qualitatively. The quantitative results showed a high degree of agreement among the judges themselves, among the predictors themselves, and also between predictors and judges. However, the ability to agree on the nature of short-range changes was not unequivocally demonstrated. Unfortunately, this study, whose method seems valuable for testing psychoanalytic hypotheses, has never been replicated.

Using typescripts and a sound film that was stopped at various points during a psychotherapy interview, Strupp (1958) studied factors such as experience and empathy that have been reported to influence therapists' responses. Over 200 subject-therapists were asked to offer their own responses to statements made by the patient in the film. This approach had the virtue of comparing therapists under standard conditions. Strupp (1962) himself, however, has stated that the degree to which a therapist's response in this situation was the same as it would be in actual psychotherapy is problematical.

Analogue studies, particularly those of the laboratory type, introduce a relatively high degree of experimental control and, to the extent that the analogue shares the essential characteristics of the clinical procedures and phenomena being investigated, this approach provides a powerful and economical means for determining the mechanisms of operation of these complex variables (Paul 1976). However, some comments on the validity of this approach are in order. One of its liabilities is the difficulty of being sure that a psychotherapeutic atmosphere exists and that it exists in some way comparable to what occurs in a natural setting. Further, the investigator working in a laboratory setting must provide some rationale that he or she is dealing with the same phenomena that have been observed clinically (Bernstein and Paul 1971, Kiesler 1971, Luborsky 1969, Luborsky and Spence 1971, Strupp and Luborsky 1962). As Bordin has stated, "The degree to which you can safely depart from the naturalistic setting is proportional to the amount you already know about the phenomena in question" (1965, p. 497). He cautions the investigator, therefore, given the crudity of our present understanding of psychotherapy, to structure his or her analogue procedures to approximate as closely as possible the conditions that obtain in everyday practice (Bordin 1966).

This advice is more easily given than followed for a number

of reasons, probably the most important of which is that analogue studies frequently involve volunteers. These are usually students who happen to have a problem, for example, a mild fear of snakes, that seldom or never causes concern in their daily lives or, more recently, mild social or sexual difficulties, for which they normally would not seek professional aid. How similar to "real" patients, in terms of such variables as symptoms, motivation, and demographic characteristics, are these analogue patients? Obviously, students represent only a small portion of the general population, and unless the more seriously disabled are chosen as subjects, only limited conclusions may be drawn from such a sample (Kiesler 1971, Marks 1978, O'Leary and Borkovec 1978).

The extent to which analogue therapists are similar to "real" therapists is also a problem. However, as long as ethical considerations are borne in mind, and as long as the programmed attitudinal and technique behaviors of the therapist are specified, investigators have more leeway in utilizing various types of individuals in manipulative studies (Kiesler 1971).

The third and crucial analogue question concerns the extent to which conclusions reached in analogue settings have meaningful application to actual psychotherapy. The generalizability of analogue change findings to "emotionally disturbed" behaviors is neither simple nor straightforward (Kiesler 1971, Luborsky 1969, Luborsky and Spence 1971, Strupp and Bergin 1969). For this reason, it is advisable not only to complement controlled experimentation by replication studies in naturalistic settings, but also to carry out research over the whole range, from the virtually unmodified clinical setting to the most abstracted laboratory conditions (Bordin 1965, Kazdin and Wilson 1978, Kiesler 1971, Stollak 1966, Strupp and Bergin 1969). By integrating the different levels of observation, it will be possible to provide a bridge between research on psychotherapy and more general psychological research in such areas as personality, attitude change, and various aspects of learning.

# CHAPTER 7

# Pragmatic and Ethical Issues

Research in psychotherapy poses a number of practical and ethical problems for which there are at present no truly satisfactory solutions. One issue concerns the issue of privacy and confidentiality. A second issue relates to the need for no-treatment or attention/placebo control groups. A third involves the utilization and implications of informed consent.

## Privacy and Confidentiality

With regard to this first issue, the relationship between patient and therapist has traditionally been a confidential and privileged one (Karasu 1980, Meltzoff and Kornreich 1970). Yet increasingly in recent years there has been external intrusion on this traditionally confidential relationship. The need for unbiased, objective data for the purpose of evaluation and research has led to the use of such devices as one-way screens, tape recorders, and motion picture cameras.

Some therapists hold that these intrusions constitute a violation of the intimate, private atmosphere of the therapeutic relationship. In addition, what if the patient, wittingly or not, reveals some antisocial or illegal acts, either past or contemplated, and this information is then on record? (Holt 1965). Furthermore, it is argued that the use of observational or recorded data for research purposes so alters the behavior of the participants that generalizations to sessions in which strict privacy is maintained are weakened. This position obviously tends to discourage research and hinders the acceptance of research findings.

Meltzoff and Kornreich (1970) cite a number of studies designed to investigate the assumption that therapeutic relationships are so unique and private as to make them inaccessible to systematic analyses by independent investigators. They conclude that there is some limited evidence that recordings, observations, and filming do have an effect on both the patient and the therapist and that this should be considered in the research design and in the interpretation of the results of any study in which these procedures were utilized. They also point out, however, that there is a long tradition, particularly in medicine, of reporting clinical findings and data that may benefit others.

## No-Treatment and Attention/Placebo Controls

The second issue that has both pragmatic and ethical implications concerns the use of a no-treatment or attention/placebo control group. While the advantages of such experimental methods are well known and widely accepted, they raise a number of problems.

As previously discussed, one problem concerns the ethics of withholding treatment from those patients in the control group who are actively seeking help, even if the purpose is to advance our knowledge, with the ultimate goal of benefitting an even greater number of individuals. This problem is compounded when one considers the possibility that treatment prohibition for control patients could continue over several months or even years (Imber et al. 1978). One way out of the conflict this produces between the humanitarian desire to help the afflicted and the logical requirements of research design is to use "rationalization." If the treatment has not already been proved effective, then perhaps it is not unethical to withhold it (O'Leary and Borkovec 1978). The major drawback of this approach is that most psychotherapists, by virtue of their very occupation, are convinced of the efficacy of the help they provide and may, therefore, be reluctant to participate in this form of research. There is, in addition, the practical difficulty of retaining patients assigned to a no-treatment group. Attrition is likely to be high, leaving the investigator with a sample certain to be biased in significant ways (Imber et al. 1978).

Several solutions to this problem have already been suggested. One is that those who apply, but who do not return for therapy after the initial intake interview, be utilized as controls. This is not logically feasible, however, because these individuals are essentially dropouts, and as such are a self-selected sample essentially different from those who remain in treatment (Hunt 1966). In addition, their unwillingness or inability to accept psychotherapy makes them poor controls for patients actually undergoing treatment (Imber et al. 1978).

A second solution is to utilize the waiting-list approach. By randomly assigning a number of individuals to what amounts to a delayed treatment group, the ethical issue is surmounted. There are, however, problems with this solution, too. First, this option is possible only when therapy is of relatively short duration. Second, it would be viable only for those patients who do not seek help elsewhere. And third, what does one do with an acutely psychotic suicidal or homicidal patient? He or she could be treated out of turn, but this would compromise the research design. Or the patient could be treated immediately and simply dropped from the study. This approach, however, is likely to destroy the representativeness of the sample by restricting its range of severity of illness.

A third solution is to use an attention/placebo condition. This has the advantage of permitting randomization of patients and of controlling for patients' expectations. However, even if it were possible to develop a theoretically inert placebo condition, it is unlikely that therapists would be willing to implement it over any length of time. And even if they were willing, their expectations about the success of this treatment condition relative to other credible conditions would differ. Such differences would serve to confound results.

O'Leary and Borkovec (1978) also question the use of an attention/placebo group on the grounds that it may be "unethical, impractical, or methodologically unsound in psychotherapy research of moderate or greater length" (p. 821). They distinguish at least three sources of harm that may occur to the patient. First, placebo conditions are inherently deceptive, even with informed-consent procedures. Thus, the investigator is responsible for determining that potential risks to patients are outweighed by the benefits expected to result from the research. The more severe the patient's problem, the less ethical it becomes to keep him or her essentially untreated for an extended period of time. There is a second concern that is particularly salient when treatments of established effectiveness exist but are not offered to the patient. This is that placebos deter the patient from seeking active treatment during the course of the study. Third, if the placebo treatment is truly ineffective, some patients may deteriorate or suffer considerable frustration as the consequence of minimal improvement. If the patient's expectations of help diminish over time or even become negative, the attention/placebo condition would become methodologically unsound as well as ethically questionable. These authors (O'Leary and Borkovec 1978) conclude that the potential short- or long-term harm to patients with moderate to severe problems who remain in a placebo condition for an extended period of time is at present unestimated.

There are a number of ways out of the dilemma produced by a placebo methodology. One is to use one of the quasi-experimental designs already described, and another is to proceed via analogues. In terms of generalizability and the confidence that can be placed in results, neither procedure is as satisfactory as random assignment of real patients, but these approximations are ways to achieve at least partial answers. A third alternative, recommended by O'Leary and Borkovec (1978), is developing more satisfactory standardized methods of control that can circumvent the ethical issues inherent in placebo methodology. Basically these methods should control for "nonspecific" therapy effects; for example, therapist contact, attention, and expectancy effects.

## Informed Consent

A third issue having both pragmatic and ethical implications that arises in the conduct of research in psychotherapy, although not unique to this type of research, is the requirement for informed consent. To assure that a patient's rights are not violated, participation in any study or experiment must be voluntary and based on the patient's, or the patient's legal surrogate's, informed consent. A number of government agencies and professional societies have provided explicit guidelines for the procedures to be followed in obtaining this consent.

These procedures include informing prospective patients of the purpose of the study, of potential benefits and risks involved in participation, and of the ways in which data will be collected and used. Patients must also be informed that they are free to withdraw from the study at any time and that such withdrawal will in no way affect their relationships with the institution, hospital, or center or its personnel. They must also be informed if random assignment to treatment, control, or waiting-list conditions is to be used. A true informed-consent approach thus solves the deception problem, inasmuch as patients give their consent to receive no treatment at all, an attentional control or treatment that is presumed to effect change in their condition.

This approach seems both reasonable and humane, and at first glance would seem to pose no problems for researchers. And it does appear quite appropriate for patients with mild to moderate problems who agree to participate in brief to moderately lengthy trials. However, as the severity of a patient's condition increases or the duration of the study becomes more protracted, or if the availability of other forms of intervention is limited, there may be a concomitant increase in a control patient's frustration, reduced motivation to seek alternative help, and possible deterioration. It is important, therefore, to monitor carefully these patients and to make appropriate referrals where necessary.

A practical drawback to the informed-consent approach is that it may, in fact, inhibit participation in some research, particularly double-blind drug studies. For example, a depressed patient who is told that he or she will be given either a new experimental drug, one of two relatively well established antidepressants, or an inert substance may not wish to run the risk of receiving either an unknown quantity or nothing at all.

One last problem with the use of informed consent is a conceptual one. How is "voluntary participation" of a committed patient in a state mental hospital or a prisoner in a penal institution to be interpreted? The patient may believe he or she has no choice, or may not be fully capable of understanding the situation. In the case of the prisoner, it is not unknown for trade-offs to occur, although this probably happens less frequently today than in the past.

Obviously, using informed consent is not a panacea for all the methodological and ethical problems that plague psychotherapy research. It is, however, still the best way of reconciling the conflict between our ethical responsibility to evaluate the efficacy of treatment and our ethical responsibility to protect the rights of human subjects.

In summary, there are three areas in which ethical issues lead to pragmatic difficulties and pragmatic issues lead to ethical problems. The invasion of privacy for the purpose of collecting the objective data necessary to systematically evaluate psychotherapy is one area. A second concerns the ethical issues involved in assigning patients with distressing problems to no-treatment or placebo conditions in order to provide baselines for evaluation of experimental treatments. The third area relates to the possible refusal to participate in a study or differential attrition that results from our ethical responsibility to obtain informed consent.

# CHAPTER 8

# Assessment Issues

Assessing the efficacy of psychotherapeutic treatment has been a major focus of psychotherapy theory and research for at least the last two decades. This section will address a number of methodological issues concerned with this assessment. These will include: the reliability and validity of techniques for measuring change; the lack of agreement among criteria; a conceptual model for assessing change; the measurement of therapeutic outcome; measures from different vantage points; issues related to follow-up procedures; statistical problems related to change and its measurement; and some special problems in measuring cost-effectiveness and cost-benefit of psychotherapy.

## Reliability and Validity

Whatever measures are chosen for evaluating the effect of psychotherapy, they should satisfy the requirements of reliability and validity (Chassen 1967, Fiske et al. 1970, Nunnally and Wilson 1975, Spitzer and Endicott 1975, Zax and Klein 1966). Although there are many kinds of reliability, they all deal essentially with consistency. For example, a highly reliable measure is one that shows relatively little variation in the measurement of a phenomenon assumed to remain constant. This constancy may be from one time to the next, in which case reliability may be thought of as stability or dependability. Or, it can occur from one observer to another. In this case, reliability pertains to the degree of agreement among observers about the existence of a certain phenomenon. In addition, the items of a reliable instrument should be positively correlated with one another. Estimates of reliability based on the average correlation among its items concern the "internal consistency" of a test. The size of the reliability coefficient of a measure depends upon both the average correlation among its items and the number of items (Nunnally 1967).

However, reliability, while necessary, is not sufficient. It is also necessary that a test instrument be a valid measure of the dimension or concept in which the investigator is interested. The validity of a test or any measuring instrument has many meanings. Actually, validity is a highly relative concept. The question is always, valid for what? Validation is always an unending process, and may take many forms: content, face, predictive or concurrent, and construct (Cronbach et al. 1972, Guilford 1965, Kerlinger 1967, Nunnally 1967).

Briefly, a measuring instrument has content validity if it has adequately sampled the theoretical universe of content consisting of all the things that can possibly be said or observed about the concept considered (Kerlinger 1967). Content validation usually involves judges evaluating each item of a scale or questionnaire for its presumed relevance to and coverage of the property being measured. Content validation is, therefore, basically judgmental.

The term *face validity* is closely related to content validity. This type of validity concerns the extent to which an instrument "looks like" it measures what it is intended to measure. The major difference between face and content validity lies in the fact that the former concerns judgments about an instrument after its construction, whereas the latter is more properly associated with the planning phase during the process of constructing a test (Nunnally 1967).

Predictive and concurrent validity are virtually the same, differing only in the time dimension. The one element characterizing them both is that prediction is made to an outside criterion, and the measuring instrument is checked, either now or in the future, against this criterion. The procedure for establishing a concurrent validity coefficient is to administer a new test and to correlate scores received on that test with scores received on another test that has already been validated.

From a theoretical standpoint, construct validity is perhaps the most important type of validity. Also, since most constructs in the behavioral sciences tend to be abstract (and the more abstract a construct, the more difficult it is to validate measures of that construct) it is also the most difficult to achieve. This is so because "in most instances the particular operations are meant to measure a variable which extends well beyond the operations in question" (Nunnally 1967, p. 84). When examining construct validity, then, the investigator is principally interested, not in prediction, but in understanding the nature of the properties being measured. He or she wants to know the "meaning" of the test.

Construct validity involves determining to what extent a test is consistent with a given theory or hypothesis (Van Dalen and Meyer 1962). It begins with a definition of the meaning of the construct. Certain results are then deduced that should or should not be observed if the construct in question has been properly defined. The investigator then goes on to determine whether the predicted results are observed; that is, whether a variety of behaviors predicted to relate to the construct actually do correlate with one another in a number of studies and/or will be similarly affected by experimental treatments (Nunnally 1967).

For example, an investigator wishes to construct a test to measure "flexibility." First, he or she defines flexibility in terms of the following expectation: flexible persons will score high on a test of creativity and artistic ability; flexible persons will relearn a maze rapidly when the goal is shifted to a new position; flexible persons will shift their attitudes more rapidly when exposed to propaganda than will nonflexible persons (Cronbach 1960). The investigator then goes on to determine if high scorers on his or her flexibility test do, in fact, exhibit the expected behaviors to a greater extent than do low scorers. If they do, he or she may conclude that the flexibility test possesses a measure of construct validity.

Construct validation is, therefore, not simply an appraisal of the test. It is also an assessment of the theory behind the test. If the predictions are borne out, evidence has been obtained that supports the hypothesized interrelations among a variety of measures of the construct being considered. As such, construct validity contrasts sharply with empiric approaches that define the validity of a measure solely in terms of its success in predicting a criterion. For example, "A purely empiric tester might say that a test is valid if it efficiently distinguishes individuals high and low in a trait. Why the test succeeds in separating the subjects of a group is of no great concern. It is enough that it does" (Kerlinger 1967, p. 449).

In psychotherapy research, a test instrument is most often used as a measure of current status before treatment and as a criterion measure at termination and follow-up. The investigator should, therefore, be aware of what evidence exists for the validity of the instrument as a measure of the construct in which he or she is interested.

## The Criterion Problem

The problems relating to such issues as research designs, patient selection, and the like can almost be regarded as secondary to basic decisions regarding what must be assessed. Disagreement exists both on the question of what conditions need treatment (for example, intrapsychic conflicts, interpersonal problems, family conflicts, or such social problems as crime and delinquency) and on the question of what outcome criteria should be used to assess the consequences of treatment.

Controversies over outcome criteria have traditionally centered on such issues as: how therapeutic change is to be assessed (for example, subjective ratings, ratings of overt behavior, psychological test results); the source of information upon which to base evaluation (for example, the patient, the therapist, an independent observer, and so on); the generality or specificity of assessment (for example, global personality ratings, ratings of such specific symptomatology as depression or anxiety, ratings of overt behavior); and whether the patient's status is to be assessed at only one point in time or whether the assessment includes the concept of change or improvement (Bergin and Lambert 1978, Bergin and Strupp 1972, Green et al. 1975, Mischel 1971, Kazdin and Wilson 1978, Strupp 1978, Strupp and Hadley 1977). However, regardless of what criteria have been chosen, the lack of relation among outcome criteria used by different researchers has been a recurrent methodological difficulty.

This state of affairs is partly due to the fact that some investigators have selected criteria for making overall judgments of success or improvement from a specific theoretical frame of reference, and these criteria are likely to be only partially related to those selected from another point of view (Paul 1976). For example, investigators with a psychoanalytic orientation, whose main concern is with intrapsychic functioning, are prone to select psychodynamic, cognitive criteria for the assessment of change in their patients. Behaviorists, in contrast, seek as criteria of change overt symptomatology and observable behavior. Others, perhaps those with a more idealistic value system, might consider as criteria for the success of treatment the enhancement of a patient's quality of life or the fulfillment of his or her positive capacities. The result is that evidence derived from different criteria is difficult to generalize. The use of different criteria also makes comparisons from one study to another ambiguous (Fiske et al. 1979, Parloff et al. 1978, Strupp and Bergin 1969).

A recent attempt to deal with this problem has been the development of multiple measurement procedures that are applicable across different types of therapeutic techniques. Consensus exists that divergent processes occur in therapeutic change and that divergent methods of criterion measurement, both objective and subjective, are needed. A multivariate approach also has the additional important advantage of being cost effective. As pointed out by a number of authors, for example, Edwards and Cronbach (1966) and Meltzoff and Kornreich (1970), the cost of multivariate analyses is trivial compared to the cost of setting up additional experiments, and such analyses greatly increase the amount of information obtained.

In general, research on the effectiveness of psychotherapy would benefit from an expanded set of outcome criteria. Techniques are likely to be differentially valuable across the available criteria, so that one specific treatment may be superior to another only on one or a few criteria. Thus, "the treatment of choice for a given patient may vary depending upon the particular outcome criterion relevant to the individual patient's problem" (Kazdin and Wilson 1978, p. 129). The necessity for evaluating change in many dimensions has been stressed repeatedly (Bergin and Lambert 1978, Kazdin and Wilson 1978, Edwards and Cronbach 1966, Fiske et al. 1970, Frank 1966, Strupp 1978, Strupp and Bloxom 1975, Zax and Klein 1966) and will be discussed in greater detail in the section "Measurement of Outcome."

## A Conceptual Model for Assessing Change

While disagreement may exist over what criteria to use when assessing therapeutic change and over ways in which to measure these criteria, there is little disagreement over the fact that a conceptual model for evaluating diverse changes is desirable. One such model has been explicated by Strupp and Hadley (1977).

Strupp and Hadley's (1977) "tripartite model" suggests that psychotherapeutic outcome be viewed from multiple vantage points: the *individual, society,* and the *mental health professional.* The term "mental health" has somewhat different meanings when viewed from these different perspectives, inasmuch as different value systems are involved. From the standpoint of society, whose concern is primarily with the prevailing standards of sanctioned conduct, mental health tends to be defined in terms of behavioral stability and

57

conformity. The individual himself wishes to be content, or happy, and consequently for him mental health is equated with a sense of well-being. For the mental health professional, mental health tends to be defined with reference to some theoretical model of a "healthy" personality structure, the most comprehensive and ambitious of which is psychoanalytic theory.

For psychotherapeutic treatment to be considered successful, deficits in any of these three areas should be remedied (Strupp and Hadley 1977). Some investigators, however, particularly those with a behavioristic orientation (for example, Kazdin and Wilson), see the requirement of change in the last area simply as "a reaffirmation of psychodynamic theory that assumes that behavioral adjustment and improved subjectively experienced improvement are not treatment goals per se, but merely reflections of the underlying personality structure that is the proper object of therapeutic reorganization" (1978, p. 117).

Whether or not one accepts this model, or any other, for the assessment of therapeutic change, there is general agreement in the following areas. Change is diverse; therefore, any single study of psychotherapy should incorporate a number of measures in order to enhance the sensitivity of the research and its comparability across studies. In addition, information about changes that have occurred or are occurring should be obtained from as many sources as possible. Among these are: the patient, the therapist, independent observers, and significant others (relatives, friends, associates, and so forth).

## Measurement of Therapeutic Outcome

While an investigator may want to focus on a specific area of interest, for example interpersonal relationships, there are advantages to having instruments with a broad coverage. Most investigators, for example, would agree about the importance of evaluating subjective distress, overt symptomatology, and impairment in functioning. An advantage to this approach is that because the behaviors of interest can be described in such a way as to avoid theoretical assumptions, a comparison of therapeutic approaches based on different theoretical principles is possible (Spitzer and Endicott 1975).

There has been, therefore, a trend towards the development of measurement procedures that could be used across different types of psychotherapy. Notwithstanding the unique goals of particular therapies, there appears to be some support for the notion that changes produced by psychotherapy may be assessed by "batteries" of instruments that, through the use of several types of measurement procedures, attempt to assess the core changes that result from any psychotherapeutic endeavor.

Waskow and Parloff (1975), for example, published a report resulting from an NIMH-sponsored attempt to recommend a battery of instruments that could provide the core of assessment in psychotherapy outcome studies. This battery has the virtues of being applicable to data resulting from studies derived from a number of theoretical orientations and of incorporating information about patients obtained from a number of different vantage points: self, therapist, independent evaluator, and relevant others. Each of these sources of information provides data relevant to psychopathology and symptomatology, and both the independent evaluator and relevant others contribute data concerning patients' social behavior and role functioning. The battery recommended by Waskow (1975) includes for the patient: the Hopkins Symptom Checklist (Derogatis, Lipman, and Covi 1973; Derogatis et al.1974); Target Complaints (Battle et al. 1966); and ten clinical scales from the MMPI (Dahlstrom, Welsh, and Dahlstrom 1972). The therapist completes only Target Complaints.

Instruments to be completed by the independent evaluator include the Symptom Scales and Role Scales of the Psychiatric Status Schedule (Endicott and Cohen 1967, Spitzer et al. 1970). Relevant others complete either the Katz Adjustment Scales (Katz and Lyerly 1963) or the Personal Adjustment and Role Skills Scales (Ellsworth 1975).

Despite the advantages of this battery, some of its tests have been questioned on a number of grounds. As the author herself points out, there are problems associated with the use of Target Complaints that are intrinsic to the use of any individualized measures. How, for example, do you combine or compare scores of different patients? How much weight should be given to each complaint? (Waskow 1975). The noncomparable data provided by the use of unique target symptoms makes statistical evaluation of outcome data exceedingly difficult.

Other objections, of which the NIMH conferees were also aware, have been raised about the use of the MMPI. For example, although the MMPI scales continue to be used frequently, the MMPI is often criticized as being an outmoded instrument.

**59**

In part, this is because the scales and the items composing them lack clear meaning. Criticism has also centered on the strongly nosological orientation of the scales and the fact that they are not designed with a specific type of therapeutic change in mind (Bergin and Lambert 1978). They also bear no relation to well established diagnostic classification systems.

Therefore, while acknowledging that a routine battery such as that recommended by Waskow (1975) could be instrumental in coordinating and accelerating the advancement of knowledge about psychotherapeutic change, Bergin and Lambert (1978) express doubts that a single core battery could be effectively applied. They cite as reasons for the doubts the differing theoretical and conceptual preferences of investigators, as well as differences concerning valued directions of change. Nevertheless, they do not rule out the development of several core batteries that could be applied to treatment situations when appropriate. Gottman and Markman (1978) also express reservations about the "core battery" concept. They consider it "a step backward in psychotherapy research" inasmuch as it persists in viewing therapy and change as uniform concepts. As they see it, change measures should be geared to what the therapy intends to accomplish.

## Measures from Different Vantage Points

The following discussion consists of brief descriptions of the types of information about patients that may be obtained from the different vantage points of the individual himself, the therapist, the independent observer, relevant others, and community members. Some limitations of data gathered from each of these perspectives will also be presented.

### Measures from Patients

The only way of tapping changes in a patient's feelings is through his or her reports, direct or indirect. Perhaps the simplest and most direct approach is to ask the patient to evaluate his or her own status. This may be done via inventories, scales, questionnaires, and checklists that assess traits, needs, and symptoms as well as other paper-and-pencil measures of personality and adjustment (Cartwright 1975, Glesser 1975, Imber 1975).

There has been, for example, a great deal of work on self-rating scales as instruments for evaluating the severity of patients' depression and anxiety. Although there are many such scales available, two of the better known depression scales are the Beck Depression Inventory (BDI) and the Zung Self-Rating Depression Scale (SDS). These will be discussed briefly to illustrate the general form of such scales.

The BDI (Beck 1967) consists of twenty-one sets of statements derived clinically on the basis of experience with depressed patients. Each set contains four or five sentences from which the patient selects the one most applicable to him or her. The BDI has been used with several large patient populations, and the means of samples of "not depressed," "mildly depressed," "moderately depressed," and "severely depressed" patients serve as normative data.

The BDI has been shown to have relatively high internal consistency and test/retest reliability (Beck 1967, Beck et al. 1974). It has also demonstrated both concurrent validity (Beck 1967, Beck et al. 1974, Metcalfe and Goldman 1965, Nussbaum et al. 1963) and construct validity (Beck 1961, 1967; Beck and Ward 1961; Gottschalk, Glesser, and Springer 1963).

The Zung SDS (Zung 1965) has also received widespread clinical and research use. It consists of twenty items, reflecting the typical affective, physiological, and psychological symptoms of depression, to which the patient responds on a four-point frequency scale. Total raw scores are converted to an SDS Index, for which norms derived from a number of validating groups are provided.

A review of the recent literature concerning the SDS provided relatively limited information about the scale's reliability (Hedlund and Vieweg 1979). Zung (1972) reports a split half reliability of + .73 for a group of psychiatric patients, and Giambra (1977) reports an internal consistency measure of + .79, based on inter-item correlations for a group of nonpatients. While these kinds of reliability are probably adequate, other data, including test/retest stability over time, would be desirable. In contrast, the SDS evidences substantial concurrent validity in its relations with a number of other depression scales. In the opinion of Hedlund and Vieweg (1979) "the literature appears to support the use of the SDS principally as a screening instrument and as an adjunctive clinical tool, not as an independent measure of clinical depression" (p. 55).

Q-sorts, which yield such measures as self-esteem and self-ideal discrepancy, have also been used relatively widely in psychotherapy outcome research. With this technique, the client or patient is asked to arrange a general series of self-descriptive statements, phrases, or adjectives into a number of piles in order of self-relevance. There are customarily eleven piles, and the number of statements, or words, that he or she is asked to place in each is designed to provide a normal statistical distribution. Several instruments utilizing this procedure, in addition to the original devised by Butler and Haigh (1954), have been developed (Bergin and Lambert 1978, Cartwright 1975). There are also techniques specifically designed to assess the outcome of behavior therapy (Kazdin and Wilson 1978, Krasner 1975). The chief advantage of the Q-sort procedure over the use of other rating methods is that it permits relatively precise comparative responses among a large number of items (Nunnally 1967). It would be out of the question, for example, to ask a patient to make paired comparisons of 100 items related to self-esteem in order to determine those items most descriptive of him or her. It would be almost as difficult to rank order the items in terms of self-relevance. In comparison to these procedures, the Q-sort is a relatively easy method for obtaining these types of data.

In addition to providing data unobtainable by other means, self-report data are relatively non-time-consuming and reasonably efficient. They are also cost-effective inasmuch as they do not require extra people to make ratings. However, if a patient can clearly perceive the significance of the information he or she provides, the question then arises: What factors other than his or her internal state are influencing the patient's statement? For example, self-report data are particularly subject to the effects of social desirability; that is, the patient may respond in a manner that he or she believes to be socially "correct." In addition, patients vary in the extent to which they are able to report accurately what they feel. For example, self-reporting may have only limited use with severely ill or semiliterate patients. Self-reports may also be affected by unconscious distortions. They may also be affected by such subtle social influences as the desire to please the therapist by expressing satisfaction and minimizing symptomatology (Frank 1966, Meltzoff and Kornreich 1970, Zax and Klein 1966). Additionally, self-reports by patients are necessarily restricted to areas such as moods, attitudes, and behaviors. It is often the case that such areas of functioning as impairment of thought processes and ability to test reality accurately must be judged by another person (Spitzer and Endicott 1975). A fundamental problem of direct patient reports, then, is the difficulty of obtaining unbiased assessment (Green et al. 1975, Paul 1976).

However, it is very important to emphasize that the fact that biases connected with self-report data *may* exist does not mean that they necessarily *do* exist in every case. For one thing, some of these biases may be of trivial magnitude and thus have little impact on the nature of the data that are obtained. Secondly, where group data are considered, it is often the case that the biases of some respondents are opposite to those of others so that they cancel one another out. For example, those patients wishing to please the therapist with their responses might very well be counterbalanced by those who are dissatisfied with their therapy and are willing to report it. Therefore, the general suspicion of the validity of self-report measures may be unwarranted. In fact, Gottman and Markman (1978) argue that there is mounting evidence that self-report measures can be highly valid.

Several indirect measures of the patient's subjective state have also been proposed. Projective tests such as the Rorschach or TAT permit measure of change in the patient's attitudes and feelings via communications whose significance is not always apparent to him or her. As such, they provide indices of a patient's style of organization of thinking and perceiving that are relatively free of such influences as social desirability (Frank 1966, Holzman 1975). Although there is little doubt that responses to projective tests can be consciously manipulated, there is considerable evidence that they are less influenced than are responses to more direct questions (Endicott and Endicott 1975).

These advantages notwithstanding, the deficiencies of projective techniques for research purposes are well documented (for example, Buros 1970). Their reported reliabilities have been low, and very little research exists to demonstrate their validity as measures of personality dimensions. In addition, they are time consuming and, in contrast to self-reports, they require personnel for administration, scoring, and interpretation. Furthermore, they bear no obvious relation to clinical improvement and must, therefore, be validated against other measures of a patient's subjective state and behavior (Frank 1966).

In spite of these disadvantages, there is recent evidence that such projectives as the TAT and Holzman Inkblot Technique, when treated as structured interviews whose content can be analyzed in the same manner as that of other interviews, have sufficient validity to be considered for possible inclusion in a test battery (Waskow 1975). They might, for example, be useful as additional instruments in the research of investigators whose theoretical orientation is compatible with the psychodynamic concepts underlying the techniques, whose patients do not object to the time involved in their administration, and who also have sufficient staff time available.

### Measures from Therapists

Prior to about 1940, it was taken for granted that the psychotherapist was the proper assessor of therapeutic outcome since he or she was in the best position to evaluate changes in the patient over the course of treatment. Around that time, however, psychotherapy researchers became increasingly sensitive to the numerous problems inherent in having the therapist as the judge of therapeutic change. Therapists' evaluations were, therefore, suspected of producing grossly biased data. There have, in fact, been several studies that show low correlations between therapists' ratings of outcome and other criteria such as patients' rating, tests, and so on (Garfield 1980; Garfield, Prager, and Bergin 1971). Today, however, there is a growing belief in the therapist as a valuable and potentially valid source of criterion information (Luborsky 1971, 1975; Strupp and Bloxom 1975). Evidence is accumulating that the therapist can provide relatively unbiased reports, particularly in the case of assessments of patient functioning (Endicott et al. 1976, Luborsky and Bachrach 1974).

There has, for example, been a good deal of research on rating scales that may be completed by clinicians for measuring change in a patient's status. Although there are many such scales, the Hamilton Rating Scale for Depression (HRSD) (Hamilton 1960, 1967) is an example of one that has been used extensively in the study of depressive illness. The HRSD consists of a seventeen-item list of symptoms to be checked in terms of severity by a clinician on the basis of an interview. Since the primary purpose of the scale is to quantify the data obtained in an interview, "its value depends entirely on the skill of the interviewer in eliciting the necessary information" (Hamilton 1967, p. 56).

A number of studies have reported good average interrater reliability for the HRSD, ranging from + .88 (Beck et al. 1975) to + .99 (Hamilton 1976), and have documented both its construct validity (Beck et al. 1974; Schwab, Bialow, and Holger 1967; Zealley and Aitken 1969) and its concurrent validity as a measure of depressive illness (Brown and Zung 1972, Beck et al. 1974, Schwab et al. 1967). Factor-analytic studies have yielded two relatively stable factors: a general depression factor that appears to reflect the severity of depressive illness; and an "agitated-retarded" factor.

However, while there exists a good deal of evidence that the HRSD is a reliable and valid measure of the severity of depressive illness, many investigators have demonstrated important differences in their results when using both clinical ratings such as the HRSD and self-report measures of depression. For this reason, they strongly encourage the use of both observer ratings and patient self-ratings to more adequately assess the nature and severity of depression (Hedland and Vieweg 1979).

The Health-Sickness Rating Scale (HSRS) is another example of a measure that has been used to reflect a therapist's evaluation of a patient's adjustment. The HSRS (Keinberg et al. 1972, Luborsky 1962) is a global assessment of severity of illness that uses a zero to 100 scale, with anchor points that are described in diagnostic and functional terms. The evaluator also has available to him brief descriptions of actual patients whose scores are distributed throughout the range of the scale.

Some investigators might find the numerical ratings too closely tied to traditional psychiatric diagnostic concepts and terminology (Waskow 1959). Nevertheless, a number of studies have shown that initial levels on the HSRS provide significant prediction of the outcome of psychotherapy (Luborsky and Bachrach 1974; Luborsky et al. 1980; Mintz, Luborsky, and Christoph 1979).

The therapist has both assets and liabilities as an evaluator of psychotherapy outcome. In the assets column, the therapist as a trained professional presumably is an expert in the assessment of abnormal behavior. He or she can rate and assess certain manifestations of illness that the patient would find impossible or extremely difficult to do. For example, a patient cannot be expected to assess loss of insight, and would find it extremely difficult to assess such symptoms as mild retardation, agitation, hypochondriasis, and delusions; whereas the therapist can rate all grades of severity of illness, from the mildest to the most severe. In addition, the therapist has unique, first-hand information about the case from beginning to termination and, at least relative to the patient or the patient's family, is apt to be more objective in his or her evaluation of outcome. Further, there is reasonably high agreement between ratings of outcome made by the therapist and those made by other clinical judges (Strupp and Bloxom 1975). Perhaps the therapist's most important asset is that he or she is "in a position to organize or evaluate all the clinical data flexibly, weighing the unique features of each case differently. . . . He can realize that goals may shift during the course of treatment, and that presenting problems may not reflect the focus of the therapeutic work as it progresses" (Mintz 1977, p. 596).

In the liabilities column, the major issue concerns the bias that is likely to be introduced due to the fact that the therapist may feel his own worth as a practitioner reflected in a patient's outcome (Luborsky et al. 1971, Meltzoff and Kornreich 1970). Although there is little evidence in the literature for this bias (Mintz 1977), it seems plausible, and is certainly possible that this lack of evidence merely represents a lack of investigation of the issue.

A second drawback to the use of the therapist as evaluator of patient outcome is the fact that studies utilizing untreated controls or waiting-list control groups have no therapist. Also, therapists' ratings of patients who have received different types of psychotherapy are probably not comparable. Therefore, investigators conducting studies with untreated, waiting-list, or alternative treatment groups are more likely to select as outcome measures those, such as tests, observer ratings, or behavioral criteria, that can be applied to all study groups (Mintz 1977).

Whatever the disadvantages of therapists' ratings of outcome, the fact is that in most psychiatric settings they are widely used. There appears to be consensus that, as far as possible, therapists' judgments should be specific, concrete, and concern the directly observable (Lorr 1975). Interestingly, however, the global outcome nine-point rating scale originally developed for the 1954 Rogers and Dymond project still enjoys considerable popularity. In fact, in Bergin and Lambert's opinion "it correlates so highly with other more complex and sophisticated ratings. . . . that it may well be the measure of choice for this purpose" (1978, p. 178).

Strupp and Bloxom (1975) also believe that global evaluations are probably the most valid measure of therapy outcome available. They do, however, point out that while these global evaluations appear to capture important aspects of therapeutic change, they do not provide information about the *nature* of the change; "they are purely relative to an insufficiently clear baseline. . . ." (1975, p. 171).

In a recent investigation that tested the relationship between psychodynamic and symptomatic outcome measures, Mintz (1981) found that ratings of simple symptomatic improvement, which were made by essentially untrained nonprofessional judges who typically took less than one minute per case to make their ratings, accounted for two thirds of the reliable variation in the expert clinicians' dynamic assessments for those patients whose initial symptoms did not improve. For those patients who symptoms did improve, there was a divergence in the two types of assessments. While additional studies are obviously needed, Mintz's (1981) findings do raise questions as to the importance of the expert clinician and the psychodynamic hypothesis of the necessity of deep personality change in the assessment of treatment outcome.

For these reasons, then, there is a trend toward the use of fairly specific measures of behavior drawn from a wide sample of situations. There are still relatively few standardized evaluation procedures designed specifically for use by the therapist. The NIMH report edited by Waskow and Parloff (1975) does, however, describe several therapist measures. Waskow (1975), for example, recommends Target Complaints (Battle et al. 1966) obtained from the therapist as part of the "core battery." Among other measures considered as promising, Lorr (1975) and Bergin and Lambert (1978) suggest the use of the Interpersonal Behavior Inventory, and Strupp and Bloxom (1975) make several suggestions for measures that are particularly likely to reflect changes occurring in psychoanalytic therapy.

In summary, while the specter of therapist bias in ratings of therapeutic outcome may have some basis in fact, the abandonment of the therapist as an informant would be a serious mistake. What is needed is a sustained effort to evaluate available instruments that seem promising and to develop additional ones that adequately reflect available psychometric techniques in dealing with complex clinical data.

## Measures from Independent Clinical Evaluators

Independent clinical evaluators have one obvious advantage over the patient, the therapist, or, in an inpatient setting, other members of the treatment team such as nurses or attendants. That is, being nonparticipants, these "independents" are less ego-involved and have no vested interest in the outcome of treatment. For this reason, they have the potential for making more accurate, unbiased observations and judgments (Luborsky 1975, Meltzoff and Kornreich 1975, Spitzer and Endicott 1975). This is particularly true if the impartial assessors have no knowledge of the treatment received. A further advantage of independent evaluators is that they usually possess some degree of expertise in observing and judging and in the use of the diagnostic instruments that aid them in making evaluations (Luborsky 1975). The degree of expertise required will, of course, depend on the level and complexity of judgments (Meltzoff and Kornreich 1970).

As is the case with information obtained from other vantage points, the data provided by independent clinical evaluators also pose potential problems. First, since it is seldom the case that independent evaluators are blind to the treatment received by the patient, their preconceptions about therapeutic effects introduce a potential bias. Moreover, if the content of therapeutic protocols provides the sources of their data, the clinical evaluators are likely to be influenced by statements related to therapeutic progress made by both patients and therapists within therapy sessions (Meltzoff and Kornreich 1970).

A second potential problem concerns the fact that some patients do not easily accept the idea of being interviewed by a stranger, particularly in an outpatient setting and if the interview bears no clear relation to their treatment. However, in Spitzer and Endicott's (1975) opinion, it is more frequently the therapist rather than the patient who expresses reluctance toward having an outsider privy to his or her personal relationship with a patient.

A more serious problem is posed by the fact that independent assessors customarily base their ratings on a single clinical interview (Kazdin and Wilson 1978). The problem here is one of validity: ". . .can one trust judgments made on the basis of contact that is necessarily limited to a short time period of one or two hours?" (Spitzer and Endicott 1975, p. 223). Spitzer and Endicott (1975) answer their own question by stating that there is no doubt that it is possible for patients, either unconsciously or deliberately, to misrepresent their customary behavior. However, all the evidence of which these investigators are aware demonstrates that, for the purpose of group comparisons, independent assessments provide valid ratings of patient behavior.

There are many types of independent clinical evaluation measures from which to choose. Luborsky (1975) presents a brief listing of the main types, including examples of each. There are measures based on interviews of relatives or other informants, including the patient himself. These can include ratings of various aspects of psychopathology; of interpersonal, occupational, and sexual adjustment; as well as measures based exclusively on behavior during the interview. There are also measures derived from diagnostic psychological tests and those based on a combination of sources, for example interviews and tests and improvement scales.

The services of independent clinical evaluators are customarily both expensive and time consuming. Therefore, it is important, when choosing assessment instruments, to select those that are as parsimonious as possible without sacrificing comprehensiveness. When possible, an interview instrument should have demonstrated reliability and validity, should have coverage appropriate to the hypotheses being tested in the study, should be standardized so that variability associated with differences in interviewing methods and coverage are minimal, and should require not much over an hour to complete. Interviews lasting two hours or more fatigue both patient and interviewer (Spitzer and Endicott 1975).

### Measures from Community Members

One of the most meaningful tests of therapeutic outcome is the change in a patient's subsequent behavior and functioning outside of the setting in which therapy takes place (Fiske 1975, Paul 1976). Respondents who provide this information are typically a spouse, parent, sibling, child, some other relative, or a friend or work associate. Information may also be collected from factual records (for example, hospital discharge and readmission rates, criminal arrest rates, parole violations, insurance claims, work records, and rates of nonpsychiatric medical utilization). These latter variables may provide important data for the conduct of comprehensive cost-effectiveness and cost-benefit analyses. By themselves, however, they cannot be considered suitable criteria of therapeutic outcome (Bergin and Lambert 1978).

In the past, "significant others" have been looked upon with some suspicion as informants. This is undoubtedly due to the belief that, relative to the degree of their emotional involvement with the patient, their reports are vulnerable to distortions and lack of objectivity (Hogarty 1975, Hogarty and Katz 1971, Kazdin and Wilson 1978). However, a number of investigators believe that there is enough empirical evidence to suggest that this assumption is unfounded (Hogarty 1975). Yet even those investigators who advocate the use of significant others stress the need for using pooled judgments obtained from several informants. The reason for this strategy is to provide not only more reliable information, but also a broader view of the patient's adjustment and behavior (Bergin and Lambert 1978, Fiske 1976).

Evaluations of community adjustment may be oriented toward interpersonal areas such as family, marital, and sexual adjustment, role performance as a wage earner or homemaker, and pursuit of recreation and free-time activities. Alternatively, these evaluations may deal with such intrapsychic and personal topics as mood, energy level, psychological level, psychological discomfort, insight, and personal care (Fiske 1975, Hogarty 1975).

Ideally, what is needed are measures of community adjustment that are reliable and valid, that require minimal skills of the administrator, that can be easily completed by mail or in person, and that assess broad parameters of social behavior and adjustment (Hogarty 1975). Obviously, measures that meet all these specifications are not to be found. This is largely because the assessment of community adjustment, particularly after termination of treatment, is subject to many more restrictions than are encountered when patient evaluations are made while the patient is still associated with the setting in which therapy took place.

Take the case of the investigator who wishes follow-up data from significant others on a sample of schizophrenics six months after their discharge from treatment. The least expensive way of obtaining this information is solicitation by mail. A spouse or parent could be asked, for example, to complete a questionnaire whose items relate to the patient's current functioning in the areas of interpersonal relations, work or school performance, and so forth. The financial gain derived from the use of this method is, however, usually offset by the loss of information due to nonresponders or by the inadequacy or incompleteness of information. In general, such problems as illiteracy, difficulty in reading comprehension, and a limited response to lengthy questionnaires and/or emotionally loaded questions are better controlled with an in-person interview than they are by mail (Hogarty 1975).

In-person interviews may be conducted by having the patient's relative return to the treatment setting or by having a staff member conduct the interview at the respondent's home. But the former method is rarely feasible, and the latter is expensive. Furthermore, respondents are often uncooperative, and frequently both the patient and his or her "significant other" have moved and cannot be located.

However, when they can be located and are willing to cooperate, they can provide highly valuable information. There are a number of measures in the literature that may be utilized for obtaining information from "significant others" about a patient's functioning. An instrument that has been highly recommended in terms of content, psychometric properties, and ease of administration is the Katz Adjustment Scales (KAS)—Relatives Form (1963) (Bergin and Lambert 1978, Fiske 1975, Hogarty 1975). One other instrument, the Ellsworth Personal Adjustment and Role Skills (PARS) scale approximates the KAS in content and development, but the KAS is more comprehensive, and has more extensive reliability and validity data (Hogarty 1975). One cautionary note: Reports should, when possible, be collected from more than one source, since only limited evidence exists of interrespondent agreement.

In summary, two points should be made. The first is that although data collected from multiple vantage points have been discussed primarily as outcome measures, these data may also be obtained at any point during therapy, including at initial evaluation. Second, the collection of data from the patient, from the therapist, from an independent clinical evaluator, and from significant others in the patient's life can be both time consuming and expensive. Nevertheless, since each provides a unique perspective, each has some degree of validity. In fact, since ratings provided by these different sources tend to correlate only moderately at best, it is important to include, when possible, outcome measures from each vantage point (Luborsky 1975).

## Issues Related to Follow-Up

There are two basic approaches that have characterized follow-up research in psychotherapy. The first is what Liberman (1978) calls the *global-archival* method. With this method, a researcher attempts to locate patients who were treated and assessed at discharge two, five, or ten years previously—in order to make a global assessment of their current condition relative to their status at the termination of treatment. Each patient is given a rating—for example, "improved," "same," or "worse"—and the percent of patients in each category is then determined.

Although many studies using this approach have been conducted, primarily in European settings, it is not used as frequently as it was in the '50s and '60s. This is because, while it may provide some valuable information, it suffers from many methodological weaknesses. For example, its lack of a control group precludes making inferences from the data, and only descriptive statements of current status relative to previous status are possible. Further, "even these statements may be of questionable merit as the original assessment procedures used to determine the patient's pathology are frequently no longer in existence or no longer available" (Liberman 1978, p. 108).

With the second major approach to follow-up, a study is conducted in which two groups of patients each receive a different form of therapy. The patients are then assessed at the end of treatment and comparisons made of the relative efficacy of the treatments. These patients are then contacted and evaluated at some future point in order to assess the longer-term comparative effectiveness of the treatments. Since comparison groups exist, inferential statements are possible; however, this approach faces many of the same methodological problems inherent in the global-archival one.

For example, the longer the period of time between the end of the study and the follow-up, the greater the likelihood that assessment devices and evaluative procedures will differ. Investigators such as Strupp and Bergin (1969), who stress the importance of having follow-up procedures as thorough, precise, and complete as those that were used during the therapy period, see this as a major drawback. A second problem with long-term follow-up is the likelihood that there will be a change in the personnel making the evaluations (Liberman 1978). Either of these factors alone or in combination can render the data obtained questionable.

Possibly for these reasons, follow-up, when conducted at all, has seldom tended to occur more than six months after the termination of therapy (Liberman 1978). For example, in their examination of four major behavior therapy journals for the year 1973, Cochrane and Sobol (1976) found only 35 percent of the studies included follow-up assessments. Further, only a third of these occurred as much as six months subsequent to the termination of therapy.

Nevertheless, in spite of all the potential difficulties, there clearly is a need for the assessment of patients at some point or points after the end of therapy in order to determine the success or effectiveness of treatment. The main questions are how long patients should be followed and what the ultimate criterion for the success of therapy is.

With regard to the first question, several investigators (for example, Strupp and Bergin 1969) believe that the lack of long-term follow-up is a serious defect relevant to both experimental and control groups. They believe that, with long-term data available, fluctuations of pathology in both experimental and control groups could be correlated with environmental and interpersonal events. This, they claim, would increase our knowledge of the natural history of conditions treated by psychotherapy, which in turn would provide some indication of the changes likely to result from therapy. Such long-term follow-up is probably most relevant for patients who have undergone psychoanalytic treatment.

In contrast, other investigators believe that there is substantial evidence that the results at the end of treatment are relatively good predictors of subsequent status (Paul 1967). Frank (1969), for example, states that the results from a number of studies substantiate the notion that a patient's condition immediately following psychotherapy can serve as a good predictor of how he or she will be five years later. Because of the considerable expense involved in follow-up investigations, Frank urges a careful weighing of their costs against potential gains.

What, then, is an optimal follow-up period? To date there is no consensus. For this reason, Gottman and Markman stress the "need for systematic investigation of follow-up patterns over varying times after treatment as a function of the target problem, the treatment program's components, and for different kinds of [patients]" (1978, p. 56).

The answer to the second question, regarding the criterion for a treatment's success, has no simple answer, especially for patients with disorders that tend to be chronic. Rosen (1969), for example, states:

From the standpoint of the individual patient, and his

> family, it is a blessing to be free of schizophrenia, even for
> a few months or a few years. To be free of it forever, is almost
> miraculous, and few therapists are miracle-workers, no mat-
> ter what their treatment methods may be [p. 750].

Stone et al. (1961) also believe that a treatment's efficacy should
be evaluated primarily in terms of its immediate results. They
contend that even if subsequent follow-up evaluations show
no statistical differences between therapeutic treatment conditions, the better treatment would be the one that achieved the
greatest amount of improvement most rapidly.

### Methodological Problems in Long-Term Follow-Up

First, there is the problem of attrition of patient samples over
time, and the ever-increasing difficulty of not only locating
patients, but also of securing their cooperation with the assessment procedures. This is particularly true when these procedures involve lengthy interviews or questionnaires. Liberman
reports that, based on his studies and other published reports,
"rarely have investigators obtained more than 50–60 percent of
an original outpatient sample after five years have elapsed"
(1978, p. 119). He also points out that diligence in the attempt
to locate former patients must be tempered by the ethic of
confidentiality. This precludes tracing former patients via relatives, friends, and associates. Unless, of course, patients have
given prior consent and have supplied names of individuals
through whom they might later be reached (Showstack et al.
1978). When this is not the case, the researcher is forced to rely
on such archival sources as city directories, bureaus of vital
statistics, and some publicly available courthouse records.

Related to attrition of patient samples is the problem of the
degree to which follow-up subjects represent the original treatment and control groups. Even if a patient can be located, it is
still open to question whether he or she will be willing to
participate in a reassessment. It is possible, for example, that
only satisfied patients will cooperate with follow-up assessments. Therefore, it is necessary to determine that follow-up
and original samples are equivalent on all relevant clinical and
demographic variables. If they are not, the internal validity of
such investigations and, therefore, their conclusions may be
compromised (Liberman 1978).

Another issue related to attrition is the fact that patients who
relapse are seldom studied. Although the evidence is sparse, it

is clear that treatment effects are not automatically maintained after the patient terminates treatment. Studies of patients who relapse might detect diagnostic subcategories of individuals who are not amenable to certain forms of treatment. For such individuals, treatment might be modified in an attempt to ensure that gains made in therapy will be more lasting (Gottman and Markman 1978, Kazdin and Wilson 1978).

A second major problem that becomes increasingly prominent as the length of the follow-up period increases is that results will almost invariably be confounded by uncontrolled treatment or diluted by the viscissitudes of time (Lambert 1976, Liberman 1978, Paul 1967, Voth and Orth 1973). "There are simply too many intervening variables during an interval between the end of treatment and a two- or five-year follow-up interview to be able to demonstrate the superiority of one treatment over another" (Cristol 1972, p. 199).

Butcher and Koss (1978), for example, cite a study conducted by Frank et al. (1959). For six months patients were treated in individual therapy, group therapy, or minimal contact therapy. Immediately after therapy, the individual therapy patients had improved significantly in social effectiveness from their pretherapy baseline, but no such improvement was noted for the other two groups. Continued negatively accelerated improvement was seen for all groups at the five-year follow-up, at which time 97 percent of the patients were rated as improved, and there was no longer any significant difference among the groups.

These findings may be explained in part in terms of the patients' behavior after the formal short-term treatment ended. Two-thirds remained in therapy for a year, and one-third were still in therapy at the end of two years. This uncontrolled treatment, in addition to any number of uncontrolled events occurring over the five-year period, renders the data collected at that time less relevant as a specific demonstration of the effectiveness of the original therapy methods.

This example highlights the extent to which intercurrent events can play an important role in patient change during the follow-up period and thereby make it difficult to demonstrate differences in effectiveness among treatments. However, there is no unequivocal empirical support for this position. Liberman cites a number of studies that show that most intercurrent events that have been studied, such as changes in family composition, marital state, or even occupational advancement, were uncorrelated with patient outcome at follow-up. He concludes that "more specific tests of hypotheses regarding the relevance and significance of intercurrent events must be performed before any firm conclusions can be drawn" (1978, p. 123).

In summary, there is consensus that the judicious use of follow-up is necessary for an adequate evaluation of the effects of psychotherapy. Even though it may not be possible to arrive at definitive conclusions concerning efficacy, such research may provide useful information regarding the process of therapeutic change. A number of methodological difficulties in the conduct of follow-up research were discussed. These included inconsistencies in the use of measuring instruments, differential patient and personnel attrition, and the occurrence of intercurrent events. How long the follow-up period should be remains problematical, but six months appears to be the most frequently utilized time period. Whatever the period chosen, there should be a careful assessment of events in patients' lives, both environmental and interpersonal, that have occurred since the end of therapy. An important theoretical and empirical endeavor would be to develop a series of appropriate categories for defining the important events in patients' lives that are likely to have therapeutic or antitherapeutic impact.

# CHAPTER 9

# Measuring Cost-Effectiveness and Cost-Benefit

Up to this point we have considered the complexity of assessing the efficacy of psychotherapy and some of the difficulties facing the researcher. This section will address methods for and problems in the assessment of the comparative efficacy of psychotherapy outcome in terms of costs and benefits. Increasingly stringent economic constraints and shifting fiscal priorities have made it incumbent upon mental health professionals to demonstrate not only that psychotherapy "works," but also how much it costs to get what. Over the past few years there has been, therefore, an increasing call for cost-effectiveness or cost-benefit analysis (CEA/CBA) to aid decision making about the use of psychotherapy.

Before discussing the implementation of these concepts, it is important to distinguish between them. Both cost-benefit analysis and cost-effectiveness analysis are concepts derived from industrial economics. Studies conducted within the cost-benefit framework allow one to compare the relative costs and benefits to society of various alternative procedures or programs. In addition, since it is the monetary value of benefits that is compared with the monetary value of costs, this procedure provides the evaluator with a yardstick for assessing the relative attractiveness of alternatives (Levin 1975).

A major difficulty exists in applying cost-benefit analysis to the problem of evaluating the comparative efficacy of various psychotherapeutic endeavors. An underlying and crucial assumption for performing cost-benefit analyses of alternatives is that the outcomes or benefits be "monetized"—that is, translated into monetary units (Levin 1975, Rothenberg 1975). Unfortunately, the outcomes of psychotherapy are difficult to transform into monetary units, and there are some who believe that some psychotherapy outcomes, for example, an increase in self-esteem or the reduction of "psychic pain," simply cannot be reflected in terms of a monetary unit.

For these reasons, cost-effectiveness analysis (CEA) has been more frequently used in the evaluation of the comparative cost-efficacy of psychotherapies (Yates 1980). With this type of analysis, it is the effectiveness with which various programs achieve particular goals (rather than the monetary values of these goals) that is linked to costs. Essentially, CEA is nothing more than comparative cost-accounting; that is, two or more programs are compared in terms of the cost per unit of goods or services delivered for achieving a standardized level of outcome. Nothing explicit is stated about benefits. It is simply assumed that the benefits of the programs are equivalent (Panzetta 1973).

For example, one might examine the various alternatives for reducing the level of depression of a sample of severely depressed hospitalized inpatients. Cost-effectiveness analysis would permit an examination of the cost of alternative therapies for achieving the same goal of alleviation of depressive symptoms. Cost-effectiveness analysis would not, however, allow comparing costs directly with benefits, because the reduction of depressive symptomatology has not been expressed in monetary units. Thus, it is a simple cost analysis of the therapeutic programs, with the least costly being the "most efficient."

To summarize,

> . . .the cost effectiveness approach enables us to rank potential program choices according to the magnitude of their effects relative to their costs, but we cannot ascertain whether a particular program is "worth it" in the sense that benefits exceed costs, because the latter are generally expressed in monetary units while the former are rendered in units of effectiveness for achieving a particular impact [Levin 1975, p. 93].

## Types of Cost Assessment Procedures

Before discussing the methods of assessing the cost of various alternative procedures, it is important to define the conceptual nature of costs. In a general sense, the cost of psychotherapy refers to the total value of the various resources used in the processes of therapy. These include both direct expenditures (what are often called accounting costs) and indirect expenditures (for example, allocated overhead such as electricity), as well as those costs that represent what have been termed *opportunity costs*. For example, the time and energies of unpaid volunteers will not be reflected in accounting costs, but they do represent resource costs since they could be used for alternative projects. Similarly, the value of client or patient time can be considered a cost, since this time represents fore-gone work and other activities.

A comprehensive perspective thus considers these types of costs as well as the psychological costs incurred by patients and others who are affected by the therapy process. It does not omit any elements, even if they could not be used in other ways. Further, wherever possible, costs are transformed into a com-parable metric, although it should be noted that comprehen-sive costing does not require that all costs be expressed in monetary units. Both patients' and therapists' time spent in psychotherapy, for example, may be expressed simply as time. However, when the purpose of the assessment is to compare the total cost-effectiveness of alternative therapies, the costs of patients' and therapists' time are customarily monetized on the basis of current wage rates.

## Methods for Cost Assessment

The measurement of costs would be a relatively simple pro-cedure if all that was necessary was a simple multiplication of the sum of salaries and fringe benefits of all personnel, pro-fessional and nonprofessional, involved in the therapeutic process by the time they put into the process. There are several "time-accounting systems" that have been specifically devel-oped to collect personnel cost data in mental health treatment facilities (Cost-effectiveness analysis 1980). This, however, is not sufficient, and even though it has been estimated that personnel costs typically account for 60 to 80 percent of the total budget (Levin 1975, Yates, Haven, and Thorensen 1979), this procedure would vastly underestimate the true cost of therapy.

In addition to the cost of personnel, it is necessary to evaluate costs in terms of facilities and equipment. In his "ingredients approach" to cost assessment, Levin (1975) recommends using the annual rental payments as an estimate of the cost of rented facilities. To obtain the annual cost of facilities that have been purchased, Levin suggests summing the estimated deprecia-tion value of the facilities and the estimated opportunity cost of the investment; that is, the benefits that the investment would accrue if put to other uses. This latter aspect can be approxi-mated by applying an appropriate rate of interest to the net value of the investment. If facilities are shared with other pro-grams or are provided by a parent enterprise, the measurement of facility costs is even more complex. For example, costs may be prorated among the individual programs. If the data required for prorating are not available, an alternative method of imputing a rental value equal to the annual rent for comparable facilities may be used.

Materials, equipment, and other such inputs may be estimated on the basis of expenditures or, if they have been donated, on the basis of their market value. Such costs typically include office supplies, telephones, food, and may also include such specialized materials as psychological tests and computer services. The value of a patient's time or that of others who become involved in the process of therapy may be appraised by multiplying the amount of time spent by current salary levels.

For a simple CEA or CBA, merely summing the above costs is sufficient. However, for analyses that seek to identify those therapies, therapists, patient types, or settings that cost more to achieve particular goals or benefits, more complex methods are needed. This becomes even more evident when distinctions between fixed and variable costs or between direct and indirect costs are used (see Levin 1975).

It should be noted that while there has been a great deal of interest in CEA and CBA over the last few years, most evaluation research has tended to ignore cost analysis, and frequently even those studies using "cost-effectiveness" or "cost-benefit" in their titles present no monetized data in their method or result sections. It has been estimated, for example, that perhaps as much as 95 percent of psychotherapy research neglects the cost of treatment. In addition, no standards for what should be included in cost analysis have been developed (Cost-effectiveness analysis 1980). While it is not suggested that every study or program conduct a cost analysis with the aim of making a CEA or CBA, such analyses can be potentially valuable in understanding how the effects of psychotherapy are related to the resources that psychotherapy consumes.

## Measurement of Effectiveness

Problems concerning the assessment of the effectiveness of psychotherapy, including those related to selecting and defining appropriate outcome criteria, have been discussed in previous sections. Little more need be said here except to note that outcome criteria must be integrated into the cost-effectiveness framework, usually by assigning arbitrary weights to the outcome measures so they may be aggregated into a single effectiveness index.

There is, however, one other general issue relating to effectiveness that should be mentioned: the time pattern of results. For example, it is often the case that in comparing the total costs for two or more programs, one will show relatively earlier effectiveness than others, even though at the end of an allotted time period, five years, for instance, there may be no differences among them or others may surpass the one showing the earliest effects. Clearly, comparisons of the programs should take this time pattern of impact into account. Levin (1975) discusses ways of accomplishing this by giving greater weight to those programs showing the earlier effectiveness.

## Measurement of Benefits

As previously mentioned, evaluations of the costs of psychotherapy are seldom conducted. However, the assessment of benefits associated with psychotherapy that can be used in cost-benefit analysis is even more problematic. This is largely because, although such analyses require that outcome data be expressed in the same units (usually monetary) with which costs are assessed, methods for making such translations have not been available. Following is a review of the problems of translating effects into monetary benefits (Cost-effectiveness analysis 1980).

### Benefits to Patients

While the most obvious benefits of psychotherapy accrue to patients, not all are easily measured or given monetary value. This is because many benefits are inherently intangible. Increased ability to hold a job or increased salary, for example, are benefits that may be given monetary value in a relatively straightforward way. In contrast, improved quality of life, reflected in such factors as the ability to enjoy oneself and to love others, cannot be assigned any unequivocal monetary value.

Some economists argue that the amount of money a patient is willing to pay for his or her therapy reflects its value to the patient. Therefore, what a patient pays is "the net value of the expected health, social and economic benefits, minus the psychological suffering, lost time, and personal costs that are incurred as a result of undergoing psychotherapy" (Cost-effectiveness analysis 1980, p. 55). This is an interesting way of conceptualizing the benefits derived by patients as a result of psychotherapy. It does not, however, consider that third-party payments often cover a good portion of the expense of therapy. In fact, this conceptual framework has never been applied in practice.

To the extent that patient benefits have been measured at all, only those that can be directly assessed and transformed have been used. For example, Binner, Halpern, and Potter (1973) conducted a CBA of community-based versus institutional therapy. Their patient population consisted of almost 600 patients who had received either inpatient or outpatient treatment. Binner et al. (1973) categorized patients by severity of dysfunction at admission, and stratified therapy intensity at four different levels. Their outcome measure was a gross one, based on a therapist rating that was transformed into a monetary unit by assigning a subjectively derived dollar value to changes in therapists' ratings. Results indicated that benefit/cost ratios were greater than 1 (benefits exceeded costs) for all combinations of impairment and intensity, but that the ratios were significantly larger for low-intensity therapy provided to less-impaired patients.

### Benefits to Those Associated with Patients

Although this idea is admittedly speculative, it is possible that, as a result of a patient's psychotherapy, his or her family and friends may find their lives improved in terms of increased productivity and time. To the extent that these factors can be monetized, this increased time and productivity can be considered a benefit of psychotherapy.

A patient's employer may also benefit from the patient's psychotherapy. The patient may become more productive and have fewer accidents and absences from work. Of course, the costs to the employer who pays for the patient's psychotherapy or who allows an employee release time for therapy must be subtracted from these benefits. Alternatively, the benefits can be considered a direct cost of psychotherapy. In either case, it is important that the analyst not count the same benefits twice.

### Benefits to Society

Perhaps the most easily evaluated benefits are those resulting from patients' maintenance of employment and reductions in the use of social, medical, or criminal services. The problem, however, is that these benefits accumulate over long periods of time, and would, therefore, have to be quite substantial in order for their impact to be evident at any given point in time along the way.

Most of these social service benefits are presented in the form of cost savings. In studies of therapy, for example, related benefits such as reduction in physician visits, drug abuse, and arrests, "the cost of each unit of service is estimated from . . . accounting records, and the reduction in use of units of social services is multipled by the unit cost to estimate monetary cost-savings benefits" (Cost-effectiveness analysis 1980, p. 56). Therefore, here, as in all cases where benefits are being attributed to the effects of psychotherapy, adequate comparison group data are crucial in order to estimate the actual amount of savings that can be attributed to therapy.

## Methods for Cost-Effectiveness Analysis

When benefits and costs cannot be evaluated in the same units, or when outcomes cannot be valued by their market prices or those of similar alternatives, the CEA is more applicable and appropriate than CBA. For example, it is difficult if not impossible to assess the benefits of an increase in self-concept or a decrease in anxiety in terms of their monetary value. Therefore, when treatments to be compared have similar goals, the simpler CEA is both an adequate and appropriate methodology. With this procedure, outcome data, for example, psychiatric patients returning to their communities after treatment in the hospital, are divided by monetary costs to form cost/effectiveness ratios. It is thus possible to determine which of several therapeutic endeavors produces the greatest amount of change at the least cost.

### Tabulation Methods

One of the simplest means of analyzing effectiveness relative to cost is to display the data in an array. Following is an example of this method, comparing the cost-effectiveness of programs designed to prevent rehospitalization of psychiatric patients. The example represents a hypothetical adaptation of Levin's (1975) cost-effectiveness comparison of anti-recidivism programs for released prisoners.

Assume that the State Department of Mental Hygiene is considering funding a number of alternative programs for reducing an apparently high rate of re-admissions of male patients to state psychiatric hospitals. The programs being considered are: job placement, community advocacy, and a combination of these two. In order to assess the relative impact of these three alternatives on the rate of rehospitalization, for a period of one year all discharged male patients returning to their communities from one of the state psychiatric facilities are assigned randomly to one of the three experimental programs or to the currently existing arrangement for discharged patients. At the end of six years the experiment is concluded, and the following results are obtained: five-year rates of rehospitalized patients were 15 percent for the job placement program, 26 percent for the community advocacy program, 12 percent for the combination package, and 37 percent for the patients who received no special treatment. Obviously, the combination program was the most successful, and normally it would be selected. However, a review of the hypothetical data presented in Table 1, which presents a cost-effectiveness comparison of the alternative programs, suggests a somewhat different interpretation of the findings.

Clearly, the normal program is the least expensive, and the combination program shows the highest average cost per patient. Average cost per patient, however, does not reflect the cost of obtaining the specified criterion, that is, the reduction in re-admissions. The sixth row of figures compares average costs for those patients who were not re-admitted over a five-year period. From these data it is evident that the normal program shows the lowest average cost, with job placement next, followed by community advocacy. The combination program is still the most expensive. However, this comparison is not entirely valid either in terms of the criterion, inasmuch as figures for the special programs include some patients who may not have been hospitalized even in the absence of these programs.

What is needed, for each of the special programs, is an estimate of the number of patients who were not rehospitalized over and beyond what could be expected under normal procedures. This is shown in row seven. Compared with the normal program, the community advocacy, job placement, and combination program "saved" an additional eleven, twenty-two, and twenty-five patients, respectively.

However, the additional costs for the special programs over that for the normal program vary considerably, and in order to reach a policy decision, it is necessary to determine the additional cost for each additional patient "saved" from rehospitalization. As the last column in Table 1 indicates, this ranges from $2,273 for the job placement program to $3,636 for community advocacy to $4,400 for the combination program. To keep one person who would have been rehospitalized under customary procedures out of the hospital for five years, the job placement program costs approximately half as much as the combination program. The community advocacy program falls in between these two. Thus, although it was demonstrated that the combination program was the most effective in reducing rates of readmission to hospital, its greatly higher cost would probably preclude it as the program of choice. From a cost-effectiveness point of view, the job placement program that can

**Table 1.** Cost-Effectiveness Comparison of Anti-Rehospitalization Programs for Discharged Psychiatric Patients

|  | Job Placement | Community Advocacy | Combination Program | Normal Program |
|---|---|---|---|---|
| Experimental population | 100 | 100 | 100 | 100 |
| Five-year rate of rehospitalization | 15% | 26% | 12% | 37% |
| Number of patients not rehospitalized | 85 | 74 | 88 | 63 |
| Total cost | $100,000 | $90,000 | $160,000 | $50,000 |
| Average cost per patient | $1,000 | $900 | $1,600 | $500 |
| Average cost per non-rehospitalized patient | $1,176 | $1,216 | $1,818 | $794 |
| Number of patients not rehospitalized compared with normal program | 22 | 11 | 25 | — |
| Additional cost beyond normal program | $50,000 | $40,000 | $110,000 | — |
| Marginal cost per additional non-rehospitalized patient | $2,273 | $3,636 | $4,400 | — |

keep one patient out of the hospital for five years at half the cost of the combined program would appear to be superior.

This illustration highlights a number of issues. The first is that the most effective program is not always the most cost-effective. Second, as may be seen from a comparison of average cost per patient, average cost per non-rehospitalized patient, and marginal cost per additional non-rehospitalized patient, the implications of cost findings differ depending on which measure is chosen. It is essential, therefore, that the appropriate cost comparison, that is, the one that reflects the specified criterion of the study, be utilized in policy decisions.

### Linear Programming

This approach to CEA incorporates not only the factors that determine the effectiveness of psychotherapy, but attempts to include information on cost limits as well. Linear programming considers budget restrictions of a program and, therefore, tries to determine the various contributions of the less effective, but also less costly, factors that contribute to a specified outcome. It is a statistical procedure aimed at selecting the exact combination of the most contributory factors feasible within budget constraints.

Through the equations for linear programming, information is obtained on which therapeutic techniques, delivery systems, and so on are most efficient and on the amounts of each resource required to implement each technique or system. These equations can also provide additional information on the minimal total costs for achieving a specified degree of effectiveness or, conversely, on which cost constraint could be fitted to yield the maximum improvement of effectiveness. These and related techniques have been used by a number of researchers to conduct cost analyses of delivery of psychotherapy (see Cost-effectiveness analysis 1980).

## Methods for Cost-Benefit Analysis

Most simply, in CBA all benefits are summed in terms of the same units (usually dollars), as are costs. Total benefits are then divided by total costs, yielding a ratio. A ratio larger than one indicates that benefits exceed costs, while a ratio less than one reflects costs in excess of benefits.

One advantage in the use of CBA over CEA is that often more than one treatment program is competing for the same funds and the goals of each program may not be the same. In such a case, it is advantageous to be able to compare the benefit/cost ratios of the different programs in order to select that program whose benefit-to-cost ratio is superior. If one wants to do this more systematically, there are statistical procedures that can be used to test the significance of different cost/benefit ratios (Carter and Newman 1976).

Halpern and Binner (1972), in their model for an output value analysis of mental health programs, employed a simple method of CBA that illustrates this procedure. It is their belief that the most important "product" produced by a mental health program is the patient who is returned to function in the community. What the investigators do, therefore, is to view improvement in therapists' ratings of patient functioning in terms of a monetizable increment in the economic value of the patient. Costs are measured by weighting the time he or she spent in each treatment status by the estimated cost of each status. A simple benefit/cost ratio is then computed.

According to the authors, this framework provides a method whereby an investigator can "analyze his programs and make decisions on the allocation of his efforts based on explicit measures of the productivity and effectiveness of his programs" (Halpern and Binner 1972, p. 51). A problem arises, however, because although this method may be useful, it suffers from a potential bias in the assignment of a quite arbitrary value (for example, $10,000) to each unit of improved patient functioning as rated by a therapist.

A similar procedure has been used by Fishman (1975), in his assessment of the effects of a community mental health center. When using his model, if the benefits of one program or program component are found to be superior to another, and there is no difference in costs between the two, the most effective is chosen. Similarly, if costs of two programs differ, but their effectiveness does not, then the least costly is chosen. The author himself points out, however, that his model is less useful in situations where a significantly more beneficial program is also significantly more costly.

### Net Benefit Analysis

The measures used for cost/benefit analysis so far discussed, that is, the ratios of benefit or effectiveness to cost, do not provide information on the total amount of costs or on the absolute benefits involved in a program or system. These amounts, as well as the amount by which benefits exceed costs, may be of some concern. For example, two programs might produce identical cost/benefit ratios of 2. For one program, this ratio may result from a benefit of $400 and a cost of $200, while the benefits and cost of the other program might be $400,000 and $200,000, respectively. Results such as these can be important in policy decisions. If no more than $4,000 is available in the budget, then the first program is the only one feasible.

It is, therefore, useful to calculate net benefits, which are defined as present-valued benefits minus present-valued costs. If the net benefit is negative, the program is obviously not worth pursuing, while with a net benefit in excess of zero the program is worth further consideration. This calculation of net benefits is one of the advantages in expressing outcomes and costs in the same units. In some instances, this net benefits information may be more useful than ratios, although it still seems desirable to consider calculations of net benefit per patient (Cost-effectiveness analysis 1980).

## Summary

A variety of methods to assess the costs and benefits of psychotherapy and to compare results generated by different studies have been described. Although special difficulties arise in applying CEA/CBA's to psychotherapy, especially those involved with transforming outcome data to monetary benefits, the general problems are not unique to psychotherapy. In all cases, the usefulness of such analyses hinges on the availability and quality of outcome data, and it would appear that greater methodological sophistication is needed before these techniques are fully applicable for psychotherapy assessments.

What, then, can we conclude from this discussion of CEA/CBA? First, they are extremely complex procedures and, in general, have not been used for comparing different psychotherapy treatments. Rather, they deal with the factors that affect the provision of such treatments, and have most often been applied when policy decisions about large-scale programs or projects are needed. Thus a major emphasis has been upon differences among treatment settings. Second, because of the difficulties associated with measuring psychotherapy's benefits in monetary terms, the literature tends to be concerned primarily with the assessment of low-cost treatments. Finally, in spite of methodological problems, it is important to recognize that CEA / CBA adds a new dimension to the assessment of the outcome of psychotherapy. As more evidence is accumulated, it will be possible to make more exact statements as to the cost-effectiveness and efficiency of psychotherapy.

# CHAPTER 10

# Statistical Issues

## Measurement of Change

The purpose of this section is to describe and discuss some statistical and psychometric issues that are important both in the reporting and interpretation of quantitative results of research. It is not meant to be exhaustive or to sanctify statistical processes. Rather, it is intended to review five major issues that arise in the conduct of psychotherapy research: the measurement of change; reliability of clinical judgments; the difference between statistical and clinical significance; the use of power analysis; and combinatory techniques for assessing the efficacy of psychotherapy.

In spite of many predictive studies of the outcome of psychotherapy (for example, Luborsky et al. 1971; Mintz, O'Brien, and Luborsky 1976), the problem of how to actually measure changes that occur as a result of psychotherapy has been relatively neglected. Much has been written on the desirability of having diverse sources of information and measures appropriate to each viewpoint (Fiske 1975a, 1976b; Fiske et al. 1970; Waskow and Parloff 1975). However, while there are a limited number of highly complex statistical papers (for example, Cronbach and Furby 1970, Manning and DuBois 1962) dealing with the methodology of measuring change, little has been written that is readily comprehensible to clinicians or that has been aimed directly at the area of psychotherapy (Mintz, Luborsky, and Christoph 1979).

Probably the most important reason for this lack is that the measurement of change is not a simple matter. "Indeed, this is a methodological area fraught with booby traps, where intuitive 'doing what comes naturally' is almost certain to lead one astray" (Cohen and Cohen 1975, p. 378). Even the methodologists appear to be unable to settle the complex issues centering on what, how, or even whether to measure change. Over a decade ago, a symposium devoted wholly to this topic was conducted (Harris 1967), yet the issues continue to be debated in the literature.

This section will discuss the advantages and disadvantages of a number of measures that have been used to assess outcome. These measures will include direct ratings of benefit or improvement, two types of change scores, and the use of final adjustment status as a criterion.

The most frequently used measure of outcome in the 1950s was therapist ratings of improvement (Vandenbos and Pino 1980). As discussed in a previous section, their use has survived to the present day. Two advantages of these direct ratings of benefits or change in the form of an overall rating on a simple scale are their flexibility in terms of unique evaluation of each patient and the ease with which they can be obtained (Mintz et al. 1979). However, the meanings of such ratings are often vague, and it is almost never clear exactly what standards were used for making these ratings. An extreme example of possible ambiguity to be found in global ratings of improvement would be the case when the therapist making the initial rating of a patient's condition is not the same person who makes the final rating. In addition, change is multidimensional, and a single global rating of improvement provides no insight into the nature of the change.

The second most frequent method of assessing outcome in psychotherapy research is pretreatment/posttreatment difference scores. This "raw gain" score is the simple difference between final and initial scores. Although intuitively appealing, since it takes into account level of patient functioning at two distinct points in time, this method is subject to serious statistical problems.

Raw change scores may be quite satisfactory when both initial and final scores are perfectly reliable, but measurements of changes associated with psychotherapy possess limited reliability (Fiske 1977). Therefore, because raw change scores reflect the measurement error of both initial and final scores, their reliability is likely to be substantially lower than that of either the initial or final scores. In addition to their tendency to be unreliable is the fact that simple change scores are necessarily dependent upon initial scores (Cohen and Cohen 1975, Green et al. 1975, Mintz et al. 1979). This fact is particularly important when patients have not been randomized to treatment groups. Although most researchers would like to assign patients randomly, often this is not feasible because of a variety of practical and ethical problems. Therefore, there are likely to be important pretreatment differences between two comparison groups, and a simple comparison of raw change scores could reflect not only treatment effects, but these group pretreatment differences as well.

At extreme score levels, ceiling effects may also distort the meaning of raw change. For example, there is obviously little room for change if the patient sample scores high on a pretest (the ceiling effect).

Another expected effect when "extreme" groups are selected for study, for example, patients high on anxiety or low on self-esteem, is regression to the mean. This concept implies that the more an initial set of observations deviates above or below the mean of the population distribution, the more a second set of observations will move in the direction of the mean, even in the absence of any true change (Bordin 1974). Suppose, for example, one is interested in the effect of crisis intervention on a sample of severely depressed patients. If they complete a depression scale prior to and at the end of therapy, it is predictable that the average for this sample will be less extreme at the second point in time regardless of whether or not the intervention was effective.

These and additional considerations have led to the recommendation of "residual" change scores (Cronbach and Furby 1970, Fiske et al. 1970, Manning and DuBois 1962). "A gain is residualized by expressing the posttest score as a deviation from the posttest-on-pretest regression line. The part of the posttest information that is linearly predictable from the pretest is thus partialled out" (Cronbach and Furby 1970, p. 68). More simply, a residual change score represents the difference between actual outcome and that which could be predicted from initial scores. The residual gain is, therefore, "a statistically adjusted measure which rescales an individual's simple gain score relative to typical gains made by others at the same initial level" (Mintz et al. 1979, p.32). Essentially, then, this approach reduces but does not completely eliminate initial group differences. However, the reliability of residual change scores is always greater than that of a comparable raw gain score (Manning and DuBois 1962).

A closely related method of reducing the effect of initial differences between groups is the analysis of covariance. Valid application of this method of adjustment for initial differences requires that the groups be chosen randomly and that measurement techniques be highly reliable. In essence, analysis of covariance adjusts for the differences in pretest means that occur as a function of random sampling error (Isaac and Michael 1971). However, as has already been pointed out, random assignment to conditions is normally the exception rather than the rule. Additionally, there is no unambiguous way to statistically equate non-equivalent groups unless measurement is error-free (Cronbach and Furby 1970). Consequently, the application of analysis of covariance to studies where initial assignment was nonrandom and where measurement cannot be expected to be error-free violates its basic assumptions. A number of methodologists (Bryk and Weisberg 1977, Cronbach and Furby 1970) agree with Lord's conclusion that "there is simply no logical or statistical procedure that can be counted on to make proper allowances for uncontrolled preexisting differences between groups" (1967, p.305).

At present there is no consensus among psychometricians on whether statistical adjustments designed to correct for initial differences among groups are good enough to yield useful inferences about "true change." In fact, a number of investigators (Adams 1978, Green et al. 1975) have heeded the suggestion made by Cronbach and Furby (1970) that, in general, we should not try to measure change. In their opinion, in most cases where questions have been formulated in terms of measuring change, these questions can usually be framed in other ways that do not involve change measures.

One strategy for measuring outcome that does not involve direct measurement of change is to use final adjustment status alone as a criterion. Green et al. (1975), for example, conclude from a study concerned with the relations among three different methods of evaluating psychotherapy outcome (final status scores, pretreatment/posttreatment difference scores, and direct ratings of global improvement) that final status measures correlated highly with each other and that they were more reliable than difference scores. In their opinion, if measures are chosen to represent the goals of therapy, final status scores provide the most appropriate measures of the extent to which therapeutic goals have been realized and are, therefore, the most appropriate measures with which to compare treatment outcomes.

However, in the opinion of Mintz et al. (1979), the argument for the use of final status as the criterion for the outcome of therapy is most cogent only when initial differences are minimal. The use of final status scores does not, therefore, really solve the problem of how to measure outcome, since the problem arises in the first place largely as the result of initial differences among groups.

Perhaps the most reasonable conclusion from this discussion

of various ways to measure the outcome of psychotherapy is that when patients are assigned to treatment groups at random, when initial differences among groups are small, when measuring instruments are error-free, and when the correlations between initial and final scores is low, then one may feel reasonably confident with almost any of the methods. However, these conditions are seldom, if ever, met. So the use of the residual gain score appears to be the most reliable and most frequently recommended method (Cronbach and Furby 1970, Green et al. 1975, Manning and DuBois 1962, Mintz et al. 1979).

## Reliability and Agreement of Clinical Judgments

In a previous section of this report, reliability was discussed primarily as it relates to test instruments for evaluating the effectiveness of psychotherapy. However, in research on psychotherapy, it is frequently the case that measurement involves the use of clinicians' judgments about such characteristics of patients as diagnosis, symptomatology, or severity of illness. Because data collected in this manner represent the subjective judgments of raters, it is important to know the degree to which the raters agree with one another. Knowledge of this agreement is crucial for determining the generality of a set of ratings.

The present section will distinguish between interrater reliability and interrater agreement, emphasizing the need for both types of evidence regarding a set of ratings. It will also describe and evaluate various procedures that have been suggested for determining these parameters.

### Agreement Versus Reliability

The basic characteristic of interrater agreement is that it represents the extent to which different raters tend to make exactly ·the same judgments about a rated subject. When numerical scales are used, interrater agreement means that exactly the same values are assigned to the subject. There are some exceptions to the requirement of identical ratings that will be discussed later, but in all cases interrater agreement presents no information about the variability among subjects. Interrater reliability, in contrast, is very much concerned with the variability among subjects. In this sense, it is "more than agreement, it is agreement with regard to discrimination among subjects" (Spitzer and Cohen 1968, pp.113–114). Interrater agreement has most often been expressed as percent agreement among judges, whereas interrater reliability is typically reported in terms of correlational or analysis of variance indices that portray whether the average difference between subjects is large relative to the degree of disagreement between judges (Mitchell 1979, Spitzer and Cohen 1968, Tinsley and Weiss 1975).

It is important to note that because agreement and reliability of ratings are different concepts, high reliability does not guarantee that raters agree in an absolute sense on the extent to which rated individuals possess the characteristic under concern. Similarly, low reliability does not necessarily indicate clear disagreement among raters. Table 2 presents hypothetical data that illustrate this point.

These data represent ratings made by three clinicians of ten patients on a nine-point depression scale. The ratings shown for Case 1, where identical ratings are made by each rater for each patient, indicate both high interrater agreement and high interrater reliability. Case 2 also shows high interrater reliability, but these ratings show low interrater agreement since no two raters gave the same rating to any patient. This low agreement is reflected in the raters' mean ratings of 3.0, 5.0, and 7.0, respectively. The ratings assigned to the patients are, however, proportional, since all patients are ordered similarly by the raters. If the relative orderings of the patients are all one is concerned with, the interrater reliability index alone serves as a satisfactory index of the ratings (Tinsley and Weiss 1975). This index does not, however, make evident the differences among the judges in their ratings. Therefore, whenever the absolute value of the ratings as defined by points on the scale are also important, interrater agreement should be reported as well (Lawlis and Lu 1971, Mitchell 1979, Tinsley and Weiss 1975).

The ratings shown for Case 3 have high interrater agreement, but low interrater reliability. This results from the fact that ratings assigned by the raters to the patients are very close for seven of the ten patients. However, the restricted variability in the ratings made by the judges causes the interrater reliability to be low. This is not an infrequent finding in psychotherapy research. It can result from a number of sources among which are homogeneity of patient characteristics or simply the fact that judges are inexperienced with the use of the scale. When interrater reliability is low, but interrater agreement is high,

**Table 2.** Hypothetical Ratings of Depression Illustrating Different Levels of Interrater Agreement and Interrater Reliability

| Patient | Case 1: High interrater agreement and high interrater reliability | | | Case 2: Low interrater agreement and high interrater reliability | | | Case 3: High interrater agreement and low interrater reliability | | |
|---|---|---|---|---|---|---|---|---|---|
| | Rater | | | Rater | | | Rater | | |
| | 1 | 2 | 3 | 1 | 2 | 3 | 1 | 2 | 3 |
| A | 1 | 1 | 1 | 1 | 3 | 5 | 5 | 4 | 4 |
| B | 2 | 2 | 2 | 1 | 3 | 5 | 5 | 4 | 3 |
| C | 3 | 3 | 3 | 2 | 4 | 6 | 5 | 4 | 5 |
| D | 3 | 3 | 3 | 2 | 4 | 6 | 4 | 4 | 5 |
| E | 4 | 4 | 4 | 3 | 5 | 7 | 5 | 4 | 3 |
| F | 5 | 5 | 5 | 3 | 5 | 7 | 5 | 5 | 4 |
| G | 6 | 6 | 6 | 4 | 6 | 8 | 4 | 4 | 5 |
| H | 7 | 7 | 7 | 4 | 6 | 8 | 5 | 5 | 4 |
| I | 8 | 8 | 8 | 5 | 7 | 9 | 4 | 5 | 3 |
| J | 9 | 9 | 9 | 5 | 7 | 9 | 5 | 5 | 5 |
| M | 4.8 | 4.8 | 4.8 | 3.0 | 5.0 | 7.0 | 4.7 | 4.4 | 4.1 |
| SD | 2.7 | 2.7 | 2.7 | 1.5 | 1.5 | 1.5 | .5 | .5 | .9 |

*Source:* Based on Tinsley, H.E.A., and Weiss, D. J. Interrater reliability and agreement of subject judgments. *Journal of Counseling Psychology,* 1975, 22, 358–376.

these possibilities can be investigated further, but "when both interrater agreement and reliability are low, the ratings are of no value and should not be used for research or applied purposes" (Tinsley and Weiss 1975, p. 360).

Interrater reliability has so far been discussed in terms of judgments made by clinicians about attributes that may be assigned scaled numerical values. There are, however, situations where the attribute being judged is one involving qualitatively different categories, for example, diagnoses. When one deals with these types of data and considers only whether judges are in complete agreement or not, the distinction that has been made between interrater reliability and interrater agreement ceases to exist. This is because agreement either is present or not, and the variability in ratings, which is central to the estimation of interrater reliability, is not an issue.

### Interrater Agreement

Only relatively recently have statistical indices been designed specifically to indicate interrater agreement. Measures designed for other purposes have, however, been used for this purpose. These measures include the percent or proportion of agreement $(P)$, the product-moment correlation between judges' ratings (r), various chi-square indices such as Contingency Coefficient $(C)$, and Kendall's coefficient of concordance $(W)$. More recently, measures specifically designed to measure interrater agreement have been developed by Lawlis and Lu (1972), Tinsley and Weiss (1975), and Cohen (1960, 1968). The following discussion describes the advantages and disadvantages of each of these techniques for estimating interrater agreement.

The most frequently used index has been percentage or proportion of agreement $(P)$. Although intuitively reasonable, this method suffers from a number of deficiencies. One problem is that it includes agreement that can be accounted for by chance alone (Cohen 1960, 1968; Diagnosis 1977; Mitchell, 1979; Spitzer and Cohen 1968; Spitzer et al. 1967; Tinsley and Weiss 1975). The true absolute agreement among raters can be overestimated by an amount related to the number of points on the scale. For example, the larger the number of raters and the fewer the points on the scale, the greater the likelihood that percent agreement will be inflated by chance factors.

Another problem with the use of percent agreement is that it is insensitive to degrees of agreement; that is, agreement is treated as an all-or-nothing phenomenon with no credit given for partial agreement and, in this sense, the percentage underestimates the actual extent of interrater agreement (Mitchell 1979, Tinsley and Weiss 1975). An example of this problem may be seen in the data of Case 2 of Table 2. These data represent perfect agreement on the relative level of each of the patients, but the percentage of absolute agreement is zero.

A third problem with $P$ is that while it is the most common method used in reporting agreement, it almost never is accompanied by a significance test (Spitzer et al. 1967).

Product-moment correlations between judges' ratings is another measure that has been used to estimate interrater agreement. As Tinsley and Weiss (1975) point out, however, this index is inappropriate as a measure of agreement, inasmuch as correlations show only proportional agreement. "If pairwise correlation has any merit in evaluating ratings, it is as a measure of interrater reliability, not interrater agreement" (p. 366).

The contingency coefficient ($C$), based on chi-square, has also been used as a measure of interrater agreement. However, $C$ and other indices based on chi-square have been criticized in this context because they index *association* and not necessarily *agreement* when applied to multilevel scales (Cohen 1960, 1968; Spitzer et al. 1967). What they test is the hypothesis that the proportions of subjects assigned by different judges to various rating categories are not significantly different. Therefore, a significant chi-square reflects only the fact that one judge's ratings are *associated* with another judge's ratings more than could be expected by chance, not that they are in more than chance *agreement*. The departure from a chance association could be in the direction of either greater agreement or greater disagreement. Therefore, the extent of agreement as such is ambiguous.

Kendall's coefficient of concordance ($W$) is also frequently used as a measure of interrater agreement. In essence, this measure gives the average rank-order correlation between each pair of raters and, as such, it too provides a measure of association, but not necessarily agreement. Further, "the frequent occurrence of tied ranks, which commonly results when the coefficient of concordance is used, makes the coefficient difficult to calculate and somewhat powerless" (Tinsley and Weiss 1975, p. 366).

What is clearly needed are measures of interrater agreement

that account for chance or random agreement and that provide for statistical tests of the significance of results. Investigators have also felt the need for measures that reflect the *degree* of agreement among judges' ratings rather than agreement in the absolute sense. The following measures take these needs into consideration.

In 1972 Lawlis and Lu reported a measure of interrater agreement for magnitude-scaled data that allows the investigator some flexibility in selecting a criterion for agreement. Rather than treating agreement in an absolute, all-or-nothing manner, Lawlis and Lu's (1972) index permits the option of defining agreement as identical ratings, as ratings that differ by one point, or as ratings that differ by no more than two points. Thus the investigator can make distinctions among agreements that are considered serious and those that are considered less important. The technique they propose is basically a chi-square test of whether the observed agreement is significantly greater or less than that which could be expected on a chance basis.

Tinsley and Weiss (1975) propose a measure of agreement (*T*) that may be used if a significant chi-square has been obtained to determine whether interrater agreement is high, moderate, or low. The maximum value of *T* is 1.0 when perfect agreement is observed, and it may range down to zero when the observed agreement is equal to that expected by chance.

Results from the Lawlis and Lu (1972) chi-square and the associated *T* index are contingent on the definition of agreement, which should be specified prior to the collection of data. In addition to specifying the definition of agreement, the rationale used in its adoption should also be specified in any report of findings. Further, when agreement is defined to include a discrepancy of one or two points, the chi-square and *T* value for agreement defined as identical ratings should also be reported. The purpose of this is to permit the reader to evaluate the extent to which an investigator's conclusions are contingent upon his or her definition of agreement (Tinsley and Weiss 1975).

When an investigator is working with categorical rather than scaled data, for example, with diagnostic categories, Cohen's (1960) kappa (*K*) provides an indication of the proportion of agreement between two raters over and above chance agreement. And, because its sampling characteristics are known, kappa (*K*) can be subjected to statistical significance testing.

The assumptions for the use of $K$ are that the subjects to be rated are independent, that the judges make their ratings independently, and that the categories to which subjects are assigned are independent, mutually exclusive, and exhaustive of the domain under consideration.

Kappa varies from negative values (for less than chance agreement) through zero (indicating chance agreement) to 1.0 (for perfect agreement between the raters). What constitutes a "satisfactory" kappa is open to some dispute. Some investigators report that a $K$ of more than .5 or .6 is acceptable (Grove et al. 1981), but others have stated that "satisfactory" agreement starts above .7; values of .6 or .7 may be "unacceptable" (Koran 1975a, 1975b). Fleiss, Cohen, and Everitt (1969) present formulas for testing whether an obtained $K$ is significant and for testing the significance of the difference between two $K$'s.

While $K$ is an improvement over percentage of agreement or the use of the contingency coefficient ($C$) inasmuch as it corrects for chance agreement when dealing with categorical data, all of these methods fail to distinguish *degree* of agreement. As pointed out by Cohen (1968), some disagreements may be considered of greater gravity than others. For example, disagreement over whether a patient is normal or schizophrenic might be regarded as more serious than disagreement over whether that patient is normal or neurotic. Therefore, a modification of $K$, called weighted kappa ($K_W$), was developed (Cohen 1968) to increase the utility of $K$ for use in studies of diagnostic agreement. Weighted $K$ ($K_W$) shares all the properties of $K$ already described, but in addition provides an index of interrater agreement when the investigator wants to provide partial credit for disagreement that is not absolute.

A perspective on $K_W$ is afforded by considering $K$ as a special case of $K_W$ for which weights of 1.0 are assigned to absolute agreements between judges, while all disagreements are weighted zero. In the case of $K_W$, the various kinds of disagreements are differentially weighted.

It is possible that an investigator might use both $K$ and $K_W$ in any given study. For example, if two clinicians were diagnosing a sample of patients as psychotic, neurotic, or personality disorder, and disagreements among these categories were differentially weighted, the investigator might want to compute $K_W$ to determine the degree of overall diagnostic agreement. However, he or she might also be interested in the extent to which there was agreement with respect to each of the individual diagnoses. The investigator could, therefore, compute $K$ to obtain the extent of agreement on whether patients were psychotic or not, neurotic or not, or a personality disorder or not (Spitzer et al. 1967).

The use of $K_W$ does not, however, provide a panacea for all the problems of interrater agreement on diagnostic classification. The extent to which it is useful "depends . . . upon the degree to which the transformed data represent psychological reality" (Tinsley and Weiss 1975, p.371). Further, when reporting findings based on $K_W$, the investigator should specify in detail the rationale upon which his or her weightings are predicated.

In addition, the use of $K$, or $K_W$, is limited to situations in which the same two judges rate each subject. There is, however, another procedure $(K_V)$ developed by Fleiss (1971) that essentially extends $K$ for measuring interrater agreement where subjects are rated by different sets of judges but where the number of judges per subject is constant. It is not necessary that all judges rate each subject. Fleiss (1971) presents formulas for testing the hypothesis that the observed agreement equals chance agreement.

### Interrater Reliability

The measure of interrater reliability most frequently used for quantitatively scaled data is the intraclass correlation (ICC). There are a number of formulas for computing ICC, all of which use the computational procedure of analysis of variance. However, in the most general terms it can be interpreted as the proportion of the total variance in judges' ratings that is due to variability among the subjects rated (Spitzer and Cohen 1968, Tinsley and Weiss 1975). It thus represents the amount of variability among subjects in relation to the amount of variability among raters. For the usual situation where a number of raters all rate each of a number of subjects, ICC may be described as the component of variance due to individuals divided by the sum of this component plus error variance (Fleiss and Cohen 1973).

An example of the use of ICC would be the following. An investigator is interested in knowing the degree of reliability among the ratings of three clinicians who have rated ten patients on an anxiety scale. An intraclass correlation is computed that indicates that the average of the intercorrelations of the three sets of ratings is .78. If the intercorrelations among raters is taken to be an indication of the reliability of ratings, then it can be said that average reliability is of the order of .78.

Values that approach the upper limit of ICC (1.00) indicate a high degree of reliability. A value of zero indicates complete lack of reliability. Negative values, while mathematically possible, are almost never observed in practice. In order to determine whether an ICC is statistically significant, an F-test is computed and interpreted with the appropriate degrees of freedom.

At present, there appears to be agreement that the intraclass correlation coefficient is the most appropriate measure of interrater reliability for scaled data. It is important to note, however, that more than one formula is available for ICC. Shrout and Fleiss (1979), for example, present a number of different formulas and provide guidelines for choosing the most appropriate one. Because of the fact that a given formula for ICC is appropriate in only limited circumstances, the investigator, when reporting his or her findings, should specify the manner in which the index was calculated.

Occasions do arise, however, when the investigator is faced with data for which the variability among subjects is so restricted that procedures based on analysis of variance (for example, ICC) are inappropriate and considerably underestimate interrater reliability. Finn (1970) has proposed a measure of reliability that avoids this problem.

For example, there is very little variability in the clinicians' ratings of patients in Case 3 shown in Table 2, and interrater reliability as estimated by ICC was low. In contrast, Finn's r for these same data is .93 (Tinsley and Weiss 1975). Thus Finn's r, which can vary from zero to +1.00, is not reduced by low within-subjects variance.

The use of Finn's procedure assumes that ratings are normally distributed and that both subjects and raters have been randomly selected, assumptions that are frequently violated in psychotherapy research. This does not, however, preclude the use of Finn's r, since it has often been observed that variations from the theoretical assumptions of a statistical technique frequently have little impact on the results of the use of that technique. Nevertheless, because the assumptions are seldom met, Tinsley and Weiss (1978) recommend the use of a stringent critical value, for example, the .01 level, when estimating the significance of interrater reliability obtained through the use of Finn's $r$.

### Interpreting the Values of Reliability and Agreement

Tests are available for determining whether $ICC$ or $K$, the two most highly recommended measures of reliability and agreement, are significantly different from chance. However, the meaning of all estimates of reliability and agreement depends on a number of interrelated factors. As pointed out by Grove et al. (1981), if the sensitivity and specificity of ratings are not perfect (some false-positive and some false-negative errors occur), then the value of $K$ (or ICC) and estimates of base rates will both be affected. Assuming a fixed sensitivity and specificity, both these coefficients vary in magnitude as base rate (frequency of occurrence of the event in the population of interest) varies. They are lowest when the base rate approaches zero. This means that when one is dealing with a very infrequent event, the reliability of judges' rating can never be high.

We are thus in the position of knowing whether agreement or reliability among judges' ratings differs from chance, but the actual interpretation of any coefficient must take into account several variables that themselves cannot be accurately measured. In addition, greater than chance agreement is hardly sufficient to establish that the rating procedure is satisfactory. One will almost always require interrater reliability or agreement to be well above the chance level, although absolute standards cannot be given. Thus, although the general results of recent studies of reliability have been encouraging, it appears that to date only provisional solutions exist to the many problems that plague this area of research.

### Summary

This section has distinguished between the concepts of interrator agreement and interrater reliability, stressed the importance of presenting both types of data where appropriate, and described and evaluated various procedures that have been suggested for determining these parameters. The appropriateness of percentage of agreement $(P)$, chi-square indices, product-moment correlations between judges' ratings, and Kendall's coefficient of concordance $(W)$ as measures of interrater agreement was discussed. The Lawlis and Lu (1972) measure, with its associated $T$ index, has been recommended for use with scaled data and has the advantage of permitting the investigator some flexibility in selecting a criterion for agreement (Tinsley and Weiss 1975).

For categorical data, for example, data relating to diagnostic agreement, Cohen's (1960) kappa (*K*) is the most widely used and the most highly recommended index of interrater agreement for cases where the same two judges rate each subject (Bartko and Carpenter 1976, Grove et al. 1981, Tinsley and Weiss 1975). For situations in which subjects are rated by different judges, but the number of judges rating each subject is the same, an extension of *K*, $K_V$, has been proposed by Fleiss (1971). Cohen's (1965) weighted kappa ($K_W$) is available when the investigator wishes to differentially weight disagreement among diagnostic or other categorical ratings. However, justification for the weights assigned to the categories must be provided.

A number of authors have recommended the intraclass correlation coefficient (ICC) as the best available choice for estimating the reliability of judges' ratings of scaled data. However, when the variability among subjects is severely restricted, ICC produces an underestimate of reliability, and Finn's (1970) *r* is a more appropriate measure.

Some final comments were made concerning the interpretation of estimates of reliability and agreement. It was stressed that in spite of the advances that have been made in the development of statistical techniques, all existing coefficients provide somewhat ambiguous solutions.

## Statistical Versus Clinical Significance

Statistical measures of significance are often misleading, largely because the word "significant" in its nontechnical meaning connotes "large," "important," or "consequential." There is, therefore, the temptation to consider a difference that is highly significant statistically as one that is also very large. However, differences found to be highly significant in the statistical sense may have little clinical relevance. The reason for this is that statistical significance may be achieved if study samples are large even though the actual effect obtained may be minimal. The significance level says nothing about the relative magnitude of the effect that has been observed. The significance level at which an investigator is willing to declare findings significant simply reflects the risk the investigator is willing to take that he or she is reporting a real effect when, in fact, there is none (Spitzer and Cohen 1968).

For example, suppose Dr. *A* is studying the effects of two different types of medications on the symptom of anxiety. He randomly assigns 200 patients to two groups of 100 patients each, administers drug $X$ to one group and drug $Y$ to the other. At the end of six weeks, he has the two groups of patients complete a self-report rating scale designed to measure level of anxiety. He then computes a t-test to determine the significance of the difference between the mean scores for the two groups. The t-value obtained is 2.58, significant at the .01 level in favor of drug $Y$. He reports, therefore, that drug $Y$ is greatly superior to drug $X$ for the treatment of anxiety. This may be a false conclusion, however, because all that he has really demonstrated is that with these two large samples of patients it is highly unlikely (a probability of 1 in 100 that the difference is due to chance) that there is *no* difference at *all* between the means of the two treatment populations from which these samples were drawn. The relative size of the difference may be trivial, and had the size of the samples been smaller, the difference may not have reached statistical significance.

A second, slightly different, example of an inconsequential but statistically significant effect is provided by the following: Dr. *B* is interested in determining the relative effectiveness of two drugs ($X$ and $Y$) in the treatment of depression. She therefore administers the Zung Depression Scale to a large number of outpatients at her clinic, and randomly assigns 100 patients who obtain a score of 70 or over to one of the two drug conditions. At the end of eight weeks, the patients again complete the depression scale, and the mean score of the group that received drug $X$ is four points lower than that of the group that received drug $Y$. This difference is statistically significant, but Dr. *B* does not make Dr. *A*'s mistake of reporting the superiority of one treatment over another, because the Zung Depression Scale has norms that provide reference points from which to evaluate findings. A decrease of four points in the mean score of the group receiving drug $X$ still leaves these patients well within the range of scores for depressed outpatients (50–78) and above the normative depressed outpatient mean score of 64. Thus, in a clinical sense, there is very little difference in the effects of the two drugs. Normative test data do, therefore, help the investigator interpret differences in outcome, at least as expressed on that test.

106

When normative data are not available and the relative efficacy of two treatments is decided by means of a statistical test between means, the problem is compounded. This is so because the units in which we measure our outcome variables are not only arbitrary, but also without absolute meaning. How large, for example, is a mean difference of 6.7 units on the ANX Test of anxiety? We have no conception of how large a point or a unit is (Cohen 1965). This fact again invites recourse to the significance test as arbiter of the decision of the effect's magnitude. It also underlines the need for a concept of magnitude, or effect size, that is sufficiently general to be useful in all situations where a variable under consideration is scaled or dichotomized. It must also yield a number that is independent of the units used to measure the particular variables being studied.

Consider, for example, the following two studies. In one, a difference of 4.87 was found on a scale of lung capacity in favor of a group of asthmatic patients treated with psychotherapy plus medical management when compared with a control group receiving medical management alone. A second study demonstrated that asthmatics treated with psychotherapy were symptom-free for eleven more days a month than were those treated with medical management alone. Which study demonstrated the largest effect of psychotherapy?

In 1969, Cohen developed a measure of effect size (ES) that he called $d$. This measure was designed to avoid arbitrary choices among outcome measures and the scales used for their measurement and to transform the magnitude of differences found to a common scale. Although the terminology used to define ES, or $d$, has varied somewhat (for example, Cohen 1969, Plutchik 1974), the following definition provided by Smith, Glass, and Miller (1980, p.41) is probably the most useful when considering the outcome of research in psychotherapy:

$$ES(d) = \frac{\overline{X}_{\text{Therapy}} - \overline{X}_{\text{Control}}}{s_x}$$

where: $\overline{X}_{\text{Therapy}}$    is the average score for the psychotherapy group on the outcome measure

$\overline{X}_{\text{Control}}$    is the average score for the control group on the outcome measure

$s_x$    is the standard deviation of the control group

This means that, if there is no difference between the therapy and control groups, the effect size will be zero, whereas if the difference is as large as one standard deviation of the control group, the effect size will be one. In essence, *d* changes raw scores to standard scores by expressing them in standard deviation units. The advantages of this procedure are: (1) that *d* is an unambiguous function of the relative magnitude of the experimental effect and does not depend on the size of the samples on which it was determined; and (2) the results of studies using different types of measures may be directly compared. ES, or *d*, becomes the common unit of measurement (Cohen 1969).

There are two different, yet interrelated, ways to interpret *d* as a measurement of the magnitude of effect. One way is in terms of the proportion of the total variance that is associated with group membership. This way of looking at *d* involves the notion of prediction. If one thinks of group membership as one variable "X" (that may take on the values of zero for the control group and 1 for the experimental group) and a subject's score on an outcome measure as another variable "Y," then the correlation *r* between X and Y can be found by any of the usual computing formulas for *r* (for example, Hays 1963). If one then squares the correlation coefficient $(r^2)$, the proportion of variance associated with group membership is obtained. The larger the proportion of variance thus "explained," the greater one's ability to predict (by knowing an individual's score on the outcome measure) to which group, experimental or control, an individual belongs.

This interpretation of *d* is closely related to that which considers it as an inverse measure of the degree of population overlap. Figure 7 presents examples of frequency distributions that demonstrate the concepts of proportion of variance associated with group membership $(r^2)$ and degree of overlap as they relate to the magnitude of experimental effect (*d*).

As may be seen from example 1 in Figure 7, when zero variance is associated with group membership $(r^2 = 0)$, the two distributions overlap completely, and the magnitude of the experimental effect is zero, as is the ability to predict group membership from a knowledge of an individual's score on the outcome measure. Conversely, example 4 depicts a situation in which all the variance is associated with group membership $(r^2 = 1.00)$, prediction of group membership from knowledge of an outcome measure score may be made precisely without

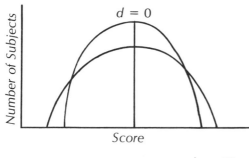

*d* = 0

*Number of Subjects*

*Score*

1. Zero variance associated
with group membership
($r^2 = 0$)

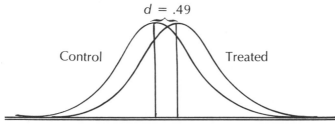

*d* = .49

Control      Treated

2. Small proportion of variance
associated with group membership
($r^2 = .06$)

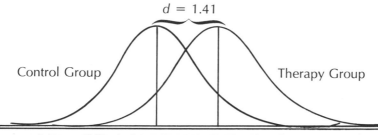

*d* = 1.41

Control Group      Therapy Group

3. Large proportion of variance associated with group membership
($r^2 = .33$)

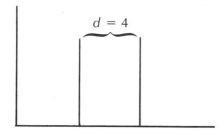

*d* = 4

4. All variance associated with
group membership
($r^2 = 1.00$)

**Figure 7.** Examples of Frequency Distributions with Different Degrees of
Overlap, Different Proportions of Variance Associated with
Group Membership, and Different Effect Sizes (*d*)

*Source:* Based on Spitzer, R. L., and Cohen, J. Common errors in quantitative research. *Interntional Journal of Psychiatry,* 1968, 6.

**109**

error, there is no overlap between distributions, and $d$ reaches a maximum of 4.

In actual clinical practice, results would never fall at either of these extremes. Therefore, actual obtained frequency distributions would more nearly approximate those shown in examples 3 and 4. As a comparison of these two indicates, the larger the proportion of variance associated with group membership $(r^2)$, the smaller the degree of overlap between the two populations, and the larger the size of the experimental effect $(d)$. Table 3 presents values of $d$ associated with differing degrees of overlap and percents of variance accounted for.

The question still remains as to what may be considered a small, medium, or large effect. Cohen (1969) operationally defines a $d$ of approximately .2 as implying a small effect. As shown in Table 3, when $d = .2$, 85.3 percent of the distributions

**Table 3.** The Degree of Overlap of Experimental and Control Group Distributions for Different Values of $d$ with Corresponding Variance Accounted for $(r^2)$

| $d$ | Degree of Overlap (%) | $r^2$ | $d$ | Degree of Overlap (%) | $r^2$ |
|-----|-----------------------|-------|-----|-----------------------|-------|
| 0   | 100.0 | 0   |     |       |     |
| 0.1 | 92.3  | 0   | 1.6 | 26.9  | .39 |
| 0.2 | 85.3  | .01 | 1.7 | 24.6  | .42 |
| 0.3 | 78.7  | .02 | 1.8 | 22.6  | .45 |
| 0.4 | 72.6  | .04 | 1.9 | 20.6  | .47 |
| 0.5 | 67.0  | .06 | 2.0 | 18.9  | .50 |
| 0.6 | 61.8  | .08 | 2.2 | 15.7  | .55 |
| 0.7 | 57.0  | .11 | 2.4 | 13.0  | .59 |
| 0.8 | 52.6  | .14 | 2.6 | 10.7  | .63 |
| 0.9 | 48.4  | .17 | 2.8 | 8.8   | .66 |
| 1.0 | 44.6  | .20 | 3.0 | 7.2   | .69 |
| 1.1 | 41.4  | .23 | 3.1 | 5.8   | .72 |
| 1.2 | 37.8  | .26 | 3.4 | 4.7   | .74 |
| 1.3 | 34.7  | .30 | 3.6 | 3.7   | .76 |
| 1.4 | 31.9  | .33 | 3.8 | 3.0   | .78 |
| 1.5 | 23.3  | .36 | 4.0 | 2.3   | .80 |

*Source:* Based on Cohen, J. Statistical power analysis for the behavioral sciences. New York: Academic Press, 1969.

of the two samples overlap, only one percent of the variance is associated with group membership, and knowledge of which group a subject belongs to will provide little in the way of predicting his or her score on the outcome measure. As an example of an effect size of this magnitude, Cohen states that it is approximately the size of the difference in mean height between fifteen- and sixteen-year-old girls (i.e., .5 inches).

A $d$ of about .5 is considered by Cohen (1969) to be a medium effect. In terms of overlap of populations, $d = .5$ indicates 67 percent overlap. In terms of correlation, $d = .5$ means that the association between group membership (experimental versus control) and an outcome measure $(Y)$ is .24. Thus, almost 6 percent $(r^2)$ of the variance of the outcome measure is "accounted for" or "explained by" group membership.

As pointed out by Cohen, "an amount not quite equal to 6% of variance may well not seem large enough to be called medium. But $d = .5$ . . . represents the difference in mean IQ between professionals and managers (about 8 points . . . )" (1969, p.24).

When the overlap between two populations is such that $d = .8$ (approximately 53 percent overlap), Cohen (1969) designates this as a large effect. In this case the correlation between group membership and outcome variable is .37, and 14 percent $(r^2)$ of the variance of the outcome variable is accounted for by group membership. It is important to note that what is here being considered large is the .8 separation between means. This difference, for example, is that represented by the mean IQ difference estimated between holders of the Ph.D. degree and typical college freshmen.

It should be obvious by now that a difference an investigator is willing to call small, medium, or large depends to a great extent upon his or her frame of reference. "We are thus reminded of the arbitrariness of this assignment of quantitative operational definitions to qualitative adjectives" (Cohen 1969, p. 24). Nevertheless, the development of a measure that unambiguously represents the magnitude of an experimental effect, that is not dependent on sample size, and that is also independent of the particular variable under consideration represents a tremendous advance in the methodology of psychotherapy research. As will be discussed shortly, this measure makes possible direct comparisons of the effectiveness of a large number of studies.

## Statistical Power Analysis

An investigator can make two kinds of interrelated errors when drawing conclusions from his or her data. The investigator can conclude that a difference between two populations exists when in fact it does not, or can conclude that a difference does not exist when in fact it does. The first kind of error (Type I) has received much attention and is taken into account by setting typically low statistical criterion levels of probability, for example, .05 or .01, for rejecting the null hypothesis (the hypothesis that no difference between groups exists). However, the second kind of error, that of concluding that no difference exists between groups when in fact it does, has been largely neglected in research in psychotherapy. If the investigator is a typical researcher in this area, not only has he or she exerted no prior control over the risk of committing this type of error (Type II), but the magnitude of the risk will be unknown (Cohen 1965, Spitzer and Cohen 1968).

The usual expectation of the investigator is that the phenomenon he or she is studying does in fact exist; for example, the patients in the experimental group who have received psychotherapy are expected to have a better outcome than those in the control group who did not. However, if only a few cases are studied, the likelihood of obtaining statistically significant results is small, even if a difference is readily apparent to the clinical eye.

It is thus highly possible for an investigator exploring differences among small samples to find himself in the converse position of hypothetical Dr. *A* discussed in the previous section. Dr. *A* was the investigator who studied the differential effectiveness of drug *X* and drug *Y* for reducing symptoms of anxiety. He found a highly statistically significant difference in favor of drug *Y*. This could, however, have been due mainly to his large samples (200 patients), and on clinical grounds the effect of the drug may very well have been trivial. It is just such issues as these with which power analysis is concerned.

### Power Analysis

"The technical term used to describe the probability of obtaining a result which is statistically significant when the phenomenon actually exists is statistical power" (Spitzer and Cohen 1968, p. 116). In somewhat simpler terms, power refers to the probability of rejecting the null hypothesis when it is in fact false, and a true difference between groups exists. A number of factors enter into the determination of statistical power.

Statistical power analysis may be viewed as the formal study of the complex relations among the following four parameters:

1. The *power* of the test (that is, the probability of correctly rejecting the null hypothesis). Theoretically, this may range from zero to 1.00.
2. The significance criterion that leads to rejecting the null hypothesis. As the criterion level increases, that is, becomes *less* stringent (i.e., goes from .01 to .05), power increases.
3. The sample size *n*. As *n* increases, power increases.
4. The magnitude of the phenomenon in the population, *d*, or effect size (ES). As this increases, power increases.

The relations among these four parameters are such that when three of them are fixed, the fourth is completely determined. Thus, since an investigator has virtually no control over the effect size in the population, once he or she decides what significance criterion and the sample size to use, "the power of his test is determined, even though he does not in general know what it is" (Cohen 1965, p. 96).

What this implies is that the problem in understanding the relations among these parameters lies in the fact that the investigator has no precise way of knowing, in advance of the study, the magnitude of the effect in the population. The investigator can, however, rely on his or her knowledge of the research area in which he is working to posit that the effect will be small, medium, or large. As previously discussed, Cohen (1969) has operationally defined a small difference between means as .2 standard deviation units, a medium difference as .5, and a large difference as approximately .8 standard deviation units. An alternative to estimating effect size on the basis of experience would be simply to select a medium effect size as a convention. Once the investigator has established three of the four parameters, he or she can then explore the implications of the relations among them *before* conducting the study, through the use of various accessible references. Cohen (1969), for example, provides a set of power tables for determining each of these parameters as a function of all the others.

While there are thus four possible ways of investigating the interrelations among sample size, effect size, significance level criterion, and power, practical applications of statistical power analysis are usually confined to only one or two. Its major use is to make rationally based decisions as to sample sizes in the planning of research. It has, however, also been used in the interpretation of completed research.

As an example of the latter usage, Cohen (1962) surveyed, from the point of view of power analysis, over seventy research articles published in the *Journal of Abnormal and Social Psychology* during the year 1960. He applied the previously discussed operational definitions of small, medium, and large effect sizes to be expected in the populations, and assumed the .05 level of significance. What he found was that the average power (probability of rejecting false null hypotheses) over the seventy studies was .18 for small effects, .48 for medium effects, and .83 for large effects. In his opinion, these power values were far too small, and he concluded that since power is a direct monotonic function of sample size, that much research in this area was being performed on samples much too small to have reasonable expectations of positive results. This, in turn, may have led to premature abandonment of fruitful lines of investigation. Cohen (1962) recommended that investigators in the area of experimental abnormal and social psychology use larger sample sizes than is customary (approximately thirty subjects in each group).

Power analysis has probably been used most frequently to determine the sample size necessary to reasonably assure the investigator that he or she may reject a false null hypothesis. One way of using power analysis in this manner would be to select a significance criterion, estimate the effect size in the population, and specify the desired power, which would then determine the sample size to be used. Cohen's (1969) power tables may be used to determine the exact relations among these parameters.

Theoretically, this would be exceedingly simple, but reality creates a number of problems. For example, an investigator wants to be highly respectable, so he chooses .01 as his significance criterion. He really has no reliable information relating to the magnitude of the effect size he expects to find in the samples he is studying, so he uses the convention of a medium size. He has had no previous experience with estimates of power and thus chooses .80 as a convention. (Cohen [1965] has pointed out that, although frequently misused, statistical conventions are nevertheless useful, and that power of .80 should be sought when no other basis for making the choice is available.) He plans to compute a t-test between the means of his two patient samples. So, with these three parameters determined, he now turns to Cohen's power tables and discovers that he will need eighty-three patients in each of his two samples if he is to stand a good chance (.80) of obtaining results significant at the .01 level if, in fact, such a difference exists between his sample means. Unfortunately, our hypothetical investigator may have nowhere near 166 patients at his disposal.

Since, as it turned out, the required $n$ exceeded his resources, the investigator still had several options open to him. He could, for example, increase his significance criterion; that is, make it less stringent. For a medium effect, a significance level of .10, and power of .80, he would need only fifty patients in each of his samples. If even this number of patients is more than he can obtain, he can reduce his chances of being able to reject a false null hypothesis and lower his power requirements.

The point of all these manipulations, which may appear to be no more than a game, is that the investigator, "by studying the relationship between $n$ and power *for his situation,* taking into account the increase in cost to achieve a given increase in power, . . . can arrive at a rational solution to the sample-size problem" (Cohen 1965, p. 98).

In conclusion, it is important to note that merely increasing sample size is no panacea for all the problems of psychological research. We have demonstrated, for example, that by utilizing very large samples, even the most clinically trivial results can be statistically significant. A large $n$ can never replace good planning, reliable and valid measures, optimally efficient experimental designs, random sampling procedures, and all the other factors that have been explored at length earlier in this report. Increasing $n$ when appropriate can, however, serve to reduce the probability of spurious negative results.

## Combinatory Techniques for Assessing the Efficacy of Psychotherapy

The term *combinatory techniques* refers to an important approach that has resulted from the rapid expansion of research dealing with the efficacy of psychotherapy. As this research has grown from a few controlled studies in the 1950s to hundreds of investigations that have used reasonably scientific standards in the 1970s, the complex nature of the results and the inconsistent findings have created many problems of interpretation. Those investigators who have attempted to review various segments of the literature have, therefore, had to develop schemas for deciding on methodological grounds which studies to include in their reviews and also for deciding on how to combine the often-conflicting results of large numbers of investigations. The present section will describe three recent approaches for dealing with these problems.

The first comprehensive attempt to categorize and review controlled outcome studies was conducted by Meltzoff and Kornreich (1970). They examined the research on comparative methods and techniques of psychotherapy in order to determine if there were any demonstrable effects of any systematic attempt to modify pathological behavior, regardless of kind or type of treatment involved.

In order to accomplish this, they reviewed 101 controlled outcome studies and divided them into adequate and questionable categories. Their criteria for an adequate study were (Meltzoff and Kornreich 1970, p.76):

1. Freedom from major design flaws that might invalidate the conclusions
2. Use of an appropriate control group and adequate sampling
3. Relative freedom from bias
4. Employment of reasonably objective, reliable, and valid criteria measures
5. Presentation of suitably analyzed and interpreted data.

A study was categorized as questionable if it did not meet these standards in one or more respects. Included in this category were analogue studies considered too limited to be generalized to clinical situations.

The authors then applied a second subdivision, based on results, to both adequate and questionable studies. Results were deemed *positive* when the balance was distinctly in favor of the group receiving therapy. *Null* results were those where no significant differences were found between treated and control groups. *Negative* results showed a balance distinctly in favor of the untreated control group.

The results of Meltzoff and Kornreich's (1970) analyses will be presented in a subsequent section of this report. In general, however, they conclude that controlled research has demonstrated significantly more desired behavioral changes in treated patients than in untreated controls, and the higher the quality of the research, the more positive the results.

The review by Meltzoff and Kornreich (1970) represents a major step forward in the attempt to combine a large number of studies and make comparative judgments about the effectiveness of various forms of therapy for various types of patients. Their method of categorizing and evaluating the studies reviewed is, however, somewhat arbitrary inasmuch as it was basically their own judgments that were involved. Since 1970, therefore, a number of other investigators have attempted to develop more explicit, less arbitrary methods and criteria for comparing the results of outcome studies of psychotherapy. With the exception of the more recent "meta-analysis" approach (Smith and Glass 1977; Smith, Glass, and Miller 1980), all have basically been variations of the so-called "box-score" method used by Luborsky, Singer, and Luborsky (1975).

### The Box-Score Method

The box-score method is essentially a way of summarizing, evaluating, and comparing, in terms of outcome, studies using different modalities or techniques of treatment. Studies that have assessed the effect of a specific modality of treatment on a specific outcome variable are examined. There can be three possible outcomes: the treatment can result in significantly positive effects, or significantly negative effects, or can have no significant effects in either direction. Studies falling into each of these three categories are simply tallied. If a majority of studies falls into one of the three categories, with fewer falling into the other two, the category containing the majority of studies is considered the "winner" and is assumed to give the best estimate of the true effect of that particular mode of treatment (Light and Smith 1971).

In 1975, Luborsky et al. examined published studies that paid at least some attention to the main criteria of controlled comparative research. The research quality of each study was evaluated according to the following twelve criteria:

1. Assignment of patients to each group was controlled, either by random assignment or by appropriate matching on important variables.

117

2. Real patients were used.
3. Therapists for each group were equally competent.
4. Therapists were not inexperienced.
5. Treatments were equally valued.
6. Outcome measures were related to target goals.
7. Treatment outcome was evaluated by independent measures.
8. Information was obtained about concurrent treatment (for example, drugs).
9. Samples of each of the compared treatments were independently evaluated.
10. Each of the compared treatments was given in equal amounts.
11. Each treatment was given in sufficient amount so that one could presume that some benefit might result.
12. Sample size was adequate.

The authors then graded each study on a scale from *A* to *E*, according to how well these "grades" fit the criteria. A grade of *A* indicated that, in general, the study met their criteria for a well-designed study. A grade of *B* indicated deficiencies on one or two criteria. *C* meant three or four criteria were partially deficient; *D* indicated partial deficiencies on three or four, with one seriously deficient; *E* reflected deficiencies so serious that the study was not included in the analysis. Independent grading judgments on sixteen randomly selected studies by two of the authors yielded a reliability coefficient of $+ .84$.

The application of the criteria and the grading process resulted in the selection of ninety-one studies for comparative analyses of results. Eight types of comparisons were made: for example, individual versus group psychotherapy, time-limited versus time-unlimited psychotherapy, and behavior therapy versus psychotherapy. For each type of comparison, a "box score" was provided, with the number of studies in which the treatments were significantly better or worse. "Tie scores," the term used for therapies showing no statistical differences, were also used.

The results of this comparative analysis of the effectiveness of various kinds of therapies will be presented in Chapter 11. The following is, therefore, presented simply as an example of their method of reporting their results:

*Box Score*

| | |
|---|---|
| Group therapy was better | 2 |
| Tie | 9 |
| Individual therapy was better | 2 |

Other investigators who have not used the term box score in their comparative analyses of large numbers of studies have used what is essentially a partial or modified version of the box-score method. For example, in 1974 May and Van Putten devised a scale to measure design relevance for studies involving schizophrenics. *Design relevance* refers to the degree of confidence with which the findings of a given study can be applied to the treatment of schizophrenia, based on the reported design, execution, and analysis of results. In this sense, it refers to the authors' judgments about the quality of the study. The scale provides criteria that are used to place a study in one of six categories, each of which is assigned a different number of points. A study placed in Category I, for example, is assigned 80 points; a Category II receives 60 points; and so on down to Category VI studies, which merit only one point.

May (1976) used this system to classify all controlled studies of the results of nonpharmacologic therapies reported up to mid-1973 and all comparable studies of pharmacologic treatment up to 1968. Findings were tabulated only for those studies that met the criteria for Categories I to IV; that is, prospective studies with six or more control patients treated in the same facility. Ratings for studies that found no benefit or worsening with a given treatment were summed and subtracted from the sum of studies reporting positive results in order to provide an overall estimate of the strength of the evidence for the therapy. A positive number indicated more support for the effectiveness than for the ineffectiveness of the therapy, and vice versa. Table 4, modified from a table provided by May (1976), exemplifies the way in which he summarized his data.

Thus, May's (1976) system produces evidence that inpatient schizophrenics treated with individual psychotherapy or standard group therapy do not improve to a greater extent than do control patients (*minus* 192 and *minus* 51 design relevance points, respectively).

It should be mentioned that Luborsky et al.'s 1975 method of presenting their data essentially ignores their grading system.

On the basis of their twelve criteria, they assigned a letter grade to each study included in their review. When presenting their box scores, however, the letter grades, which presumably reflected their estimates of the methodological soundness of the studies, are never again mentioned. In contrast, results as reported by May (1976) in his version of the box-score method do reflect his system of classification. However, while Luborsky et al. (1975) provide the reader with the number of studies on which their various comparisons were based, May (1976) does not include this data, a fact that makes interpretation of the evidence for effectiveness for any comparison somewhat ambiguous.

Nevertheless, we may obtain some perspective on the weightings shown in Table 4 (which are typical in size for most of the comparisons among nonpharmacological therapies) by knowing that the evidence in favor of antipsychotic drugs over control treatments was +7,080.

Investigations that have used somewhat "weaker" or partial versions of the box-score method are exemplified by a report of Weissman's (1979). In this paper, evidence was presented for the efficacy of five types of psychotherapy alone, in comparison with, and in combination with pharmacotherapy. The five psychotherapies included cognitive therapy, behavioral approaches, interpersonal psychotherapy, group therapy, and marital therapy. No explicit criteria for the selection of the studies used in the analyses were presented. Although seventeen studies were included, only twelve were complete at the time of writing. Five were still in progress. The relatively small amount of data available for any one type of therapy or combination of therapies thus precluded the use of the more formal

**Table 4.** Weight of Evidence from Controlled Studies of Schizophrenia to 1973

|  | Comparison | Evidence for Effectiveness |
|---|---|---|
|  | Individual versus Control | −192 |
| Inpatient | Group (Standard) versus Control | − 51 |
| Psychotherapy | Group (Reality-Activity) versus Control | +100 |
|  | Group (Reality-Activity) versus Standard | + 51 |

Source: Based on May, P.R.A. Pharmacotherapy of schizophrenia in relation to alternative treatment methods. In G. Sedvall, B. Uvnas, and Y. Zotterman (Eds.), *Antipsychotic Drugs: Pharmacodynamics and Pharmacokinetics.* New York: Pergamon Press, 1976.

box-score method of Luborsky et al. (1975). Nevertheless, evidence for the efficacy of the various therapies is presented, and limited comparisons are made.

## Critique of the Box-Score Method

While it may be argued that the box-score method is less arbitrary and more explicit than the method used by Meltzoff and Kornreich (1970), Kazdin and Wilson (1978) present a number of criticisms of the method. Although these criticisms are specific to the method as used by Luborsky et al. (1975), they would apply to most reviews that have used this combinative approach or modified versions of it in their data analysis.

First, Kazdin and Wilson (1978) point out that so many of the experiments cited by Luborsky et al. (1975) have flawed designs that the "best" studies are not necessarily much better than the poorest studies. In essence, Luborsky and his colleagues (1975) graded on a curve. Kazdin and Wilson (1978) claim that there is simply not enough data available to decide that the "better" studies show any different trends with regard to statistical significance than do the "poorer" studies.

A second criticism of the box-score strategy is that by essentially ignoring their own grading system, Luborsky et al. (1975) often give equal weight to different investigations, despite great differences in methodology and in outcome criteria. This procedure is a "kind of majority rule whereby two poor experiments are given twice as much weight as a single sound one" (Gardner 1966, p. 416). It is this criticism from which May's (1976) version of the method may be considered exempt. His assignment of points to a study and method of summation over studies does reflect, at least indirectly, the overall quality of the studies on which he based his results.

In addition to the fact that Luborsky et al.'s (1975) scoring system is not reflected in their box scores, Kazdin and Wilson (1978) present illustrations to show that the scoring system itself is arbitrary and relatively unreliable. For example, the two studies that Luborsky et al. (1975) graded highest (B+) (Gelder et al. 1967 and Sloane et al. 1975) were characterized by Kazdin and Wilson (1978) as having major methodological flaws. At the lower end of the scale, Luborsky et al. (1975) gave Cooper (1963); Cooper, Gelder, and Marks (1965); and Marks and Gelder (1967) a C grade. However, Kazdin and Wilson (1975) thought that these studies had so many design deficiencies that they were not even reviewed in their book.

Fourth, even though Luborsky et al. (1975) concluded that behavior therapy is "tied" with other psychotherapies in effectiveness, Kazdin and Wilson (1978) point out that behavior therapy was slightly or significantly more effective than the alternative treatments in almost all cases. Fifth, Kazdin and Wilson (1978) criticize the box-score method as providing no rational, statistical basis for combining the results of different investigations, regardless of what their ratings are. For example, in Luborsky et al.'s (1975) comparison of behavior therapy and psychotherapy, thirteen studies showed "tied" scores and six showed results in favor of behavior therapy. The authors then concluded that these results indicate that there are no differences in outcome between these two modalities. Such a judgment is obviously arbitrary, and it is likely that an evaluator representing another point of view might come up with an entirely different conclusion.

Finally, Kazdin and Wilson (1978) claim that the box-score approach obscures the real differences between techniques that happen to be given the same global labels. Behavior therapy is not synonymous with systematic desensitization or "cognitive modification" or rational therapy; nor is psychotherapy the same as psychoanalysis, brief psychoanalytically oriented therapy, dynamic group therapy, or supportive counseling. The box-score strategy tends to reify the convenient labels that are given to describe therapeutic endeavors.

Smith, Glass, and Miller (1980) also make some cogent criticisms of this method. In their opinion, its most serious shortcoming is that it ignores considerations of sample size in the studies integrated. Quite simply, large samples are likely to produce more statistically significant findings than small samples. Thus it is possible that nine small-sample studies could yield results falling just short of the specified level of statistical significance, while a tenth large-sample study showed significant results. Although one's intuition might warn against accepting such a tally at face value, the box score is still one for the therapy and nine against it.

A second deficiency pointed out by these authors is that it discards good descriptive information. For example, "To know that aversive conditioning beats directed imagery in 25 of 30 studies—if, in fact, it does—is not to know whether it wins by a nose or a walkaway" (Smith, Glass, and Miller 1980, p. 38).

These various criticisms of the box-score strategy are cogent and largely appropriate, and they highlight the need for a more defensible way of judging the (often) conflicting results of large numbers of investigations that deal with the same general problems. The following discussion of meta-analysis represents Smith, Glass, and Miller's (1980) attempt to overcome the deficiencies of past techniques.

## Meta-Analysis of Outcome Studies

Meta-analysis, the integration of large numbers of research studies through statistical analysis of the data of individual studies, was first described by Glass (1976). It was used by Smith and Glass in 1977 to integrate the results of 375 psychotherapy outcome studies, and in a more extended analysis of 475 outcome studies in 1980 (Smith, Glass, and Miller).

Smith and Glass (1977) present a number of criteria that a study must meet to be included in a meta-analysis. First, it must have at least one therapy treatment group that is compared to an untreated or waiting-list control group or to a different therapy group. Rigor of research design is not a selection criterion, but is, rather, one of several characteristics to be related to the effect of the treatment in that study. As an historical note, it might be mentioned that Luborsky et al's (1975) finding that the research quality of each study reviewed did not determine the trend in any given group of studies played a part in the Smith and Glass (1977) decision to include studies regardless of quality.

Second, all studies selected must meet the definition of psychotherapy provided by Meltzoff and Kornreich (1970):

> Psychotherapy is taken to mean the informed and planful application of techniques derived from established psychological principles, by persons qualified through training and experience to understand these principles and to apply these techniques with the intention of assisting individuals to modify such personal characteristics as feelings, values, attitudes, and behaviors which are judged by the therapist to be maladaptive or maladjustive [p. 6].

This criterion leads to the exclusion of such therapies as pharmacotherapy, hypnotherapy, bibliotherapy, occupational therapy, peer counseling, and marathon encounter groups. Included, however, are counseling studies, analogue studies, and dissertations whose methods fit the above definition.

For each study that is included in a meta-analysis, information of the following type is obtained: date and form of publication, type of therapy employed, duration of therapy, professional affiliation and number of years' experience of the therapist, diagnosis, age and IQ of patients, source of patients and method of assignment to groups, therapist-patient similarity, type and reactivity or "fake-ability" of outcome measures, patient attrition, internal validity of the research design, and effect size.

As conceived by Smith, Glass, and Miller (1980), the most important feature of an outcome study is the magnitude of the effect of the therapy employed. The concept of effect size as an unambiguous common unit of measurement of the relative magnitude of an experimental effect that does not depend on the size of the samples on which it was determined has already been discussed at length. At this point it is, however, worth repeating that the magnitude of effect, or effect size, is the average difference on an outcome measure between the treated and control subjects divided by the standard deviation of the outcome scores of the control group. Thus, effect size is expressed in terms of standard deviation units. If no difference exists between the therapy and control groups, the effect size will be zero. But when the difference is as large as one standard deviation of the control group, the effect size will be one. For practical purposes, it may range from −3, indicating an extremely deleterious effect of therapy, to +3, indicating that, in comparison with the control group, therapy had a highly beneficial effect.

Figures 8 and 9 demonstrate the way in which this concept of effect size is used in meta-analysis. Figure 8 shows the percentile equivalents of the various standard deviation units of a normal distribution. It illustrates the fact that a point that is one standard deviation unit above the mean corresponds to a percentile score of 84. Similarly, for every position on the horizontal axis of the normal curve, there is a corresponding percentile point.

Figure 9 illustrates the case of an effect size of +1 when a therapy group is compared with a control group. A patient who scored at the mean of the control group (50th percentile) prior to therapy on a given measure rose to the 84th percentile (plus one standard deviation) of the control group after treatment. Therefore, the average patient in the therapy group showed an improvement of 34 percentile points over the average patient in the control group on the outcome measure under consideration.

124

It is important to note that an effect size may be calculated on any outcome variable a researcher chooses to measure and that in many cases a study may yield more than one effect size, since effects might be measured on more than one type of outcome variable. Typical outcome measures on which effect sizes are obtained are self-esteem, anxiety, depression, work/school achievement, physiological stress, and so on. Mixing different outcomes is also defensible on a number of grounds, including the fact that all outcome measures are more or less

**Figure 8.** Percentile Equivalents of the Various Standard Deviation Units

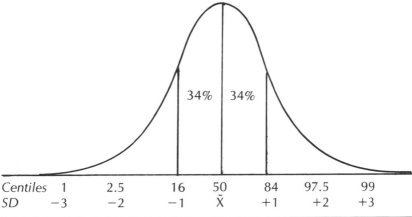

| Centiles | 1 | 2.5 | 16 | 50 | 84 | 97.5 | 99 |
| --- | --- | --- | --- | --- | --- | --- | --- |
| SD | $-3$ | $-2$ | $-1$ | $\bar{X}$ | $+1$ | $+2$ | $+3$ |

related to "well-being," and so at a general level are comparable (Smith and Glass 1977).

The effect sizes of the separate studies that meet the criteria for inclusion in a meta-analysis become the "dependent variables." The "independent variables" include such forms of treatment as transactional analysis and reality therapy. Parloff (1981) also notes that of all the therapies studied, 49 percent were group therapies.

Parloff (1981) points out that generalizations from the meta-analyses are limited. One reason for limited generalizations relates to the fact that the patients represented in the survey were not the typical clientele served by most psychotherapists. Sixty-two percent of the 1,766 reported treatment effects were derived from subjects who either responded to an advertisement or who were directly solicited by the experimenter. Furthermore, only 3 percent were described as "depressed," a

**125**

diagnosis that accounts for approximately half of all patients seen in the "real" world.

The therapists in the studies surveyed by Smith, Glass, and Miller (1980) are also considered by Parloff (1981) to be non-representative of therapists in general, inasmuch as the large majority were relatively inexperienced. Furthermore, not only were the therapists biased in favor of a particular form of treatment in 88 percent of the 475 studies reviewed, but Parloff quotes the authors as stating that "Where the allegiance was in favor of the therapy, the magnitude of effect was greatest.

---

**Figure 9.**   Results of an Outcome Study Showing an Effect Size of +1.00

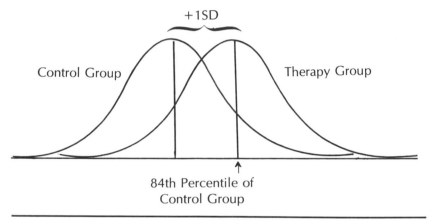

84th Percentile of
Control Group

---

Where there was bias against the therapy, the effect was least" (Smith, Glass, and Miller 1980, p. 120).

It is important to note that this critique by Parloff (1981) is not meant to impugn the significance of what he calls "this elegant survey." Rather, it is meant to show that as a consequence of the research field's dependence on voluntary participation, the body of evidence for the effectiveness of psychotherapy does not seem to fully represent psychotherapy as it is actually offered to the public.

It thus appears that although meta-analysis is an important new statistical advance, considerably more research, particularly more research that adequately represents psychotherapy as currently practiced, is needed before existing conflicts among facts and conflicts among interpretations can be resolved.

# CHAPTER 11

# Issues of Effectiveness

The previous sections of this report have examined the major methodological problems and issues associated with research in psychotherapy. We have considered such fundamental matters as the problem of defining the patient, the therapists, and the therapy; the nature of controls; the problem of selection and assignment of patients; the structure of research designs for psychotherapy evaluation; the problem of ethics; and the many problems associated with assessment. Despite these many complex problems and despite the lack of solutions for some of them, many researchers have attempted to carry out psychotherapy outcome studies.

At the outset these studies were largely descriptive, anecdotal, and uncontrolled. Gradually, beginning in the 1950s, a number of attempts were made to introduce control or comparison groups into psychotherapy research. And over the ensuing years, a large body of literature of this type has accumulated. Most of these controlled studies were carried out in academic settings using relatively inexperienced therapists and only slightly or moderately disturbed "patients." And these studies were usually carried out over relatively short periods of time. According to Parloff et al. (1978), there are, in fact, no long-term well-controlled studies of psychotherapy.*

Unfortunately, the literature on the effectiveness of psychotherapy has been reviewed rather haphazardly. Different

---

* The major long-term study of psychotherapy was reported from the Menninger Clinic (Kernberg et al. 1972) and involved a comparison of twenty-one patients who entered long-term psychoanalysis with twenty-one patients seen in psychoanalytically oriented psychotherapy. Those in analysis were seen for an average of over 800 hours, while those in psychotherapy averaged almost 300 hours of therapy. Psychological tests and evaluation interviews were conducted initially, at termination, and two years after treatment was completed. Where possible, relatives, therapists, and supervisors were also interviewed. No audio- or videotapes were made of the sessions.

The results indicated that some patients improved on various measures and others did not or got worse. On the Health-Sickness Rating Scale, there was no difference in improvement between those in psychoanalysis and those in analytic psychotherapy. Outcome data are not provided, although patients judged to have high ego strength tended to do better with both modes of therapy.

The study has been criticized on a number of grounds, including the lack of blind ratings and the lack of an untreated control group.

reviewers have selected studies to examine largely arbitrarily. Their evaluations of the adequacy or inadequacy of the studies cited have often been based on arbitrary criteria or the criteria have not been specified at all. Sometimes a box-score method has been used to attempt to arrive at a conclusion about effectiveness in the face of conflicting results. More recently, a meta-analysis of results of different investigations has attempted to use a sophisticated new statistical methodology in an effort to combine the results of diverse experiments (Smith, Glass, and Miller 1980).

Given these problems and divergent approaches it would not be expected that there will be any simple or consistent answers to the question of for whom and under what conditions psychotherapy is effective. However, it is worthwhile to summarize and evaluate the various efforts that have been made to review the literature on controlled studies of the effectiveness of psychotherapy. It should be clear that no attempt will be made to re-examine every study that has been published. Instead, the careful major reviews of the literature reported by such individuals as Bergin and Lambert (1978); Eysenck (1952); Kazdin and Wilson (1978); Luborsky, Singer, and Luborsky (1975); May (1975); Meltzoff and Kornreich (1970); Parloff et al. (1978); and Smith, Glass, and Miller (1980) will be examined for their selection of studies, for the adequacy of their analyses, and for their conclusions.

The proposed integration of these and other reviews will be carried out primarily in terms of different therapeutic modalities but an attempt will be made to introduce an historic perspective as well. This integration will address the questions: To what extent does each therapeutic approach provide controlled evidence of effectiveness? and To what extent must conclusions be qualified?

## The Issue of Effectiveness Is Raised

In 1952, Eysenck published the results of a review of twenty-four articles, representing mostly uncontrolled investigations, that described the outcome of psychotherapy. Some of the reports were based on psychoanalytic therapies and others were of a variety of types that he labeled "eclectic." For each study, Eysenck estimated the percent of patients who improved.

For two reports in which no-treatment control groups were included, Eysenck calculated a "spontaneous" improvement rate for untreated patients of approximately 64 percent. When he calculated comparable statistics for the various treatment conditions, he found that for most studies about two-thirds of the patients improved, a figure almost identical to the spontaneous improvement rate. For investigations using psychoanalytic treatment, the improvement rate was estimated to be 44 percent, below that for the purported controls.

It should be emphasized that the major data source for Eysenck's controls was from insurance company files of individuals who had submitted mental disability claims. The insurance company reported that without therapy 44 percent of the claimants had returned to work by the end of one year, and that 61 percent had returned to work by the end of two years.

This review by Eysenck, which threw doubt on the efficacy of psychotherapy, raised a storm of criticism and led to a number of rebuttals (Bergin 1971; Kiesler 1966; Lambert 1976; Luborsky 1954, 1972; Malan 1973; Meltzoff and Kornreich 1970; Rosenzweig 1954; and Strupp 1963). Critics pointed out that many of the studies cited were ambiguous concerning the degree and nature of the outcomes. The nature and quality of the treatments were also poorly specified. The control group data were also challenged as not representative, not comparable to those of the treated patients, and also not free of the influence of various remedies such as sedatives, tonics, and reassurance. In addition, it was pointed out that work disability is only tenuously related to the kinds of life problems and symptoms that bring an individual to psychotherapeutic treatment, and that people may return to work while still suffering from anxiety, depression, phobias, and character disorders. Finally, these critics have noted errors in Eysenck's data and reporting of statistics.

In a later paper, Eysenck (1966) updated his original review by adding eleven new studies. The new review supported his original conclusions about the non-effectiveness of psychotherapy of the psychoanalytic variety. But it did claim that behavioral therapies (particularly systematic desensitization) are more effective than doing nothing. Among the criticisms of this paper is that Eysenck used a biased selection of studies to draw his conclusions. According to Meltzoff and Kornreich (1970), there were at least seventy published controlled studies of psychotherapy by 1965, most of which were not included in Eysenck's review.

Bergin and Lambert (1978) concluded that reviews published by Eysenck do not resolve the basic issues raised about the efficacy of psychotherapy. This is because (1) the cases reported in the different studies are not comparable; (2) the criteria of outcome are highly variable; (3) the quality and amount of psychotherapy received was often unknown; (4) follow-up was often haphazard; and (5) evaluations were usually based on the therapists' impressions, and thus were potentially biased.

One of the important points that Bergin (1971) and Bergin and Lambert (1978) made is that Eysenck's estimate of the rate of spontaneous remission for untreated cases is too high. In Bergin's and Lambert's (1978) examination of thirty-four controlled studies, they concluded that the median spontaneous remission rate in untreated (or minimally treated patients) is about 43 percent rather than the 67 percent suggested earlier by Eysenck.

In a follow-up review of literature published since the original Eysenck paper (1952), one of his collaborators, Rackman (1973) examined outcome data from twenty-three studies of verbal therapies in contrast to behavioral therapies. In arriving at his sample of studies, he excluded subjects who were delinquents, or who had psychosomatic complaints, on the grounds that such patients are not neurotic. He also excluded seventeen studies on methodological grounds such as the use of projective measures for outcomes, the exclusion of subjects who left therapy before treatment was completed, and inconsistency among outcome measures when several were used in the same investigation.

Rackman (1973) concluded that the spontaneous remission rate is much higher than the 30 percent figure that Bergin had suggested in his earlier report (1971) and that it is closer to 65 percent.

The issue of the extent to which untreated control patients "spontaneously" recover is still largely unresolved. This is due to the fact that the criteria for recovery are ambiguous and obviously depend on whether one is concerned with a particular symptom such as a phobia, or whether one is concerned with personality changes or improvement in functioning (social relations, work, and so on). Secondly, relatively few studies have considered, because of practical or ethical reasons, control or untreated patients over long periods of time; for example, a year or more. Finally, the spontaneous recovery rate depends upon the types of patients studied (for example, schizophrenics versus adjustment reactions of married life), the ages of the patients, and the extent to which untreated patients seek out sources of help other than the particular therapy at issue.

However, one need not look for a single magic number that somehow reflects the rate of spontaneous remission, since this has been reported to vary greatly in different investigations. Instead, one may simply examine a series of controlled studies of psychotherapy and empirically determine the differences in recovery on a variety of measures of the treated and untreated groups. This approach has been adopted by a number of investigators. Let us examine some of the major conclusions resulting from this approach.

## First Major Response to the Challenge

In 1970, Meltzoff and Kornreich took up the challenge posed by Eysenck (1952, 1966). They reported the results of 101 controlled outcome studies that had been published in the decades of the 1950s and the 1960s. They pointed out that the contention that there is a paucity of controlled outcome studies of psychotherapy is simply untrue. "On the contrary, every five-year period since 1950 has brought a steadily *increasing* number of outcome studies. From every point of view (design, sampling, criteria, nature of controls, data analysis), the quality of the research has improved along with the quantity" (p. 174).

In their review, Meltzoff and Kornreich asked the basic question of whether anyone has been able to demonstrate that individuals with emotional disturbances of any type can be more benefited by psychotherapy of any variety than by lack of it over the same time span. Without distinguishing between type or duration of therapy or type of patient, they reviewed 101 controlled studies of the outcome of psychotherapy. These studies were divided into "adequate" and "questionable" categories. Using their own judgment and without giving details in every case, they defined adequate studies by the criteria listed on page 116 of the present report.

In summarizing the results of outcome research of individual and group psychotherapy, Meltzoff and Kornreich (1970) pointed out that the ratio of adequate to questionable studies before 1960 was 18 to 25; since 1960 the ratio has been 39 to 19 in favor of adequate studies. Of the 101 investigations reviewed, 80 percent yielded positive results and 20 percent yielded null or negative results. Altogether, 56 percent were considered sufficiently adequate in design and execution for valid conclusions to be drawn, and 44 percent were doubtful. Among the adequate studies, 54 percent showed desirable outcome effects that could be considered major, central, or multiple; 30 percent of the outcomes were minor, restricted, or limited; and 16 percent were null or negative, all as compared to the results obtained from the control groups.

Meltzoff and Kornreich (1970) also attempted to explain, at least partially, the failures of psychotherapy to bring about desirable changes. They noted that in about one-half of the studies where no significant differences were found between the treated and control groups, studies were included in which verbal therapies had been used with chronic schizophrenic patients. Another group of failures of psychotherapy was associated with studies of delinquents and with drug addicts, patients who are known to be difficult to treat with any degree of success.

Overall, however, Meltzoff and Kornreich (1970) concluded from their review of the literature of the 1950s and 1960s that a wide variety of types of psychotherapy applied to a wide range of disorders under controlled conditions showed improvements in various indices of adjustment that were significantly greater than could be expected on the basis of the passage of time alone as indicated by what happened to the control group patients. The evidence did not allow any statements about the *degree* of effectiveness of different modalities of treatment. However, an important point made by Meltzoff and Kornreich (1970) was that the better the estimated quality of the research, the greater the likelihood that positive results would be obtained.

## Further Refinements

The review by Meltzoff and Kornreich (1970) contained an element of arbitrariness in their interpretations of the various studies. This was true both in terms of the judged adequacy of the experiments, as well as the interpretation of their outcomes. As a result, several other investigators attempted to develop more explicit methods for evaluating experiments. One of these alternative approaches is the box-score method (Luborsky, Singer, and Luborsky 1975), and the other is meta-analysis (Smith, Glass, and Miller 1980).

The first major application of the box-score method was made by Luborsky et al. (1975) to a variety of brief psychotherapies for nonpsychotic conditions. These authors identified thirteen studies in the literature in which individual therapies were compared with group therapies, whether or not a separate control group was used. In addition, they found eight studies in which time-limited treatment was compared with time-unlimited treatment. The variety of comparisons made is shown in Table 5.

### Results of the Box-Score Method

Each investigation was evaluated by Luborsky, Singer, and Luborsky (1975) in terms of a list of twelve criteria for adequacy of design and methodology, which has been previously discussed, and was then given a letter grade ranging from $A$ to $E$.

**Table 5.** Comparisons of Different Modalities of Psychotherapy

| Therapy Modalities Compared | Number of Investigations |
| --- | --- |
| Individual versus group | 13 |
| Time limited versus time unlimited | 8 |
| Client-centered versus psycho-<br>analytically oriented | 5 |
| Behavior therapy versus verbal<br>therapies | 19 |
| Psychotherapy versus drug therapy | 8 |
| Psychotherapy versus drug therapy<br>plus psychotherapy | 16 |
| Drug therapy plus psychotherapy<br>versus drug therapy | 11 |
| Psychotherapy plus medical care<br>versus medical care | 11 |
| Total | 91 |

*Source:* Luborsky, L., Singer, B., and Luborsky, Lise. Comparative studies of psychotherapies: Is it true that "Everyone has won and all must have prizes"? *Archives of General Psychiatry,* 1975, *32*, 995–1008.

All studies dealt with young adults or adults, and the majority of them were nonpsychotic patients. Deliberately excluded were all childhood disorders and a wide range of common adult problems including addictive behaviors, sexual problems, and psychotic disorders. Luborsky et al. (1975) also reported, as did Meltzoff and Kornreich (1970), that the more recent investigations were methodologically sounder than were earlier investigations.

# CHAPTER 12

# Outcome Research by Therapy Modality

## Individual Therapy

Using the box-score method, Luborsky, Singer, and Luborsky (1975) compared the different therapies. For example, when group therapies were compared with individual psychotherapies, eight of the thirteen studies showed no significant differences between the two modalities of treatment. Of the remaining five studies, three showed that individual therapy was better and two showed that group therapy was better. These results, demonstrating few if any differences between individual and group therapy, were confirmed whether all the studies were compared or whether a comparison was made of only the "good" studies; that is, those rated *A* or *B*. Therefore, on the basis of the Luborsky et al. (1975) review, there seems to be no reason to choose short-term individual therapy over short-term group therapy.

The same approach was applied to the eight studies in which time-limited treatment was compared with time-unlimited treatment (the latter term is probably a misnomer since time-limited treatment usually refers to a fixed number of sessions such as twelve or twenty; time-unlimited treatment may go on for six to twelve months or more, but is not meant to imply long-term psychoanalytic treatment that may continue for many years.) Of the eight studies in which time-limited treatment was compared with time-unlimited treatment, there were no significant differences found in five. In two investigations, time-limited treatment produced significantly better results than did time-unlimited treatment. And in one, time-unlimited therapy was superior.

Client-centered therapy was compared with other types of verbal therapies such as Adlerian or psychoanalytic, and no significant differences were found in four out of the five studies evaluated.

Finally, of the nineteen comparisons between behavior therapy and other types of verbal therapies, thirteen showed no significant differences. The remaining six investigations reported that patients exposed to behavior therapy did significantly better in reducing phobias or anxiety states than did those exposed to a short-term verbal therapy. However, in the judgment of Luborsky et al. (1975), five of these latter six studies were rated *C* or *D* in quality. In addition, the term "behavior therapy" in most cases meant only one technique of treatment; namely, systematic desensitization.

Luborsky et al. (1975) drew several conclusions from their observations:

1. With the exception of studies using drugs, there are few differences between the outcomes associated with different types of therapies (psychoanalytic, client-centered, behavior, and so on).
2. The better-controlled studies do not show a different trend in the data than do the less-well-controlled studies.
3. Brief therapies do not seem inferior in outcome as compared to longer-term therapies.
4. Results may reflect the psychotherapeutic elements that most therapies have in common.

Several important points may be raised about the review by Luborsky, Singer, and Luborsky (1975). First, most of the studies are relatively brief, seldom lasting more than a few months. Second, many were carried out in academic settings (for example, college clinics) using only mildly disturbed student-patients, and one might not expect any large-scale changes to occur in connection with any form of brief therapy. Third, the outcome measures used in many of these investigations (anxiety reduction, MMPI scores, and so forth) may be too simple to reflect adequately the complexity of changes that may in fact occur in some cases. And, as Strupp and Hadley (1977) have pointed out, a tripartite model may be needed to gather input data from the individual, the therapist, and society ("significant others") in order to obtain a comprehensive image of the changes that take place in an individual. Typically, this was not done. Fourth, it is interesting to note that although Meltzoff and Kornreich (1970) cited 101 controlled outcome studies of psychotherapy in 1970, Luborsky, Singer, and Luborsky referred to only 91 studies in 1975. No explicit rationale is given for the omissions or for the studies selected.

The meta-analysis of individual psychotherapies has produced results that are fairly consistent with those reported by Luborsky et al. (1975). Smith, Glass, and Miller (1980) located every published study (including Ph.D. dissertations) that compared a treated psychotherapy group of patients with some kind of control group, and in each case calculated the effect size. These authors located 475 controlled studies. A separate effect size was calculated for each outcome measure. Therefore, since most studies used several outcome measures, a total of 1,766 effect size measures were derived from the 475 controlled studies. Considering all these measures, the average ES was .85 units in favor of the treated patients. This means that the average person who received psychotherapy of any type (that is, one who was initially at the 50th percentile of the control group distribution) was better off at the end of therapy than 80 percent of these persons who were in the control group. If the analysis is made using only untreated controls so that placebo controls and counseling controls are excluded, the ES is found to be .93 of a standard deviation unit instead of .85.

In order to appreciate the magnitude of this effect it may be compared with effect sizes obtained in other types of investigations. Alcoholics treated with drugs alone improved over the untreated controls to the extent of producing an ES of .77 units. The effect of cigarette smoking on development of lung cancer produced an ES of .60. The conclusion that Smith, Glass, and Miller (1980) reach is that the beneficial effects of psychotherapy are substantial.

In an effort to describe the average characteristics of patients and therapists included in all 475 studies, Smith et al. (1980) report that when all studies are combined it appears that patients are twenty-two years old on the average. In addition, they have received seventeen hours of therapy from therapists who have had about three and a half years of experience; and outcome measures were obtained four months after therapy began. These simple figures clearly imply that, despite the large number of outcome studies cited, most are done with college students who receive brief therapy from relatively inexperienced therapists. These facts should be borne in mind when evaluating the results of the meta-analysis.

One of the meta-analyses carried out by Smith et al. (1980) compared the relative amount of change that occurs when using different measures of outcome. They found that the largest benefit of therapy occurred in terms of symptom improvement (ES = .78) and the smallest benefit occurred in educational and social functioning (ES = .50). Self-esteem improved more than did work achievement.

Seventy-two of the 475 studies compared two different types

of therapies. It was found that behavioral therapies (loosely defined) had larger effect sizes than verbal therapies (loosely defined). But this superiority was related to type of outcome index used. When measuring anxiety, the behavioral therapies were .23 units superior to the verbal ones, whereas life-adjustment measures showed no difference between these two types of therapies. When therapies were broken down by traditional schools, it was found that systematic desensitization produced the largest beneficial effect (ES = .91) while Gestalt therapy produced the lowest (ES = .26). Psychodynamic therapies (ES = .59) had an effect that was comparable to transactional analysis (ES = .58) and client-centered therapy (ES = .63).

An interesting finding is that the estimated "internal reliability" of the studies correlated near zero with effect size, meaning that the "good" studies did not show a better effect than did the "poor" studies. In fact, almost all the quantitative variables correlated close to zero with ES. The largest (although still relatively small) correlation with ES was something called "reactivity of outcome indicator" (ES = .18). This implies that the more easily an outcome indicator can be faked (that is, the more obvious the social desirabilities of the items), the larger the effects reported in the investigation. The other relatively large correlation was between effect size and "percent males in the patient group" (ES = .13). Apparently, this means that the greater the percent of males in the treated group the poorer the outcome of therapy.

Some other important findings are that duration of therapy and experience of therapist were both unrelated to therapeutic effect size. However, it should be kept in mind that most therapists used in such studies had relatively little experience beyond their initial training.

A relatively small number of studies have been meta-analyzed for specific diagnostic groups. For fifteen studies of psychotherapy as applied to alcoholism, the ES was found to be .96, which is higher than for psychotherapy in general. The longer the alcoholism therapy was continued the greater the success rate. For thirteen studies of psychotherapeutic treatment of asthma the ES was .85. It was found that both utilization of medical services and subjective symptoms such as anxiety decreased as a result of therapy. Similarly, recovery from surgery was hastened as a result of psychotherapy but the effect size was somewhat smaller (ES = .50).

In examining these findings it seems that psychotherapy has somewhat better outcomes than are obtained in the control conditions; there is little else that one can conclude. Most therapies have comparable effect sizes, but most are based on short-term applications of the therapy to young people. Duration of therapy and experience of the therapist seem to be unrelated to outcome—a statement contrary to the practical experience of most psychotherapists *and* inconsistent with the report by Luborsky et al. (1980) that reported twenty-three studies in which there was a clear trend for duration to be related to improvement. This finding again may reflect the brief exposures to psychotherapy provided by relatively inexperienced therapists. Furthermore, all the elaborate data analyses do not demonstrate what treatments work best with which patients.

As has been discussed earlier, meta-analysis, despite its apparent statistical sophistication, has led other statisticians to raise questions about the methodology. At best, meta-analysis can reflect only what investigators are actually doing in their controlled research. Thus, if experiments use only young patients, nothing can be said about old patients. If few investigators do psychotherapy with schizophrenics then this issue will not be available for meta-analysis. And similarly, if no long-term controlled studies of psychotherapy are published, all the meta-analyses will concern short-term therapy only.

## Behavior Therapy

In 1978, Kazdin and Wilson published an extensive review of behavior therapy both from the point of view of its diverse approaches and its effectiveness. Behavior therapy was broadly defined "as the application of principles derived from experimental psychology for the alleviation of human suffering and the enhancement of human functioning" (p. 46) and included such techniques as systematic desensitization, aversion therapy, operant conditioning, and others. All studies were reviewed in which a behavioral treatment was compared either to a specific alternative form of treatment or to routine medical management or to no formal treatment. Only prospective studies were reviewed, both neurotic as well as psychotic patients were included, and patients of all ages were considered. The studies were also grouped into seven major areas as shown on Table 6.

In view of Kazdin and Wilson's (1978) critique of box-score methodology, it is instructive to consider their approach when making some tentative generalizations. Basically, they conclude that no method of combining data from different experiments is adequate, simply because the majority of investigations had so many design problems that meaningful interpretations were seldom possible. The result is that they provide no rating system for studies, no box scores, and no formal statistics; they simply make rather tentative generalizations from a perusal of whatever trends exist.

These tentative conclusions may be described as follows. Of fifteen investigations of patients (often college students) with neurotic disorders (mostly phobias and anxieties) the behavioral treatments were usually more effective than "psychotherapy" (twelve out of fifteen comparisons) and were equally effective in three. In four studies of sexual functioning that were reviewed, behavioral techniques were superior to psychotherapy in all cases. Similar superiority of behavioral methods of therapy were found in seven out of eight studies of obese patients seeking to lose weight. In nine studies of alcoholic patients, the results appeared difficult to summarize, but aversion techniques and community reinforcement programs were usually found to work better than traditional psychotherapies. Of eight studies of behavior therapy for specific self-care or ward behaviors of hospitalized patients, as compared to routine hospital care, seven studies indicated greater improvement for the behavioral methods. Similar findings

**Table 6.**   Major Areas of Application of Behavior Therapy

| Area | Number of Investigations |
|---|---|
| Neurotic disorders | 15 |
| Sexual dysfunctions | 4 |
| Addictive behaviors | 16 |
| Psychotic disorders | 15 |
| Delinquency | 5 |
| Childhood disorders | 5 |
| Mental retardation | 9 |
| Total | 69 |

*Source:* From Kazdin, A. E., and Wilson, G. T. *Evaluation of Behavior Therapy: Issues, Evidence, and Research Strategies.* Cambridge, MA: Ballinger Publishing Company, 1978.

were reported when behavior therapy (reinforcement approaches) was compared to individual or milieu therapy for psychotic patients (reinforcement therapy superior in five out of seven studies).

In their review Kazdin and Wilson (1978) devote considerable attention to the book by Sloan et al. (1975), which had been described by a number of reviewers as one of the best comparative studies of psychotherapy in the literature. In their investigation, outpatients suffering from neurotic or personality disorders were treated by "behavior" therapy or by psychoanalytically oriented psychotherapy, and were compared to a waiting-list control group. Ratings of symptoms, general adjustment, and overall improvement were made by the therapists, the patients, and, where possible, by an informant. The results revealed that both modes of therapy produced better outcomes at the end of treatment than were found in the waiting-list controls. However, behavior therapy was superior to psychotherapy in the measure of overall improvement.

Kazdin and Wilson (1978) criticize the study on several grounds: (1) they suggest that the patient's behavior in the clinical situation is not a good sample of his or her behavior in the natural environment; (2) it is difficult if not impossible to keep the assessors blind to the treatments received by the patients; (3) the correlations between ratings made by the different types of assessors (self, therapist, other, and so on) are close to zero, suggesting either the different goals of these assessors or the possible unreliability of the measures; (4) the use of an omnibus treatment package called "behavior therapy" makes it impossible to identify the critical change-producing variables; and (5) the treatment of different types of problems treated by widely differing techniques makes it difficult to identify the specific effects of a specific treatment. Although one may question the appropriateness or specificity of these criticisms, it is worth remembering that even well-done clinical trials may be subject to attack on various methodological grounds.

The application of behavior therapy to adolescents and children was also reviewed. Behavior therapy was reported to be superior to reform school, probation, individual psychotherapy, and no treatment in four out of five of the studies. In the treatment of enuresis, the "bell and pad" method was reported to be more effective than random wakenings or "routine treatment" in four out of the five studies. Nine investigations were cited that were concerned with conduct problems and/or retarded children. Ratings of overt play or classroom behavior were the most common outcome measures used. In almost all cases the control group consisted of children who received drugs. Behavior therapy had better outcomes than drug therapy in four of the investigations.

Kazdin and Wilson (1978) therefore conclude that a variety of brief behavioral therapy methods have tended to be superior to a variety of verbal therapies for a range of conditions. It should be kept in mind, however, that target symptoms were often quite narrow in focus, and that the behavior therapies were often used for conditions to which verbal therapies are seldom applied; for example, self-care behaviors of ward patients, or obese patients. It seems evident that future research of behavioral therapies should compare types of patients or problems for which verbal therapies are typically used, and should do this over a reasonable period of time, using multiple measures of outcome.

Given the qualitative way in which these behavior therapy studies are presented by Kazdin and Wilson (1978) it would not be surprising to discover that other qualitative surveys of the same or similar literature might come to different conclusions.

For example, in partial agreement and partial opposition to Kazdin and Wilson (1975), Parloff et al. (1978) report that behavior therapy, particularly in the form of token economies, has been helpful primarily with regard to ward adjustment, but has had little impact on the bulk of psychotic manifestations such as agitated depression, manic behaviors, hallucinations, and disordered thinking. Very little data are available on the extent to which desirable behavior changes persist outside the hospital setting. Parloff et al.'s (1978) conclusion highlights the point made earlier; that is, that the narrowness of focus of outcome measures may inadvertently make behavior therapy appear more effective than it is.

Parloff et al. (1978) also provide some tentative conclusions about other conditions to which behavior therapy has been applied. With regard to the treatment of childhood autisms, psychodynamically oriented treatment has apparently had no beneficial effects. In contrast, a few studies using small numbers of children have reported some benefits of behavior therapy on such children.

In addition, neurotic anxiety patients have benefited from systematic desensitization, as have many patients with phobias. Studies of psychodynamic therapies generally do not use control groups; therefore, no conclusions about their efficacy can be drawn in this context.

Treatment for sexual dysfunctions have included individual psychotherapy, psychoanalysis, group therapy, hypnosis, various behavioral techniques, and specific "sex therapies." "Despite the few controlled studies, reviewers of the sexual dysfunctions literature agree that a combination of some form of graduated exposure to the anxiety-inducing sexual stimulation, information regarding sexual anatomy, physiology, plus technique, plus some form of social skills training is effective with most of the sexual dysfunctions" (Parloff et al. 1978, p. 185).

Regarding the problem of obesity, both behavioral and non-behavioral techniques of therapy have had relatively little long-term effects. This conclusion also holds for the treatment of anorexia nervosa, and for the treatment of smoking problems.

Small-sample studies have shown that behavioral therapy techniques have been able to reduce hyperactive behavior in children. Similar studies with small samples have reported that operant conditioning approaches to enuresis are often successful.

These comments based on the Parloff et al. (1978) report indicate that qualitative surveys of the literature can often lead to conflicting conclusions when different investigators evaluate the same domains. For example, both Parloff et al. (1978) and Luborsky et al. (1975) give relatively less emphasis to the supposed beneficial outcomes of behavior therapy than do Kazdin and Wilson (1975). One limitation of the Parloff et al. (1978) review is that their evaluations are based upon no formal evaluation schema. Their conclusions are dependent upon the subjective weights given to different papers and often are based upon a small number of investigations. Although preference was given to controlled research, naturalistic and single-case studies were also included.

The descriptions that have been given from the work of Meltzoff and Kornreich (1970); Luborsky, Singer, and Luborsky (1975); Kazdin and Wilson (1978); and Parloff et al. (1978) demonstrate the possible problems and inconsistencies that can result from the attempt to review large amounts of published literature using only subjective judgments or statistically weak box-score methods.

## Marital and Family Therapy

The vicissitudes of the review process can perhaps best be seen by considering the literature on marital and family therapy. In their review of psychosocial treatments for schizophrenia, Mosher and Keith (1980) reported on only three studies of family therapy for schizophrenics. In contrast, Gurman and Kniskern (1978) review almost 200 studies of marital and family therapy, at least 13 of which were conducted with inpatients, many of whom were schizophrenics. A selection process of greater or lesser explicitness must therefore take place in all reviews and obviously the conclusions must be at least partly a function of the experiments that are included.

Gurman and Kniskern (1978) point out that the field of marital and family therapy has only recently evolved, with eight of the nine relevant journals having been initiated since 1973. Most states do not have licensing boards for marital and family therapists and no unified set of training procedures yet exists. Schools of practice center around charismatic leaders; therapists come from diverse professions (for example, sociology, nursing, social work, psychiatry), and there is no generally accepted unifying theory to guide practice. Although Gurman and Kniskern (1978) located 200 studies (some unpublished and many through contacting colleagues in the field), most of these investigations are uncontrolled, and most represent global ratings (therapists' opinions) about what happens to patients who undergo marital and family therapy.

In an effort to apply a kind of box-score analysis to the studies that were reviewed, Gurman et al. (1978) drew up a list of criteria for estimating the adequacy of the reported research. Each item on the list was assigned a numerical weight. For example, controlled assignment (randomization or matching) to treatment conditions was worth five points. Measurement of the outcome variable *both* before and after the treatment was worth five points. Lack of contamination of major independent variables (using therapists of equal skill in the different treatment, for example) was also worth five points. A whole series of other criteria were worth one point each. These included: appropriate statistical analysis, three months or more follow-up, use of multiple outcome measures, and having the therapist and the investigator be two different people. Based on total assigned scores, each experiment was rated from "poor" to "very good."

Gurman et al. (1978) begin their analysis with a summary of 118 mostly uncontrolled studies of marital and family therapy in which an estimate was made of improvement rates. Overall, the different types of nonbehavioral marital therapies produce improvement rates of 61–65 percent, which is comparable to those produced by non-marital individual therapy. From part of these data an estimate was also made of deterioration rates (patient got "worse") and these ranged from 0 percent to 16.6 percent, with an average of 5.4 percent. Gurman and Kniskern (1978) claim that the limited evidence on the application of individual therapy to marital problems produces a deterioration rate of about 12 percent.

These rather gross estimates should be considered in relation to a number of facts. First, most of the research is uncontrolled. Second, family studies typically use relatively inexperienced therapists in outpatient settings. Third, the types of problems for which families seek help are not always the kind for which traditional diagnostic labels, such as schizophrenia and depression, are available. Families are defined as having problems of communication, intimacy, dependency, autonomy conflict, and so forth, along with problems of delinquency, drug addiction, alcoholism, anorexia nervosa, and, sometimes, psychosis. Fourth, family therapies are typically very brief, and rarely last more than one to twenty sessions. Finally, family therapy research has special problems related to what is measured as evidence of the outcome of therapy. For example, if a child is the identified patient, and the parents are in conflict over how to deal with the child's problems, should outcome be measured by changes in the child's behavior, the parents' conflicts, or both? Therefore, the figures on "improvement" and "deterioration" can be only very rough guesses as to the outcomes of treatment.

Gurman and Kniskern (1978) also report on the studies in which a control or comparison group was included. Of forty-four comparative studies, thirty-one treatments by conjoint marital therapy methods were reported superior in comparison to individual therapy, communication-training, or verbal counseling; eleven studies showed ties; and in two studies the "other" method was superior. Of twenty-one studies of family therapy, as compared to individual therapy, parent counseling, client-centered therapy, eclectic treatment, or hospital treatment, "every study to date that has compared family therapy with other types of treatment has shown family therapy to be equal or superior. . . . There have now appeared 30 comparisons of nonbehavioral marital and family therapy with individual or group therapy of the identified patient. In 22 (73 percent) of these, marital-family treatment emerged superior, with no differences found in seven studies" (Gurman and Kniskern 1978, pp. 835, 844). These authors make the strong statement that "when one member of a family system or one dyadic relationship within the family present themselves for treatment with problems involving family living, then marital-family therapy represents a more effective general treatment strategy than does individual therapy" (p. 844).

Unfortunately, this kind of conclusion is based on the same fallacy associated with the claim that behavior therapy is more effective than individual psychoanalytically oriented therapy. If one measures only phobias, then a reduction in phobias will often seem to occur more quickly through systematic desensitization than through psychoanalytic therapy. Similarly, if one measures only communication difficulties, then it may appear that family or marital therapy works more quickly than do other forms of individual therapy. This implies that if one is to make a fair comparison of therapies, each has to be conducted under the best of conditions using a wide variety of outcome measures including those for which each therapy has specifically been developed. Only then will these box-score tabulations avoid ambiguity.

In addition to comparative studies of marital/family therapy, there are fifteen recent investigations in which nonbehavioral marital therapies were compared with untreated control groups, and sixteen studies in which family therapies were compared with untreated controls. One should keep in mind that all such comparisons were conducted over short periods of time, in view of the frequently cited fact that untreated control groups cannot ethically or practically remain untreated for more than brief periods. To illustrate this point, the average number of treatment sessions was only nine. In addition, in most of these studies there were no follow-up evaluations.

Gurman et al.'s (1978) box score indicated that ten studies showed marital therapy significantly more effective than the controls, four showed no differences, and one showed the controls superior to the marital therapy group. Eight of the sixteen studies of family therapy reported that patients exposed to family therapy did significantly better on various outcome criteria than did the control patients; seven studies reported no differences; and in one study the control patients did better than the family therapy patients. These figures do not reflect differences in the results as a function of the adequacy ratings of the different studies.

Gurman and Kniskern (1978) also review a number of studies using behavioral techniques as applied to marital counseling. Unfortunately, most of these are analogue studies carried out in university settings using small numbers of college students as patients, with infrequent follow-up. In fact "there does not yet exist even one controlled comparative study of behavioral couples therapy with real clients involved in severely disturbed relationships" (Gurman and Kniskern 1978, p. 852).

Behavioral techniques have also been used in family interventions. Inexperienced therapists are typically used (under supervision) and although target behaviors have often been found to change in desired ways, almost no evidence exists that desired changes generalize to other settings. Behavioral family studies are also characterized by a high rate of patient dropouts from treatment and refusals to be followed up. Despite these problems behavioral family treatment has been reported more effective than no treatment or alternative treatments in ten out of eleven comparisons. One should keep in mind that here, too, the outcome focus is usually on a single target behavior such as verbal abuse, school fighting, or withdrawal.

Gurman and Kniskern (1978) draw a number of general conclusions from their review of the literature on marital and family therapy. Although at present these are relatively new modalities of treatment, and although they are typically carried out over rather short periods, there is suggestive evidence that couples marital therapy and family therapy appear to be at least as effective or possibly more effective than individual therapy for a wide variety of interpersonal problems within a family. This statement is made even though there is little agreement on goals or techniques among the different "schools" of family therapy.

## Group Psychotherapy

Not everyone who has attempted to review the literature on the outcome of psychotherapy has been concerned with box scores, control groups, or meta-analyses. For example, Parloff and Dies (1977) examined the literature from 1966 to 1975 on the outcome of group psychotherapy from the point of view of what they called a "clinical analysis rather than a rigorous scientific autopsy" (p. 282).

They used three criteria for selecting studies for their review: (1) that one or more forms of group therapy were included; (2) that subjects were "real" patients; and (3) that there was a reasonable basis for attributing the effects of the therapy to the group procedures. Although these criteria sound straight-forward enough, their implementation required a number of arbitrary judgments. For example, encounter groups, growth groups, *est* groups, and self-help groups were all excluded from the survey. The only types of patients studied were psycho-neurotics, schizophrenics, addicts, and criminal offenders. Standards of research design were relaxed sufficiently to per-mit including investigations without control groups. But the standards did require that measures be obtained before and after the designated treatment period. Over 100 studies were screened; 38 were finally selected for summary. These included eighteen dealing with group therapy as applied to schizo-phrenics, six on psychoneuroses, ten on crime and delin-quency, and five on addictions. Descriptions of the various studies are not detailed and it is not possible to independently assess the reported results. What is evident, however, is that in many cases relatively small numbers of patients were studied and only a limited number of group therapists were used.

The conclusions can be stated as follows. In mental hospital settings there were seven investigations. These compared patients given group therapy with patients given the usual hospital treatment. Five of these seven studies reported no special benefits that resulted from adding group therapy to the usual hospital regimens. Two studies compared group therapy in the hospital with a special program (behavioral or non-directive). No differences were found.

Six other studies compared inpatients given group therapy with other patients given group therapy plus some special treatment approach such as drugs, videotape feedback, ward activity, or "forced" social interactions. It was reported that the combined treatment approach was superior to the group therapy alone in five of the six studies. Unfortunately, here again drug treatment was not controlled in most of these in-vestigations, and the results may simply reflect the well estab-lished fact that drug therapy in a mental hospital is the most highly efficacious procedure of any currently used.

Considering after-care programs for schizophrenics, three studies have reported no differences in the effects of individual or group psychotherapy (given the fact that patients had access to medications), one reported mixed results, and one reported better outcomes for group-therapy-treated patients than those given no treatment at all. In one investigation, after-care patients given a psychotropic medication did better than those given group psychotherapy alone. Parloff and Dies (1977) conclude: "In summary, 'group psychotherapy' as an undefined treatment form for post-hospital schizophrenics does not appear to contribute uniquely or consistently to the amelioration of such target treatment areas as reduced rates of rehospitalization, improved vocational adjustment, or diminished psychopathology or enhanced social effectiveness" (p. 295). It is important to emphasize their point that group therapy at present is largely an undefined treatment practice having many idiosyncratic elements related to who does the treatment.

Parloff and Dies (1977) also briefly describe six investigations in which "psychoneurotic" patients given group therapy were compared with similar patients exposed to some other form of treatment (for example, individual therapy, systematic desensitization, and so on). The results of these studies are mixed and somewhat confusing. One reported that alternative sessions improved the benefits attributed to group therapy for neurotic patients (Truax and Wargo 1969), while the opposite was found for schizophrenics and juvenile delinquents (Truax et al. 1966, Traux et al. 1970). Another investigation found group therapy to be less effective than muscle relaxation training. Still another study did not use appropriate statistical comparisons so no conclusions could be drawn. Finally, the most interesting of the studies (Gelder et al. 1967) compared three groups of phobic patients: one that received individual therapy, one that received group therapy, and one that received systematic desensitization. A variety of outcome measures were used. The results demonstrated that the patients' phobias decreased fastest with systematic desensitization, but that the differences among the patient groups largely disappeared by the end of a year of treatment. In addition, one out of four patients in the systematic desensitization condition dropped out of treatment while none of the patients receiving group or individual therapy withdrew from treatment.

These data suggest that the effects of treatment may also depend on the duration of treatment; psychosocial therapies may take longer to have an effect, but the effect may last longer. Secondly, differential dropout and attrition rates may be an important source of bias in attempting to compare different therapies and may, in fact, invalidate the interpretations one makes of differences in outcome. Finally, one may argue that dropout rates themselves may be considered a kind of outcome measure, in that they reflect patients' acceptance of particular modes of treatment.

Group therapy techniques have also been applied to delinquent and adult offenders. With the exception of one group of sex offenders who apparently benefited by group therapy, the results of most of the ten studies cited were almost uniformly disappointing. "Group therapy with adult offenders seems to be of little value" (Parloff and Dies 1977, p. 305).

Finally, Parloff et al. (1977) briefly describe five studies of inpatient narcotic addicts or alcoholics. All these studies were limited by small groups of patients treated over short periods of time (for example, a seventeen-hour marathon versus daily group therapy for two weeks) and one had no control group. In four of the studies, there were no outcome measures relevant to the target complaints (that is, drug or alcohol abuse). Their conclusion is that there is no convincing research evidence that group therapy has any beneficial effects in the treatment of alcoholics and drug addicts.

In summary, the review of thirty-eight of the "better" studies of group therapy as applied to various patient groups has led to the conclusion that this modality of treatment as described in the recent literature has little value in the treatment of schizophrenics, psychoneurotics, delinquents, and drug-abusing patients. However, this conclusion should be qualified in several ways.

First, Parloff and Dies (1977) point out that although most clinicians work with outpatients who attend group therapy meetings on a voluntary basis, most of the controlled published research has been done (for reasons of convenience?) in institutional settings. However, patients in such settings are least likely to benefit from brief group therapy (Stotsky and Zolik 1965, Meltzoff and Kornreich 1970, Bednar and Lawlis 1971). In their opinion, it is possible that private practitioners may increasingly be treating a class of relatively well-functioning patients who are concerned mainly with problems of life style and personal philosophy. The prognosis for such patients is considerably better than for patients with major psychiatric or social difficulties in hospitals and prisons.

Second, Parloff and Dies (1977) point out that the published studies of group therapy are not at all representative of the way therapy is conducted by private practitioners in terms of length of therapy and degree of experience of therapists. The published research cites such figures as six, ten, or fifteen sessions of group therapy with the average in most categories less than ten. The therapists who actually do the research may be graduate students or residents with limited experience in this field.

A third point made by Parloff et al. (1977) is that the term "group therapy" is rarely defined in any but the most global or ambiguous terms, such as "supportive," "directive," or "analytically oriented." Such vague descriptions provide no meaningful data on what actually transpires in the group therapy setting, nor do they allow replication of the experiment by an independent investigator. The probable variation among group therapists in style, techniques, and theory implies that no generalization at all can be made about some vague process called "group therapy." In this context, as is also true in regard to individual therapy, the appropriate question should be: What techniques of treatment, administered by what kinds of therapists to what kinds of patients, over what durations, produce beneficial results? Parloff et al. (1977) conclude that the most useful strategy for research is not to attempt to answer global questions like "Does group therapy work?" but rather to state explicit assumptions or hypotheses about limited aspects of therapy and to test the implications of these hypotheses.

## Social and Milieu Treatment in Schizophrenia

Although it is widely accepted that psychotropic drugs are the major treatment modality for schizophrenia, there has also been considerable interest in the use of social and milieu treatments for this disorder. Such treatments include group meetings, therapeutic communities, halfway houses, day hospitals, and after-care programs, modalities that have been in use for some time.

In 1970, Meltzoff and Kornreich examined twenty-five studies of therapeutic programs designed primarily to treat schizophrenics in institutionalized settings by means of a combinative approach that utilizes drugs, social and educational programs, and multiple personnel rather than a single thera-pist. Most such programs had a limited goal, such as improve-ments in self-care behavior on the ward, and most had no control or comparison conditions as reference points.

Regarding the outcome of these therapeutic programs, Melt-zoff and Kornreich (1970) claimed that fifteen of these studies showed major positive results, six showed minor positive results, and four showed no or negative results. Given the complexity of the interventions and the lack of controls, it is difficult to draw any firm conclusions from these claims.

Interest in the problem of institutional treatments for schizo-phrenic patients continued, however, and in 1975 May re-viewed the literature again. This time, studies that did not use a control group were excluded, as were single patient experi-ments in which the patient was his own control. May evaluated each reported investigation in terms of four general categories, as well as subclasses within categories. His first category (I) was defined as solid, substantial, well-designed research. The second category (II) included research whose results might be accepted with some reservations. The third category (III) defined investigations that had design defects to such a degree that any conclusions should be treated as tenuous or uncertain. May used category IV to define uncontrolled experiments, retrospective surveys, and the like. The various therapies were divided into a few broad categories: inpatient hospital milieu therapy; outpatient after-care therapy; inpatient individual therapy; inpatient group therapy; outpatient group therapy; and various combinations of drugs with therapy. Table 7 lists the numbers of studies considered under each of these rubrics.

**Table 7.**   Controlled Studies of Social and Milieu Treatment for Schizo-phrenic Patients

| Therapeutic Modality | Number of Investigations |
|---|:---:|
| Inpatient Hospital Milieu Therapy | 18 |
| Outpatient Aftercare Programs | 7 |
| Inpatient Individual Therapy | 5 |
| Inpatient Group Therapy | 14 |
| Outpatient Group Therapy | 7 |
| Total | 51 |

*Source:* From May, P. R. A. Schizophrenia: Evaluation of treatment methods. In A. M. Freedman, H. I. Kaplan, and B. J. Sadock (Eds.), *Comprehensive Textbook of Psy-chiatry—II.* Vol. 1. Baltimore: The Williams & Wilkins Company, 1975.

May pointed out that of the eighteen controlled studies of milieu therapy most were contaminated by unmeasured drug or ECT administration. In other words, some of the patients in both experimental and control groups received medications or ECT so that this was, therefore, an uncontrolled factor whose effects could not be predicted. According to May, twelve of the eighteen studies had serious design defects and in all of these patients were reported to receive mild to moderate benefits. Among the six more highly rated experiments, four showed positive or mixed results, one showed no effects of treatment, and one demonstrated a negative effect. May speculated on the basis of these ambiguous results that inpatient milieu programs may possibly improve social behavior to some degree, but will not have any effect on the fundamental psychotic process.

Seven controlled studies of outpatient after-care programs reported positive results. The evidence indicated that outpatient after-care combined with drug treatment improved the patients' ability to work and remain in the community and seemed to prevent recurrence of symptoms. However, there is seldom improvement over the patients' previous best levels of functioning. May concluded that treatment and support of schizophrenics in the community is the most efficacious mode of preventing relapse.

Only five controlled studies compared inpatient individual psychotherapy with no treatment or with milieu treatment, and all but one were contaminated by unmeasured drug effects. Almost all these investigations found little or no differences between the individual therapy inpatients and the controls.

Of the fourteen studies that compared patients who received inpatient group therapy with patients who received no special treatment procedure, most did not indicate the extent to which patients were taking medication. In most of these studies there was either a slight benefit of group therapy or no significant effect. Contamination of effects by drug or ECT administration made the results equivocal.

Seven studies examined the effects of group therapy on outpatient schizophrenics. Although the number of investigations was small there was an indication that group therapy had some slight benefits, and that groups that focused on real-life activities did somewhat better than those that focused on insight. Finally, controlled studies in which drugs were compared with psychotherapy plus drugs showed that there is little difference in outcome between these two conditions.

May also examined studies of behavior therapy for schizophrenics and concluded that most were of type IV; that is, basically uncontrolled. He reviewed four controlled studies, which suggested some possible benefits resulting from the application of operant conditioning techniques, but he stated that the relative values and interactions of behavioral and drug therapies cannot be determined from the available literature.

Overall, the review by May (1975) of fifty-one studies concerned with social and milieu treatment of schizophrenic patients produced little to be enthusiastic about. Many of the studies were poorly designed and executed, and the results were often contaminated by the fact that drugs and electroshock therapy were administered on a nonrandom basis to patients who "needed" them. Sometimes the findings of even the "better" studies were inconsistent; and beneficial effects, when reported, were moderate at best. This same viewpoint is reported by Parloff et al. (1978). Their later evaluation of the literature led them to conclude that both individual and group psychotherapies have little effect on outcome with schizophrenic patients.

An important contribution to this literature was published in a book in 1977 by Paul and Lentz. They described a study that compared three groups of severely debilitated chronic inpatients who were equated on a number of variables including age, sex, diagnosis, and chronicity. One group received the "usual" hospital treatment program, another received "milieu" (or therapeutic community) therapy, and the third received "social-learning" (token-economy) therapy. Each of these treatment modalities was defined by manuals, and medications were administered as deemed appropriate by the physicians involved. The social-learning approach emphasized the development of self-maintenance, communication and vocational skills, and a general re-educational approach. Assessments of staff, patients, and programs were continued for over four years, and release and relapse rates were determined over a year-and-a-half follow-up period.

The results indicated that 90 percent of released patients treated by the social-learning approach remained in the community for the follow-up period, while 70 percent of the released patients treated by milieu therapy remained in the community. Of those released patients treated by the usual hospital procedures, less than 50 percent remained in the community for a year and a half. Cost-effectiveness analyses showed that the social-learning program was the least expensive to operate. Despite these apparently impressive findings, they have had relatively little impact on current hospital-treatment procedures.

A later update on the application of social and milieu treatments for schizophrenia is provided by Mosher and Keith

(1980). They reviewed group, individual, and family therapy and community-support approaches. Their conclusions are also pessimistic.

They point out that the experimental literature on the role of group therapy in the treatment of schizophrenia is complex and difficult to unravel for the following reasons. Some studies compared hospitalized patients exposed to group therapy versus patients not so exposed. Other patient studies compared patients given group therapy to patients given a complex of in-hospital treatments that included group therapy as one component. Other investigations compared group therapy against individual therapy with outpatients. Still other investigations compared outpatients exposed to group therapy with outpatients who did not receive group therapy (this meant that they usually received psychotropic medications of some sort).

Despite these heterogeneous comparisons, patients, settings and treatments, Mosher and Keith (1980) try to provide some tentative conclusions. In six studies of inpatients who were exposed to relatively brief periods of group therapy (approximately ten to thirty sessions) it was found that the treated schizophrenic patients did not do significantly better, on a variety of measures, than did patients who did not receive group therapy but were simply exposed to the usual hospital conditions (which could include medications, social work counseling, vocational guidance, and so forth).

Another set of comparisons involved inpatients who were exposed to group therapy, and who were then compared to other inpatients who were exposed to group therapy, plus some other type of psychosocial treatment (for example, paired-patient meetings, videotape feedback, or extra group sessions). Five such experiments were reviewed (most done in the early 1970s or before) and the conclusion that Mosher et al. (1980) reached was that the combined treatment tended to produce better results than did the group treatment alone. Mosher and Keith (1980) admit that the noncomparability of patients and settings, the use of extremely short treatment periods, and the narrow outcome measures used make the intergration of results of these different studies difficult at best.

Five investigations compared group and individual therapy for outpatients, most of whom were former schizophrenic inpatients. For the different studies, the N's ranged from 24 to 152 patients. Therapy sessions were often fifteen to thirty minutes long; the duration of treatments was not always specified. The results showed, on most outcome measures, no significant differences between the group therapy and individual therapy conditions.

In their review of research on family therapy for schizophrenics, Mosher and Keith (1980) cite only three controlled studies (Goldstein et al. 1978; Langsley et al. 1968; and RoTrack, Wellisch, and Schooler 1977). In each case, family therapy was given for relatively brief periods (five, ten, or twelve visits) and medications were administered "as needed" in the judgment of the psychiatrists. The patients exposed to family therapy were compared with other schizophrenic patients given individual therapy, or inpatient treatment. Results demonstrated few differences between the patient groups.

Finally, Mosher and Keith (1980) briefly discuss research on community support systems; these include such settings as cooperative apartments, halfway houses, and rehabilitation centers. Unfortunately, although there are a number of published reports providing basic statistics (employment rates, rehospitalization rates, and so on) regarding what happens to former patients in various community support systems, there is an almost complete absence of controlled studies. However, NIMH has recently funded eighteen pilot demonstration community support programs so that the possibility exists of significant new research data in the near future.

# CHAPTER 13

# Drug/Psychotherapy Outcome Research by Diagnosis

The reviews of psychotherapy outcome studies have been of two general types: those that compare a variety of therapies and those that are primarily focused upon a particular diagnosis or a particular subgroup of patients. The previous pages have dealt largely with the former approach while the following pages are largely concerned with the latter. The following sections will deal with the treatment of schizophrenia, depression, nonpsychotic disorders, and somatic illnesses, and will be particularly concerned with the interactions of psychotherapy and pharmacotherapy.

## For Schizophrenia

Although there are a few reports in the literature that are concerned with the application of psychotherapy to schizophrenia, there has been little interest in continuing such studies ever since the essentially negative results of May (1968) and Grinspoon, Ewalt, and Shader (1972). These investigations demonstrated that drug treatment of hospitalized patients was more effective than psychotherapy alone, and that combined drugs plus psychotherapy was not more effective than drugs alone. These results were obtained using a variety of outcome measures and using psychotherapists at several levels of skill.

The results of these investigations were summarized by Feinsinger and Gunderson (1972), who found only five studies describing the psychotherapeutic treatment of schizophrenics that had used appropriate control groups. They concluded that the results of the May (1968) experiment should be accepted. May found that ego-supportive psychotherapy, given to acute schizophrenic patients once or twice a week for periods up to one year by relatively inexperienced therapists, had little or no advantage over the use of drugs alone in terms of therapy outcome. The Grinspoon, Ewalt, and Shader (1972) study provided psychoanalytic psychotherapy to chronic schizophrenics by senior analysts at least twice a week for two years. They found that the patients showed little or no benefit in outcome over the control patients given drug-oriented treatment in a state hospital.

Taken together, the five studies cited offered persuasive evidence that "drugs alone are the single most powerful and economical treatment for schizophrenic patients within 1- and 2-year time limits." (Feinsinger and Gunderson 1972, p. 47).

Since the appearance of the Feinsinger and Gunderson (1972) review, several other attempts have been made to examine the literature on the interaction of drugs with either psychotherapy or some form of psychosocial treatment. For example, Hollon and Beck (1976) consider in detail fourteen studies concerned with the interactions of drugs and psychotherapy in acute and chronic psychotic patients and in- and outpatients.

In seven studies published in the 1950s and 1960s and based on chronic inpatient populations, drug and psychotherapy combinations did not produce effects that were superior to those produced by the administration of drugs alone.

In the 1960s several major studies were conducted with relatively large numbers of new or recently admitted schizophrenic patients. In a Veterans Administration Collaborative Study (Gorham et al. 1964), one group of patients was given thioridazine only, a second group received thirty-six sessions of group therapy, and a third group received combined drug and group therapy. Results showed that the two groups that received the drug were equivalent to one another and both were superior to the patients who received only group therapy.

The major study by May (1968) and its five-year follow-up (May, Tuma, and Dixon 1976) of "first admission" schizophrenic patients also demonstrated that the patients who received drugs (stelazine or chlorpromazine) showed the best response on a variety of measures. Patients given drugs plus psychotherapy ("supportive, reality oriented," averaging forty-nine hours per patient) did about as well as the patients given drugs alone. All other treatment conditions (ECT, milieu alone, psychotherapy alone) were less effective. The five-year follow-up demonstrated that those patients treated with psychotherapy alone had the largest number of subsequent relapses. A similar study by Shader et al. (1969) using a smaller number of newly admitted patients essentially confirmed the findings reported by May (1968).

A small study ($N = 36$ patients) that partially replicated the conditions of the May (1968) investigation was concerned with the role of "experienced versus inexperienced" therapists (Karon and Vandenbos 1970, 1972). These researchers reported that those patients receiving both drugs (phenothiazine) and psychotherapy did better than those receiving drugs alone, and that patients treated by experienced therapists did somewhat better than those treated by inexperienced ones. These results, based on only twelve patients per group, are discrepant with most other studies. May and Tuma (1970) have provided a critique of the methodology of this investigation including the following points: (1) "drug only" patients who did not show a rapid improvement were transferred to another hospital; (2) assignment of patients to experienced versus inexperienced therapists was not made on a random basis; (3) some patients refused to be tested. Hollon and Beck (1978) conclude from their overall examination of the literature that drugs alone are the most effective treatment for recently admitted schizophrenics and that psychotherapy contributes little additional benefit.

The overall conclusions reached by Hollon and Beck (1978) concern both substantive issues and methodological problems. From the viewpoint of major conclusions, they state that, in the treatment of schizophrenics, the effectiveness of drugs and the ineffectiveness of psychotherapy have been fairly well established. Combined treatments have rarely been reported to be any more effective than drug treatment alone.

With regard to methodological issues, they point out that the effects of drugs, psychotherapies, and their combinations should be evaluated in relation to specific diagnostic groups and types of problems. Therapy modalities should be defined as explicitly as possible, as should other possibly relevant variables. Overall, they claim "the comparative literature appears to be in its infancy" (Hollon and Beck 1978, p. 486).

A similar conclusion was reached by Klein et al. (1980) after reviewing the relatively small number of studies concerned with the interaction of drugs and psychotherapy. In addition, they state that the frequent practice of providing psychotherapy to outpatient schizophrenics who are being treated by drugs does not rest on any convincing evidence of effectiveness.

Klein et al. (1980) also provide a critique of treatment studies with the hope that psychopharmacologic research in the future will be more satisfactory than many such studies published in the past. They describe several problems or flaws.

One outstanding flaw in most studies is the inadequate specification of the patient groups. This includes failing to specify not only the obvious demographic characteristics of the patients, but also research diagnoses and such things as length of illness, response to previous treatments, developmental history, and familial history.

A second flaw in many studies is the use of sample sizes that are too small to detect real drug effects even if they exist. Klein et al. (1980) recommend that groups of patients and placebo controls should consist of approximately thirty patients each or more.

Another problem is concerned with the use of fixed dosage levels. If an open pilot study has not already established a probably effective dosage, then the entire investigation may be wasted. It is recommended that the evaluating clinician have the option of increasing the dose level when an adequate clinical response is not obtained.

Some studies give the active medication for too short a period. This can lead to a situation where cumulative effects of this drug are missed. Another aspect of this problem is the need for establishing dose-effect curves and to do this separately for each diagnostic entity.

These problems of psychopharmacology research listed by Klein et al. (1980) may help account for some of the discrepancies in this literature. They point up the need for improvements in methodological sophistication as well as the need for more investigations.

There is one additional related area that has received considerable attention in recent years. And that concerns the role of antipsychotic drugs in preventing relapse in schizophrenic patients who have been discharged from inpatient hospital facilities. This literature will be examined in the following section.

## Antipsychotic Drugs in Relation to Relapse

The effectiveness of antipsychotic drugs for the treatment of acute schizophrenia has been established by the results of many well-controlled, double-blind investigations (Davis et al. 1980). Patients given antipsychotic medications show marked improvements over patients given placebos over brief (six-week) trials. In the majority of instances typical schizophrenic symptoms such as hallucinations and delusions diminish or disappear, and behavior tempos tend to become "normalized." Evidence for decreases in thought disorders such as overinclusive thinking, bizarreness, and flight of ideas has also been documented (Spohn et al. 1977).

One of the important issues that has only recently been addressed concerns the effects on relapse rates of the administration of "maintenance" psychotropic medications, with or without concomitant psychotherapy. The classic study by May (1968) and its five-year follow-up (May, Tuma, and Dixon 1976) found that patients in the group that did not receive psychotropic medication spent about twice as many days in the hospital after discharge as did patients who were treated with drugs. This finding stimulated a number of controlled investigations in different countries and settings on the issue of whether drug treatment during follow-up may prevent relapse.

In the period between 1959 and 1978, twenty-nine controlled studies were published in which discharged schizophrenic patients were given either antipsychotic drugs or placebos on a random assignment basis. Evidence was accumulated to show that side effects did not bias the double-blind studies, and that the use of "active placebos" (that is, those that produced some side effects themselves) did not increase the relapse rate as compared to those patients who received inactive traditional placebos. The results of these twenty-nine investigations show that schizophrenic patients given maintenance antipsychotic drugs while in the community have an average relapse rate of 19 percent, while comparable patients maintained on a placebo show a 55 percent relapse rate. This difference, based on a total of 3,519 patients, is highly significant. The results thus strongly support the use of maintenance antipsychotic medication to prevent relapse. These general findings were further supported by Hogarty et al. (1979). However, Davis et al. (1980) do point out that approximately 25 percent of schizophrenics improve significantly on placebo alone, and that there are obviously a number of unexplored (or unknown) variables that must be operating in this situation. Only future research can resolve this kind of issue.

## For Depression

Hollon and Beck (1978) point out that although many investigations have demonstrated that both tricyclic medications and MAO inhibitors decrease depression in both unipolar and bipolar depressed patients, very few studies have compared either behavioral or traditional psychotherapies with control groups in actual clinical populations.

Drug/psychotherapy interaction studies are also very few and only seven such studies are reviewed (Daneman 1961, Covi et al. 1974, Friedman 1975, Klerman et al. 1974, Weissman et al. 1974, Rush et al. 1977, and Davenport et al. 1975). The conclusions reached by Hollon and Beck (1978) may be briefly summarized as follows: Tricyclic antidepressant medication alone effectively reduced depressive symptoms. Traditional psychotherapies (individual analytically oriented therapy, group analytically oriented therapy, marital therapy, and interpersonal psychotherapy) seemed to have no effect on *depressive symptoms* but may have had limited benefits on certain aspects of social functioning. Cognitive therapy (as defined by Rush et al. [1977]) was the only psychotherapy reported to decrease depressive symptoms and to be more effective than tricyclic medications. Hollon and Beck (1978) consider that, at best, the combination of treatments may broaden the spectrum of phenomena affected.

Since the Hollon and Beck (1978) review, Weissman has provided a more up-to-date evaluation of this literature and has included a number of investigations that were not included in their analysis. Weissman (1979) reports that Liberman's 1975 review of 200 articles concluded that not one controlled trial of psychotherapy included an adequately diagnosed, homogeneous sample of depressed patients and used sample sizes of greater than ten patients. Most studies of depression included unselected populations of disturbed individuals in whom feelings of depression accompanied the disorder, but for whom depression was not necessarily the primary diagnosis. These conclusions were also reached by Cristol (1972) and by Luborsky, Singer, and Luborsky (1975) in their independent reviews of outcome studies.

However, since that time the situation has changed and the review by Weissman in 1979 reported seventeen controlled clinical trials concerned with the psychological treatment of depression. Some are concerned with a comparison of psychotherapy with no-treatment controls, some are concerned with a comparison of psychotherapy with drug therapy, and some are concerned with the interaction of the two.

Weissman defined psychotherapy as a dialogue specifically directed at bringing about a desired psychological and/or social change in the patient. Such changes include reduction of symptoms, improved adaptation, better social functioning, increased self-esteem, and greater assertiveness.

In reviewing the seventeen studies it appeared that five were still in progress (as of 1979) so that complete outcome data were available for only twelve investigations. These studies, grouped under the heading of "cognitive therapy," "behavior therapy," "interpersonal therapy (IPT)," and "group and marital therapy," all represent short-term approaches. For example, the cognitive approach averaged around five weeks of therapy, and the IPT approach averaged twenty-four weeks. The sample sizes for the different investigations varied from 24 to 196 patients.

No formal analysis of the overall data was made; that is, no box-score method was used nor was meta-analysis applied to the data. Unfortunately, the fact that Weissman presented only "significant" results makes it more difficult to apply these more sophisticated methods of data analysis.

Despite these limitations, Weissman drew some conclusions. She reported that "cognitive" therapy was more effective than behavior therapy, drug therapy (imipramine), or no active treatment (waiting-list controls). However, she also pointed out that sample sizes in the various treatment cells were small (less than ten per cell) and that only one of the five studies used research diagnostic criteria.

With regard to the six completed studies of behavior therapy (loosely defined), Weissman reported that "self-control" therapy produced more improvement than waiting-list or nonspecific group attendance, that self control was more successful than social skills training (for example, verbal and assertiveness skills enhancement), and that groups that monitored daily activities were more effective than nondirective groups.

Of the three studies of "interpersonal psychotherapy," one was still in progress so that outcome data were available only on two. The results indicated that both IPT and drug therapy were more effective than nonscheduled or placebo conditions, that drug therapy (Elavil) reduced the relapse rate, and the combined drug and IPT treatments were additive in their effects.

The two studies of group and marital therapy showed that patients improved more than did low-contact controls, and that the effects of psychotherapy combined with imipramine treatment were additive.

Overall, it appeared that any form of psychotherapy for depressed patients produced better results than doing nothing or having limited contacts. It appeared that drugs alone are also effective, and that the effects of psychotherapy plus drugs are additive. These results are limited, however, by the qualifications stated earlier; that is: relatively brief periods of therapy, limited drug trials, small number of patients per treatment condition, and lack of standard diagnostic assessments.

Weissman's conclusions, therefore, present an optimistic view of the effects of the interaction of drugs and psychotherapy for the treatment of depressive illness. Her interpretation of a wider range of studies than were reviewed by Hollon and Beck (1978) is that the effects of antidepressant medication plus certain forms of psychotherapy are additive and that more benefits accrue from their combination than from the use of either modality alone. The occasional concerns voiced about negative interactions have not been verified by empirical research (Rounsaville, Klerman, and Weissman 1981).

## For Psychoneuroses

The literature in this area is complex and somewhat difficult to interpret. Hollon and Beck (1978) describe three early studies (Gibbs, Wilkins, and Lauterbach 1957; Lorr et al. 1961; and Lorr et al. 1962) in which mixed psychoneurotic patients were given psychotherapy alone, or in combination with chlorpromazine, meprobamate, or chlordiazepoxide. Although relatively large numbers of patients were studied, the three investigations provided little information regarding the effects of drug/psychotherapy combinations. This was due to several reasons: (1) the heterogeneity of the samples: (2) the absence of analysis by diagnostic subtypes; (3) the brevity and lack of specificity of the psychotherapies; and (4) the high attrition rates that occurred.

During the 1960s and early 1970s four more investigations provided controlled clinical trials of the interactions of drugs and psychotherapy. According to Hollon and Beck (1978), three of the four studies found significant advantages of the drug/psychotherapy combination over psychotherapy alone. However, criticisms of these studies include the fact that the "psychotherapy" was given for an extremely brief period in most cases (four weeks), that the nature of the psychotherapy was unspecified, and that only single therapists were involved in each experiment, thus severely limiting the possibility of generalizing any of the findings.

In the review by Luborsky, Singer, and Luborsky (1975) the same issue was also examined. These authors used the box-score method in an effort to rationalize their conclusions to some degree. They reported that in cases where drug therapy alone was compared to psychotherapy alone, seven out of eight comparisons showed drug treatment to be superior. When drug treatment plus psychotherapy was compared to psychotherapy alone, thirteen out of sixteen studies found the combination to be superior. When drug treatment plus psychotherapy was compared to drugs alone, five out of eleven studies reported ties, and six reported the combination to be superior. These various reports thus imply that drug therapy, either alone or in combination, tends to be better than psychotherapy alone when applied to nonpsychotic conditions.

Luborsky et al. (1975) did not present an evaluation of each study in detail, and they may have been less critical than Hollon and Beck (1978) of some of the design, selection, and statistical flaws in the research. A more conservative estimate would suggest that there may be limited benefits of combining drugs with psychotherapy for mixed psychoneurotic patients, but that only future research using more precise diagnostic and outcome criteria can resolve the apparent inconsistencies.

## For Phobias and Anxiety States

In recent years a number of investigations have compared the efficacy of drugs combined with psychotherapy in the treatment of phobic and anxiety states (Lipsedge et al. 1973, Solym et al. 1973, Zitrin et al. 1976). In each experiment the patient samples were relatively homogenous (most were outpatients with agoraphobia), the techniques of therapy were fairly explicit (most involved systematic desensitization), and all used an antidepressant medication (either TCA or MAOI).

The results of these studies demonstrated that drugs alone or drugs combined with systematic desensitization were equally effective, and better than placebos in agoraphobic patients. However, no clear-cut increase in effectiveness was demonstrated for the combination over either treatment alone (Hollon and Beck 1978).

A more recent controlled study of drug/psychotherapy interactions for phobias and panic attacks was published by Zitrin, Klein, and Woerner (1978). They compared three conditions: behavior therapy with imipramine; behavior therapy with placebo; and supportive therapy with imipramine. The results indicated that any combination treatment that included imipramine was superior, in producing marked or moderate improvement, to behavior therapy with placebo.

The meta-analyses of drug therapy also throws some light

on the issue of combination therapies that include drugs for anxiety conditions. Smith, Glass, and Miller (1980) report that the average effect size for antianxiety agents in comparison to placebo conditions was +.62. This finding may be contrasted with the average effect size (based on only seven observations) in which an antianxiety agent was combined with psychotherapy of some type. The effect size in this case was +.27, thus suggesting the possibility of a slight inhibitory effect of psychotherapy, a finding contrary to the experience of most clinicians.

## For Other Nonpsychotic Conditions

Hollon and Beck (1978) examined in detail thirty-one controlled studies involving comparisons of patients undergoing psychotherapy with or without medications or placebo pills. No attempt was made to use a box-score analysis or a meta-analysis; but enough information is provided for most of the studies so that the reader may often judge how adequate the critiques are and how valid the conclusions are.

Hollon and Beck (1978) point out that they are reviewing only controlled studies of drug/psychotherapy combinations in which assignment of patients to different conditions is made on a random basis. However, despite attempts by many investigators to use true experimental designs, there are frequent problems that occur in clinical research that limit the interpretations one may draw from the experiment. Problems that are encountered frequently include high rates of attrition, poor compliance with the treatment protocol, uncontrolled lengths of treatment, inadequate sample sizes, questionable statistical analyses, and failure to control or measure extraneous sources of psychotherapeutic treatment.

In addition to the problems of implementation that exist, problems of interpretation also exist when examining the interaction of two or more treatments. For example, Uhlenhuth, Lipman, and Covi (1969) suggest that there are four possible types of interactions that may occur. These are: (1) *additivity*, when the separate effects of each of the treatments are linearly added; (2) *potentiation*, where the effects of the two treatments are greater than the simple sum of each separate treatment effect; (3) *inhibition*; where the effects of the combination are less than the effects of either treatment alone; and (4) *reciprocation*, where the joint action of the two treatments is equal to the larger of the individual treatment effects. Given the fact that more than one outcome measure is typically used, it is often possible for several different patterns of interaction to occur simultaneously.

The strongest statement of the nature of the interaction between drugs and psychotherapy has been stated by Karasu (1981). After reviewing the literature of the 1970s, he concludes that psychotherapy and pharmacotherapy tend to be additive in their effects. However, although potentially integrative, each has differential effects or loci of outcome. Drugs have their major manifestations upon symptom formation and affective distress, whereas psychotherapy more directly influences interpersonal relations and social adjustment. Each is activated and sustained on a different time schedule. Drugs may take effect sooner, may be of shorter duration, and may be used prophylactically. The results of psychotherapy, though, may not reveal themselves until a later time, but may last longer. Finally, and more speculatively, drugs may be more useful for time-limited and autonomous "state" disorders, while psychotherapy may be more useful for long-lasting "trait" disorders.

## For Medically Ill Patients

In 1973, Malan reviewed a number of reports on the outcomes of psychotherapy research. After critically examining the reviews by Eysenck (1965), Meltzoff and Kornreich (1970), Bergin (1971), and several others, he concluded that the pessimism that had been expressed by some writers on the efficacy of psychotherapy is unwarranted and based largely on the use of inadequately done researches. The major problem, according to Malan (1973), is the general reliance on outcome criteria that do not do justice to the complexity of the human personality.

Despite the frequently cited negative findings and the general lack of impact of research on clinical practice, one striking positive conclusion resulted from his review. In five out of five studies in which a group of medical patients were given some kind of group or individual psychotherapy, their problems (medical and psychological) improved more than did those of a control group of patients given medical treatment alone. This was the only context in which there was complete agreement among researchers on the benefits of psychotherapy.

Five studies on a topic, however, is only a beginning, and this issue was re-examined by Luborsky, Singer, and Luborsky in 1975. They identified eleven studies in which patients with "psychosomatic" symptoms; that is, ulcers, colitis, asthma, or dermatoses, were treated by standard medical regimens and were then compared with similar patients who were treated by a combination of psychotherapy plus medical regimens. Using their box-score method for evaluating the results, they reported that in nine studies psychotherapy plus medical regimen was more effective in influencing the target symptoms than was medical treatment alone. In one study there was a tie, and in one study the results of the medical treatment was better than the results of the combination. Thus, the Luborsky et al. (1975) review appeared to generally confirm Malan's (1973) conclusion about the benefits of combined treatment.

For several years the issue was left unexplored until Conte and Karasu (1981) again examined the available literature. This time they identified eighteen investigations in which a control condition of some degree of adequacy was included. The literature also indicated that a variety of therapeutic approaches have been used, including psychoanalytic, supportive, and didactic therapies. In addition, a wide variety of medical illnesses had been considered in this research. They included: peptic ulcers (three studies), ulcerative colitis (two studies), functional abdominal disorders (one study), asthma (two studies), migraine (one study), skin diseases (two studies), cardiovascular disease (six studies), and essential hypertension (one study). Investigations using biofeedback, relaxation, and behavior modification were not considered.

In the review each study was assessed as "good," "adequate," or "poor" on the basis of criteria suggested by May (1975) that considered such factors as method of assignment to groups, size of groups, definition of improvement, methods of assessment, and adequacy of follow-up. Overall, there were seven "good" reports, six "adequate" reports, and five "poor" ones. Eight studies involved some form of group therapy and ten involved individual therapy.

The results indicated that of the thirteen studies rated as "good" or "adequate," eight reported greater improvement for patients given combined therapy and medical treatment than those given medical treatment alone. Five of these studies showed no significant differences between the experimental and control groups.

Some of the possible reasons given by Conte and Karasu for the contradictory outcomes are the following: (1) difficulty of providing long-term control groups; (2) inappropriate exposure of often unmotivated patients to psychiatric treatment; (3) high dropout rates; (4) highly heterogeneous patients; (5) lack of standardization of the psychotherapy being offered; and (6) inadequate outcome measures.

## A Meta-Analysis of Drug/Psychotherapy Interactions

All of the reviews thus far cited on the interaction of drugs and psychotherapy were based on interpretations of selected studies by the authors of the reviews (for example, May 1975, Parloff et al. 1978). In contrast, Smith, Glass, and Miller (1980) included in their book an additional but separate meta-analysis concerning the effects of drug therapy on psychological disorders. However, rather than attempting to review all studies of psychotropic medication (estimated to total over 25,000 as of 1980), they selected a random sample of recent studies in which a control group was included. They attempted to answer the following questions:

1. What are the overall therapeutic benefits of drug treatments on patients with psychological disorders?
2. What kinds of patients have benefited most from psychotropic drugs?
3. On what kinds of outcomes has drug therapy had its greatest effects?
4. What are the general and specific effects of psychotropic drugs?
5. Is drug therapy more or less effective than psychotherapy?
6. Does drug therapy facilitate or inhibit the effects of psychotherapy?
7. How do the characteristics of the studies (such as methodological adequacy) relate to their outcomes?

Smith, Glass, and Miller begin their analysis by examining thirteen major reviews of the drug literature, in which anywhere from 18 to 159 double-blind placebo controlled studies were included. The reviews were concerned with antipsychotic or antidepressant drugs. The results of an examination of over 800 studies revealed that approximately one-quarter (28 percent) showed no difference between drug-treated and control patients, while significant differences were found in the remainder of the studies. Surveys of reports comparing drug plus psychotherapy with drug alone or psychotherapy alone led to inconsistent conclusions.

In their meta-analysis, Smith et al. (1980) selected 151 drug studies stratified to include approximately equal numbers of articles in three major drug categories: antipsychotic, anti-anxiety, and antidepressant. Detailed information was extracted from each article and coded and the results were then subjected to a meta-analysis to determine the effect size for each individual study and for all studies combined. Because there was often more than one outcome measure in a particular study, over 560 measures of effect size were obtained from the 151 experiments. The data were analyzed in a variety of ways.

The results showed that the effect size obtained when drug therapy was compared to a placebo control group was +.40. When psychotherapy was compared to a control group the effect size was +.30. This figure is much smaller than the effect size reported earlier in the book for 475 studies of psychotherapy where the effect size was estimated to be +.85. The difference may be due to the fact that drug therapy is typically given to more severely ill patients (schizophrenics, manic depressives, and so on).

When drug therapy is given with psychotherapy and the combination compared to a control group, the combined effect is less than the sum of the two separate effects; that is, approximately +.60 standard deviation units. Other major results are presented in Table 8.

Smith, Glass, and Miller (1980) concluded that combining drug therapy with psychotherapy produces better effects than either alone, even though the effects are not strictly additive.

It thus appears that the meta-analysis of drug studies provides different conclusions concerning the interactions of drugs and psychotherapy in schizophrenic patients than those of May (1975), Parloff et al. (1978), and Hollen and Beck (1978).

The reasons for these discrepancies are not obvious. They could conceivably have to do with the selection of studies used for the meta-analysis, or with the subjective weights given to different studies, or could reflect some artifact of the method itself. Thus, for example, the carefully done study by May (1968) using over 200 patients, many therapists, relatively long-term treatments, and a five-year follow-up would be given the same weight in a meta-analysis as any study that used small numbers of subjects, few therapists, and no follow-up.

**Table 8.**  Major Findings of a Meta-Analysis of Drug / Psychotherapy Interactions

1. Outpatients responded to drugs more favorably (+.60) than did inpatients (+.47).
2. Drugs plus psychotherapy is better for psychotic patients (+.80) than for nonpsychotic patients (+.37).
3. Drugs alone produce greater beneficial effects with anxious patients (+.66) than with depressed patients (+.37) or with schizophrenic patients (+.49).
4. Antianxiety agents produce larger effects (+.62) than do antidepressants (+.40) or antipsychotic agents (+.43).
5. Benzodiazepines produce larger effect sizes (average = +.73) than do phenothiazines (+.48), carbamates (+.55), tricyclics (+.44), monoamine oxidase inhibitors (+.29), or hypnotics (+.24).
6. Somatic symptoms are more affected by drug therapy (+.56) than are psychological symptoms (+.39).
7. Ratings of change tend to show larger effect sizes (approximately +.54) than do formal psychological tests (+.26).
8. "Open" studies show only slightly larger effect sizes (+.62) than do double-blind studies (+.49).
9. Patient age, sex, and length of treatment are not correlated with effect size.
10. Studies with larger percents of black patients tend to show smaller effect sizes.

*Source:* From Smith, M. L., Glass, G. V., and Miller, T. I. *The Benefits of Psychotherapy.* Baltimore: The Johns Hopkins University Press, 1980.

# CHAPTER 14

# Age-Related Studies of Psychotherapy Outcome

Although most discussions of the outcome of psychotherapy research have been organized around either the type of therapy used or the diagnoses of the patients, a few reviews have dealt with the application of psychotherapy to different age groups. The present summary will examine this literature for children, for adolescents, and for the elderly. Almost all of the research that has been cited earlier has dealt with the broad range of ages in the middle that we loosely call "adult."

## Children

Child psychotherapy research is no match in quantity or quality for research with adults (Barrett, Hampe, and Miller 1978). Their review in the *Handbook of Psychotherapy and Behavior Change* (1978) contains few recent references and ignores the large number of single case studies that exist, on the assumption that they are essentially irrelevant to the controlled-research literature. A key issue that is given attention is the rate of "spontaneous" recovery of children with problems who are not formally treated by psychotherapy. In an earlier review by Levitt (1963) in which children were followed-up for an average of about five years, he claimed to find an improvement rate of approximately 78 percent. Such a high rate of spontaneous improvement obviously makes it very difficult to prove that psychotherapy can have beneficial effects. A later review by Levitt (1975) concluded that the percent improvement of "untreated" controls was more likely about 65 percent. No major objection has been given to this estimate although some authors point out that the spontaneous remission rate must certainly be related to diagnosis (Miller et al. 1978). One large-scale, controlled study of children with phobias (Miller et al. 1972), found that the treated younger children (six to ten years) showed a 96 percent improvement rate while a comparable group of waiting-list-control children showed an improvement rate of 57 percent. For older phobic children the success rate with treatment was the same as the improvement rate of the waiting-list controls (45 percent). Motivation of the parents seemed to be positively correlated with the success of the outcome.

Given the paucity of controlled outcome studies of the effect of psychotherapy on children, Barrett et al. (1978) drew few conclusions, and some of them are primarily methodological. They pointed out, for example, that the high "spontaneous" improvement rate among children implies the need for relatively larger numbers of patients in treatment studies. In addition, response to psychotherapy appears to depend heavily upon diagnosis and developmental age of the child.

## Adolescents

Although there had been reviews of psychotherapy outcome with special groups such as schizophrenics or children, there had been no such reviews for adolescents until that of Tramontana (1980). He identified thirty-five non-case studies published between 1967 and 1977 in which the primary focus was on adolescents aged twelve to eighteen, and in which outcome was quantified in some way. However, only fifteen of the studies were conducted with the use of a control or comparison group. Both individual and group therapy were included.

Tramontana (1980) concluded that only three studies were sufficiently well designed and executed to provide convincing evidence that psychotherapy (individual in one case, group in another, and both combined in the third) produced better outcomes than was found in the control patients. Outcome measures included school and work performance and indices of legal difficulties. One controlled study of institutionalized delinquents did find that two new correctional institutions, one run on transactional analysis principles and the other on behavior modification principles, had lower recidivism rates than other traditionally run institutions.

Tramontana (1980) also stated that in all studies reviewed 73 percent of the patients receiving psychotherapy were reported to show a positive outcome whereas only 29 percent of the control cases at termination of therapy showed a positive outcome. These statistics of improvement could be overestimates in view of the fact that the therapists and researchers were often the same people. In addition, the studies from which the outcome rates were derived differed greatly in terms of methodological adequacy, outcome criteria, the kinds of treatment interventions used, therapist characteristics, and the kinds of clients and problems studied. Positive outcomes at follow-up are reported to be 68 percent for the adolescents who received psychotherapy and 48 percent for those who did not.

The review makes the important point that the use of the term "spontaneous remission" to describe the positive outcome of the untreated controls has no explanatory value. It tends to imply that the change process is random and not specifiable, whereas there are potentially identifiable factors producing positive changes even in the absence of formal psychotherapy. These could include education, pastoral counseling, good family relations, and successful life experiences.

Tramontana (1980) concludes that multidimensional assessments are essential for research with children and adolescents because of the changing nature of the patient simply as a result of development trends. Adolescent adjustment is probably more variable than that of adults as a function of both age and varying situational demands.

Although some investigators assume that long-lasting changes as measured by follow-up assessments should be produced by psychotherapy, this is debatable. "No one would insist that just because the benefits of a particular medical treatment may fade in time—so that additional treatment becomes necessary—the initial treatment was necessarily without value" (Tramontana 1980, p.447). Finally, Tramontana (1980) believes that previous research on adolescents has been too narrow in at least two ways: (1) disproportionate emphasis has been given to group therapy studies of delinquents; and (2) measures such as re-institutionalization are not sensitive to the many small changes that may occur in an individual. Potentially useful measures such as sociometric indices have seldom been used even though the improvement of peer relations is often considered an important goal of therapy.

## The Elderly

Despite the increase in the number of people over the age of sixty-five, the research literature for this age group is quite limited. The sparse literature in this field is reviewed by Sparacino (1978), who notes that in both England and the United States mental health workers have tended to avoid treating elderly patients by means of psychotherapy. However, there are many reasons for this state of affairs. For example, many elderly people have difficulty getting to mental health centers; others have limited money for payment or limited insurance coverage; and others are in such poor physical health that they cannot leave their residences. The view that diminished cognitive capacity and ego strength in the elderly is a deterrent for psychotherapy may be a more pessimistic view than is warranted.

Studies of age in relation to prognosis are inconsistent. In fact some studies indicate that younger patients are more likely to drop out of a variety of medical and psychological treatments than are older patients. Other studies indicate that aged people tend to see psychotherapy as a sign of weakness and a limitation on their sense of independence.

Psychotherapists have differed considerably in their theoretical accounts of how best to provide psychotherapy for the elderly and on what models to use. Disagreements exist on such factors as: the role of insight, the role of passive relating, the role of confrontation, and the role of active environmental intervention.

Very few studies with the elderly have used formal experimental methods and control groups. In one (Godbale and Verinis 1974), elderly patients exposed to either brief supportive psychotherapy or brief "confrontational psychotherapy" did better on a variety of measures than did the control group given only two evaluation interviews. In another investigation (Schultz 1976), elderly patients in a home reported higher self-reports on such measures as happiness, hope, and physical health as a result of regular visits by college students as compared to control patients who were not visited.

Overall, the literature on psychotherapy for the aged is largely anecdotal and greatly in need of expansion.

# CHAPTER 15

# Negative Effects of Psychotherapy

Any technology known to be effective may be used for harm as well as benefit. This notion presumably applies to psychotherapy as well. To the extent that evidence accumulates demonstrating the effectiveness of psychotherapy, one might reasonably assume that some evidence will also be found to indicate that psychotherapy also has "negative" or "deterioration" effects. Such a view has been proposed most forcefully by Bergin, beginning in 1963. He has continued to publish provocative papers on the possibility of deterioration effects in psychotherapy (Bergin 1966, 1971).

As one might expect, obtaining unequivocal evidence on this issue is not easy; psychotherapists are not strongly motivated to describe their failures. However, several papers give figures on the number of patients who improve, the number who remain unchanged, and the number who get worse. Such reports are often not part of controlled studies, but simply opinions (estimates) by the treating psychotherapist of how well he or she did. In cases where a control group was used, deterioration effects might be indicated by evidence that the treated patients did worse than the untreated patients. Such reports are extremely rare.

In view of this, Bergin has tended to rely on an indirect measure of possible deterioration effects. He assumes that even if a treated patient group receives the same or better average ratings on measures of adjustment and symptoms as an untreated group, the existence of deterioration effects in the treated patients will be revealed by the fact that some patients will improve a great deal and others will deteriorate a great deal. The net effect of this possible outcome is that the variability of scores on outcome measures will be higher in the treated group than in the control group. This logic also assumes that treated patients are being compared with untreated patients, a possibility that occurs only with short-term therapies.

The concept of negative effects of psychotherapy has been challenged by several investigators. Basically, they have attempted to show that there is little or no evidence that the variability of outcome scores is significantly greater in treated patients than in untreated patients (Gottman 1973, May 1971).

In response to these critics, Lambert, Bergin, and Collins (1976) have reported on forty-eight studies in an effort to show that the phenomenon of deterioration occurs, and that it occurs among many types of patients treated with a variety of techniques.

Because of the obvious importance of the issue, Strupp et al. (1976) decided to re-examine in detail all of the forty-eight studies cited by Lamberg, Bergin, and Collins (1976) in support of their deterioration hypothesis. After reviewing this evidence, Strupp et al. (1976) came to quite different conclusions. They stated that nearly all of the forty-eight studies cited by Lambert et al. (1976) show major errors or deficiencies of methodology that make any conclusions quite tenuous. The criticisms of the studies include the following points, among others:

- Use of inexperienced therapists, such as paraprofessionals, medical students, graduate students or residents
- High dropout rates of patients from treatment
- Use of schizophrenics in some studies, who tend in general to have a deteriorating course regardless of treatment
- Use of single (often only global) outcome criteria
- Inclusion of unimproved patients in the negative effects category
- Use of outcome ratings of unknown reliability
- Failure to take account of differences between experimental and control group patients before therapy
- Arbitrary assumptions that increases in anxiety or defensiveness are *necessarily* negative effects of therapy
- Failure to distinguish between negative effects of therapy and *relapses* after therapy.

The one study free of most of these sources of error (Sloane et al. 1975) reports a negative effect of therapy of about 3–6 percent, which was similar to the rate of untreated waiting-list controls.

There is also one other important issue reported on in detail only by Strupp, Hadley, and Gomes-Schwartz (1977). They raise the question of whether it is always evident what a negative effect of therapy is. In order to arrive at some kind of empirical answer to this question, they decided to poll 150 psychotherapists of a wide range of theoretical orientations, by means of a mail questionnaire. Seventy therapists responded. Basically, the therapists were asked if they believe there are negative effects of psychotherapy; what such effects are; and to suggest possible reasons for them.

The results showed that the clinicians overwhelmingly agreed that negative effects of psychotherapy do occasionally occur. Such effects may take a variety of different forms: (1) exacerbation of presenting symptoms; (2) appearance of new symptoms; (3) patients' misuse of therapy (such as sustained dependence on the therapist); (4) development of negative attitudes by the patient toward him- or herself (such as feelings of failure or self-contempt); and (5) disillusionment of the patient about therapy in general or about his or her own therapist. These interesting comments by the clinicians suggest a much more sophisticated concept of negative effects than was originally proposed by Bergin. But most of the kinds of measures implied above have never been systematically measured by researchers. It is thus evident that a serious new evaluation of the "deterioration hypothesis" will require the development of new psychometric instruments.

The clinicians also made a number of interesting points about the interpretation of negative effects. Some of them pointed out that negative effects are judged as such by an observer; what is a negative effect is therefore a value judgment. Negative effects depend on abstruse theoretical issues as well as the patients' overt behavior. For example, do transient transference effects indicate negative effects of therapy? They depend also on what one considers desirable from the viewpoint of society and the family, as well as the patient. Should the concept of negative effects be applied only to the identified patient or can it apply to the family system or the larger society in which the patient is embedded?

Finally, the clinicians were asked their opinions on possible reasons for deterioration effects. In response to this question they offered a wide variety of hypotheses. They suggested that negative effects could be produced by certain personality characteristics of the therapist such as coldness, hostility, seductiveness, pessimism, and narcissism. Certain patient qualities such as low motivation and a masochistic character structure could also contribute to a poor outcome of psychotherapy. Errors in technique, inappropriate goals, technical rigidity, misuse of interpretations, fostering dependency, and breaches of confidentiality were also mentioned as possible sources of negative effects. What is perhaps puzzling is that there is so little research evidence for the existence of all these possible sources of negative therapeutic effects.

After their extensive review of the evidence, Strupp et al. (1976) make the important point that in a pluralistic society, in which mental health can mean different things to different people, there is no simple or general way to define positive or negative effects. In their words:

> In increasing numbers, patients enter psychotherapy not for the cure of traditional "symptoms" but (at least, ostensibly) for the purpose of finding meaning in their lives, for actualizing themselves, or for maximizing their potential. In our pluralistic society the term "mental health" has assumed a multiplicity of meanings. If conceptions of mental health are fuzzier than ever, how can we determine whether a particular intervention has led to improvement, deterioration, or no change? Unless we make certain assumptions and develop a generally acceptable set of criteria concerning mental health, it is more or less meaningless to speak of "improvement" or a negative effect from psychotherapy—and it is even less possible to compare the relative effectiveness of treatments in different studies [Strupp et al. 1976, p.57].

One may conclude that the available empirical data are inadequate to demonstrate either the nature, the frequency, or the causes of deterioration.

# CHAPTER 16

# Cost-Effectiveness and Cost-Benefit Studies of Psychotherapy

In recent years a new dimension has been added to the problem of evaluating the effectiveness of psychotherapy. In addition to looking at traditional outcome measures such as symptom reduction or social functioning, efforts have been made to estimate the relative costs and benefits of different psychotherapeutic approaches. Two different methods have been used. Cost-benefit analysis (CBA) compares the estimated monetary value of benefits of psychotherapy against the monetary value of its costs. Unfortunately, it is often very difficult, if not impossible, to transform the outcomes of psychotherapy—increases in self-esteem or decreases in depression—into monetary units. As a result, an alternative procedure called cost-effectiveness analysis (CEA) has been more frequently used to evaluate therapies. In CEA two or more programs or therapies are compared in terms of the costs required to achieve a given outcome. Nothing is explicitly stated about benefits. It is simply assumed that the benefits of the program being compared are the same.

One of the earliest studies dealing with the relative costs of psychotherapy was conducted in West Germany in the 1950s. Duehrssen (cited in Sharfstein 1978) attempted to follow approximately 1,000 patients who received psychoanalytically oriented psychotherapy. Patients were evaluated at the beginning of therapy and again five years later, after they had received an average of 100 hours of treatment. Twelve percent ended treatment prematurely, and twelve percent continued privately after their insured limit of 200 visits ran out. Out of the original sample, 845 patients provided follow-up information either through interviews or questionnaires.

The results showed that these patients had an averge of 5.3 hospital days per year for any kind of illness prior to treatment and only .78 hospital days per year during the five-year follow-up period. Patient satisfaction was high, with 81 percent of the patients reporting that they felt strongly that they had been helped by the treatment. Unfortunately, this study did not use a randomly selected control group of comparable patients so that there is no way of judging the role of psychotherapy in the apparent benefits.

The most thorough review of the literature on the application of CEA / CBA to psychotherapy has been provided by Yates and Newman (1980). Although there are a number of studies of CEA or CBA in psychotherapy settings, these authors point out that the range of therapies and patient populations is so limited that no generalizations are yet possible. This research has focused on three major areas; specifically, it has been carried out to: (1) investigate variables related to the delivery of care (variables such as intensity of inpatient treatment); (2) compare alternative drug treatment programs; and (3) compare the effects of psychotherapy on medical utilization.

With regard to the first area of research, several studies have examined the costs of more and less intensive treatment programs in mental hospitals. Intensity was defined either in terms of patient / therapist ratios or amount of patient contacts per week. Five such studies reached the conclusion that the more intensive therapy was more cost-effective or more cost-beneficial than was less intensive therapy in an inpatient setting, although none of the studies used random assignment to the different levels of intensity of inpatient treatment. One study of milieu therapy reported it to be less effective and more costly than other forms of inpatient treatment.

Seven investigations have compared community-based programs for adult schizophrenics with institutional programs. These investigations found that, in general, community-based programs of treatment are more cost-effective and cost-beneficial than institutional treatment. This is due primarily to the difference in the overhead cost of housing, feeding, and supervising patients in hospitals rather than to better outcome per se. These results, however, should be considered tentative at best because the various studies suffered from one or another of several methodological problems. To wit: (1) lack of random assignment of patients to the different conditions; (2) lack of a no-treatment, or placebo treatment, condition; (3) arbitrary rules for transforming therapist ratings of outcome into dollars; (4) frequent exclusion of some or all costs that the community must bear for the care of deinstitutionalized patients; and (5) omission of some indirect costs of deinstitutionalization (for example, reduction in real estate values possibly caused by the stigma of mentally ill patients in the community). One of the more methodologically rigorous of the studies (Weisbrod 1979) found that a community-based therapy program was more cost-beneficial than an inpatient program for schizophrenic patients.

Another area of application of CEA/CBA analysis is in the residential versus institutional treatment of problem children, expecially juvenile delinquents. Four studies of this type were reported and all tended to find that delinquents in special token economy/therapy programs did better than those in boys' schools and that such programs were less costly. These studies suffered from a lack of random assignment of delinquents to the different programs. In addition, they failed to consider the potential costs of free volunteer and student services.

Seven studies have been concerned with comparing services rendered by professionals with those rendered by paraprofessionals. Most of these investigations have shown that paraprofessionals (nurses or parents, for example) may, after training, treat disturbed children as well as do professionals and at somewhat less cost. However, these studies also suffer from various methodological weaknesses. For example, they tended to include only operations costs and thereby underestimated the drain on community resources required by "live-in therapists" (parents). In addition, the patients were not randomly assigned to the different conditions.

Five investigations were concerned with the cost-effectiveness of drug-treatment programs for heroin addiction. Generally speaking, the results indicated that all programs, be they methadone maintenance, therapeutic communities, inpatient detoxification, or contingency contracting, had benefit/cost ratios greater than one. Paying a client ten dollars for each day he or she could provide a drug-free urine sample was the simplest effective treatment. Limitations of some of these studies included inadequate benefit data, lack of control groups, or nonrandom assignments of patients.

Yates and Newman (1980) review one last area: the effect of psychotherapy on medical utilization. Eight studies have attempted to define the cost-benefits of psychotherapy on medical utilization. All the studies report a reduction in the use of general medical services. However, according to Yates and Newman (1980) none of the studies used random assignment of patients and no-treatment control groups. One interpretation that has been suggested for the decline in use of medical services after minimal therapeutic contacts is that patients relabel their problems as psychological rather than medical.

Yates and Newman (1980) conclude that some approaches to cost-effectiveness and cost-benefit analysis can be applied in most psychotherapy settings. In a preliminary and tentative

way they suggest that "the economics of delivering psychotherapy, including the salary of the care provider, the residential or outpatient nature of the program, duration of contact
with therapists during participation in the program, and
length of participation in the program, all seem to determine
cost-effectiveness or cost-benefit more than the techniques
applied" (p. 181).

In a series of researches at Kaiser-Permanente by Cummings
and Follette (1976) spanning eighteen years, brief psychotherapy was reported to reduce medical utilization in somaticizing patients complaining of somatic disorders to the extent
that the savings in medical costs far offset the cost of providing
the psychotherapy. Closely matched somaticizing patients
who did not receive psychotherapy and who did not, thereby,
reduce their medical utilization were used as "controls," a
methodological flaw necessitated by the fact that treatment
could not be denied to patients seeking psychotherapy. This
methodological difficulty is attenuated by the twenty-eight
replications in widely differing settings (such as Group Health
Insurance of Washington, Pennsylvania Blue Shield, and so
on), all of which demonstrated the Cummings-Follette effect,
as reported by Jones and Vischi (1979).

## The Effect of Psychotherapy on
## Medical Utilization—A Meta-Analysis

In 1980, Schlessinger, Mumford, and Glass reported on the
use of meta-analysis to evaluate psychotherapy's effect on the
use of general medical services. Using the data from the 475
controlled psychotherapy outcome studies reported by Smith,
Glass, and Miller (1980), they identified twenty studies in
which a medical care index was used as one of the outcome
measures. This included such indices as the number of emer-
gency room visits and the number of hospitalizations. The
average effect size in favor of the psychotherapy groups was
+.74, which compares favorably with the average effect size of
+.78 for symptom improvement. These findings do not permit
assigning a dollar value to effect sizes, but the results imply
that psychotherapy has some cost-saving results.

Schlessinger et al. (1980) then review eleven retrospective,
quasi-experiments, based on clinical records, that deal with
patients' use of medical services with or without psychotherapy. Combining all the data into one time series, they
conclude that patients who receive psychotherapy show a 25

percent reduction in the use of medical services, and begin to approach the use rate of the control patients. However, these authors point out that this result may be misleading because of "regression to the mean" artifacts. In other words, if the time of entering psychotherapy happens to be a peak time of medical utilization, then one would expect medical use to decrease not only as a result of the psychotherapy but simply because peak values in any time series are likely to be followed by lower values. Thus, the analysis of retrospective data is not conclusive concerning the role of psychotherapy in medical use.

Consequently, Schlessinger et al. (1980) provided meta-analyses of three sets of experimental studies: one concerned with the effects of psychotherapy on alcoholism, one with its effects on asthma, and one with its effects on recovery from surgery. These authors located twenty experiments dealing with alcoholism. Meta-analysis showed the psychotherapy groups to be +.96 units higher on the average than the control groups, although the treatment effect decreased considerably over a twelve-month period to the level of the control group.

A similar meta-analysis of twelve studies of asthmatic patients demonstrated that those patients receiving psychotherapy were +.85 units higher than the controls, and that they used fewer medical services. Finally, patients facing surgery who were exposed to some form of psychological interventions (psychotherapy, hypnotherapy, educational programs, and so forth) did better than the control patients. The average effect size for ten studies was +.50. In addition, experimental patients stayed in the hospital almost two days less than the control patients.

These results of the meta-analyses imply that the experimental group patients would have a financial benefit over the controls, but the methods of a CEA or CBA analysis have not been used in any of these investigations. It is, therefore, impossible to establish any detailed cost/effectiveness ratios from the information provided. The area of CE and CB analysis represents a relatively new and promising technical innovation for analyzing the outcomes of psychotherapy research.

# CHAPTER 17

# Problems and Alternatives

The preceding material has been based largely on reviews of the psychotherapy outcome literature published during the past three decades. These reviews represent the considered judgments of experts in research design, psychotherapy, or both. And they provide a kind of intellectual history of an era. In broad terms, these reviews reveal steady growth in the number of research studies dedicated to measuring psychotherapy outcomes. They also reveal an increasing preoccupation with the details of methodology and an increasing concern with meeting the rigorous standards of laboratory research.

Over the years, various aspects of research have been made more explicit. For example, greater and greater attention has been focused on defining patient samples. Today, investigators do not merely sample a handful of clinic patients who happen to come in during a certain period. Increasingly, research diagnostic criteria are used to diagnose the patients (with psychometric tests often added) to provide precise figures on how depressed or anxious each patient is.

Another variable that has been specified to a greater degree in recent research is the technique of treatment. In many earlier studies, the therapy would be specified simply as psychoanalytically oriented, supportive, or behavioral. The inadequacy of such descriptions has been frequently stated with the result that, increasingly, "manuals" are prepared by advocates of particular schools of psychotherapy so that the therapists are more likely to do the same sorts of things. In addition, audio- or videotape recordings help independent assessors determine whether the therapists are, in fact, following specified guidelines for therapy.

Attention has also been focused on more precise specification of outcomes. Not only do investigators encourage the therapist to make global ratings of improvement, as was done in the old days, but the *patient* often completes a battery of tests on many aspects of his or her feelings and personality. And since society and the patient's family have a stake in the outcome of psychotherapy, various "significant others" are asked to rate the patient's behavior and life-style.

Still another variable that has received increasing attention is the personality of the therapist. In earlier studies, it was simply enough to say that one or more trained (or trainee) therapists were carrying out the treatment. Then asking whether the therapist was warm, empathic, and genuine became fashionable. Other researchers concerned themselves with categorizing therapists as $A$ or $B$. This was determined by a therapist's score on a test of vocational interests. Although this interest in specifying the therapist's personality or values continues, it does so in the face of repeated failure to show any significant connections between these variables and the outcome of psychotherapy (Luborsky et al. 1971, Razin 1977). To complicate matters, most therapists seem reluctant to be tested in the same ways or to the same degrees as their patients.

Finally, increased attention has been paid to the problem of control groups. As everyone knows, the laboratory model of causality that provides the paradigm that researchers follow says that we cannot identify causal agents without having a control group (or a control condition) to compare outcomes against. Although countless reports of psychotherapy outcome do not use them, increasingly control groups have been included in recent research. Not only are untreated patients used as controls, but patients on waiting lists are used, as are patients given various other or modified forms of psychotherapy or drug therapy. However, this trend toward greater use of controls has created many problems, both ethical and methodological. These problems were evaluated in earlier sections of this report.

Thus, we have an apparent picture of robust growth of research, healthy skepticism, increased precision, and more sophisticated methodology. However, the complex waxing and waning of optimism (or pessimism) is based only on the subjective evaluations of small segments of the research literature.

Many associate the beginnings of the critical evaluation of psychotherapy outcome research with the review by Eysenck (1952). This review was based on twenty-four reports that he collected from various sources, most of which did not describe any controlled investigations of psychotherapy. The arguments were indirect and inferential, and statistics were uncritically pooled. But instead of being ignored, the review stimulated despair, anger, criticism, and rebuttals. Some believe (for example, Meltzoff and Kornreich 1970, Bergin and Lambert 1978, Vandenbos and Pine 1980) that Eysenck's arguments have been undermined and defeated. But a paper published in 1980 in a prestigious psychological journal has resurrected Eysenck's critique and has argued that his claims have never been adequately refuted (Erwin 1980).

It may be argued that Eysenck's mode of reviewing the literature, that is, haphazardly selecting articles with a critique designed to support a prejudice, served as a model for most of the reviews that followed. With one exception (Smith, Glass, and Miller 1980), all reviewers of the literature have exercised a great deal of personal judgment in terms of what they select to review and how the review itself is carried out. Some reviews of the literature have examined as few as nine studies (Cross 1964), fifteen studies (Cristol 1972), twenty-four studies (Eysenck 1952), or forty-eight studies (Bergin 1971).

This implies again that the reviewer subjectively selects articles for evaluation. Some reviewers have claimed to select only controlled studies, but other critics have often attacked these articles on methodological grounds. For example, although Luborsky, Singer, and Luborsky (1975) included nineteen controlled studies of "behavior therapy" in their review of the literature, Kazdin and Wilson (1978) cite fifty-one controlled studies of behavior therapy, and at the same time question the methodological adequacy of Luborsky et al.'s box-score method. Kazdin and Wilson claim, in fact, that so many methodological weaknesses pervade the published research that very little can be concluded from it. Despite this opinion, where Luborsky et al. (1975) conclude that behavior therapy is about as effective as "verbal" therapies (whatever they are), Kazdin and Wilson (1978) conclude that behavioral therapies are more effective than verbal therapies in most comparisons. In a similar vein, Malan (1973), using different standards of evidence than Meltzoff and Kornreich (1970), concludes that only 4 of their 101 cited studies are of truly adequate design, but that these "good" studies reveal psychotherapy's effectiveness.

Bergin's reanalysis (1963) of data cited by Eysenck (1952) also illustrates the idiosyncratic elements involved in evaluating research reports. Eysenck claimed that the rate of improvement of patients who were psychoanalyzed at the Berlin Psychoanalytic Institute was approximately 39 percent, a figure derived from somewhat ambiguous reports. In contrast, Bergin (1971) derived a 91 percent rate of improvement from the same data. This difference, and the other examples cited thus far, "clearly shows the importance of the evaluator in appraisals of outcome data" (Garfield 1981, p. 179).

To illustrate some of the diversity of opinion resulting from the various reviews of the literature, a number of authors may be quoted or cited. In 1964, Cross stated that the "efficacy [of psychotherapy] has not been scientifically demonstrated beyond a reasonable doubt" (p. 416). In 1966, after reviewing fourteen controlled studies of psychotherapy, Dittman stated that his own "conclusions are modest, and are, moreover, diluted by confusion" (p. 74). On a more optimistic note, Meltzoff and Kornreich (1970) concluded that "the effectiveness of psychotherapy with a wide variety of patient types has already been amply demonstrated." More cautiously, Bergin (1971) stated that "psychotherapy, as practiced over the last forty years, has had an average effect that is modestly positive" (p. 263). Malan, in 1973, arrived at a mixed conclusion after his review of the literature. He stated that "the evidence for the effectiveness of psychotherapy is now fairly strong; that there is considerable evidence that dynamic psychotherapy is effective in psychosomatic conditions; but, that the evidence in favor of dynamic psychotherapy . . . [for] neurosis and character disorders . . . is weak in the extreme" (p. 725). Parenthetically, the "considerable evidence" for the effectiveness of dynamic psychotherapy in psychosomatic conditions is based on five investigations, in one of which psychotherapy consisted of brief group meetings with ulcer patients (Chappell and Stevenson 1936), and the others involved unspecified forms of "dynamic" psychotherapy.

The review by Luborsky, Singer, and Luborsky (1975) concludes that "everyone has won and all must have prizes" (p. 995) meaning that psychotherapy appears to benefit patients, but that the limited comparative evidence that exists does not reveal that any one psychotherapy is more effective than any other. Frank (1979) concludes from his review of the literature that "psychotherapy . . . [is] more effective than informal, unplanned help. Unfortunately, . . . these efforts are not impressively more effective" (p. 310).

That these conclusions do not apply only to individual therapy may be illustrated by citing several reviews of other modalities of treatment. In a survey covering forty-two years (1921–1963) of group psychotherapy with psychotics, Stotsky and Zolik (1965) concluded: "The results of controlled experimental studies do not give clear endorsement for the use of group therapy as an independent modality" (p. 339). In 1971, the review by Bednar and Lawlis came to the same conclusion. More recently, Parloff and Dies (1977) reviewed the group psychotherapy outcome literature for the period 1966 to 1975. They were particularly concerned with "real" patients rather than volunteer college students or growth potential groups. Their analysis covered group therapy as used with schizophrenics, psychoneurotics, offenders, and addicts. They concluded that the research evidence indicated that group therapy had little or no effect on schizophrenics or addicts and that the evidence was too limited or irrelevant to make any decisions about its effects on delinquents or psychoneurotics. They wrote: "Very little can be concluded regarding the efficacy of group psychotherapy" (p. 313). Essentially similar conclusions of little or no *proven* efficacy have been reached in reviews of the literature on family and marital therapy (Gurman and Kniskern 1978) and social and milieu treatments (Mosher and Keith 1980). It thus appears that most of the reviews cited have concluded either that the various forms of psychotherapy are not particularly effective, or that their effectiveness is moderate at best.

The only recent reviewers of the literature who present their conclusions in somewhat stronger terms are Luborsky et al. (1975) and Smith, Glass, and Miller (1980). Their technique has been described earlier and some criticisms made, but it may be worth recapitulating a few points. Since these authors included only controlled studies of psychotherapy outcome, they relied heavily on academic studies performed by graduate students doing Ph.D. dissertations using college student volunteers as patients. This may be inferred from their statement that the average age of the patients is twenty-two and that 56 percent of the studies were done in college facilities or schools. As we stated earlier, if there are few controlled studies in the research literature on the elderly, or on drug addicts, then a meta-analysis of all studies cannot reveal anything about the elderly or about drug addicts.

In addition, some (many?) of the published investigations may be subtly biased. This possible bias concerns the fact that students rapidly learn that only "positive" results get their dissertation through the graduate committees, and there is thus strong motivation to discover some significant differences in line with their hypotheses. Another pressure for "significant" results is the fact that most journals tend not to publish experiments in which no significant differences were obtained. For example, in one survey of 294 articles published in well-known psychology journals, 97 percent of the articles concluded that a difference found between an experimental group and a control group was significant at the 5 percent level or better (Sterling 1959). The point is that many of the studies used by Smith, Glass, and Miller (1980) in their meta-analysis may be biased toward positive results that favor psychotherapy.

Even if this is not so, other statisticians have challenged Smith et al.'s (1980) interpretation of the magnitude of the psychotherapy effect (Gallo 1978). Whether the magnitude of the psychotherapy effect is medium or small remains a moot point; no one has claimed that it is large.

Finally, in criticism of meta-analysis, Garfield (1980) has stated:

> I question the meaningfulness of combining studies that differ in as many ways as the published and unpublished studies used in this analysis. Also, although much is made of an average effect size, it does not have any real operational or clinical meaning for me. The type of criterion used in the studies is of some consequence, *and comparison with a control group is only one aspect of evaluation treatment effectiveness* [italics added] [p. 180].

We have examined closely the differences among the different reviews and have seen the inconsistencies and ambiguities. Reviewing the literature in any field is not a simple process; and it is exceedingly difficult in the field of psychotherapy research. The reviews are selective, incomplete, biased toward certain types of methodologies, and subject to the vagaries of any complex inferential process. Evidently, the same investigations are sometimes interpreted differently depending on how reviewers weight different aspects of the experiment (for example, control groups, randomization, multiple outcome measures, follow-ups).

## Relation of Research and Practice in Psychotherapy

An important question that clinicians often ask is "What is the relation between theory and practice?" A parallel question might be asked about psychotherapy research: "What is the relation between research findings, particularly as reflected in reviews of the literature, and clinical practice?" To put it still another way, "Does research have an impact on therapeutic practice?"

Parloff and Dies (1977) have given their answer: there is "indisputable evidence that clinicians have long been able to resist the offerings of the researcher . . ." (p. 281). There appears to be an "inconsistency between the clinicians' day-to-day observations regarding the apparent utility of their efforts and the researchers' failure to furnish enthusiastic confirmation" (Parloff and Dies 1977, p. 312).

This belief in a lack of correlation between research and practice has been elaborated more fully by Wolpe (1981) and by Garfield (1981). Wolpe (1981) claims that psychoanalytic theory and practice continue to dominate the field despite the fact that "the clinical effectiveness of psychoanalytic therapy has never been established (and) . . . not a single one of the theory's main propositions has ever been supported by scientifically acceptable evidence" (p. 159). In contrast, a behavioral theory of neurosis, which Wolpe believes is based on evidence of learning and conditioning in the laboratory, continues to have relatively little impact on clinical practice. Wolpe rejects the criticism that behavior therapy is nonverbal or that it is narrow in focus, pointing out that it has been applied successfully not only to phobias and sexual problems, "but to the whole range of neurotic problems including the most complex social neuroses and so-called existential problems" (p. 162).

Garfield (1981) considers the problem from a different perspective. He points out that "in spite of repeated and often harsh criticisms of psychotherapy's effectiveness, psychotherapeutic activities have continued to grow and develop in various ways" (p. 175). This growth is evidenced in several different ways. The first is the large increase in the number of people providing psychotherapeutic services. They include not only psychiatrists and psychologists, but social workers, nurses, pastoral counselors, and lay people with various types of training. A second sign of growth is the large increase in types of psychotherapies that have become available, including such therapies as transactional analysis, transcendental meditation, primal scream therapy, and dozens of variants on these themes.

What is most important to emphasize is that this expansion of the clinical field of psychotherapy has occurred alongside the parallel expansion of research, much of which seemed to show that psychotherapy was either ineffective or marginally effective.

Garfield (1981) makes one other interesting point. As the number of variants of psychotherapy increased, a smaller and smaller percent of them were even examined in a research context. As the versions of psychoanalytically influenced therapies proliferated, fewer of them were examined for effectiveness. Increased research effort went into brief therapies, such as systematic desensitization, which could be described in detail and carried out in a few sessions with motivated college students who reported anxiety states or snake phobias. The fact is "that most psychotherapies have received no systematic research evaluation, but this fact has not deterred the followers or, apparently, the potential clients of these therapies" (Garfield 1981, p. 178). Research reviews have no impact on patients (or potential patients) even in the unlikely event that they have an influence on therapists.

There is one other kind of evidence for this statement. New psychotherapies have appeared with regularity on the clinical scene. Some are clear offshoots of a few major schools, as is the case with the neo-Freudian therapies. Some are derivative of the general behavioristic tradition. More recently, we see the appearance of various forms of cognitive therapies, as well as variants of existential approaches. We hear reference made to bibliotherapy, telephone therapy, poetry therapy, and others too esoteric to even classify.

What is important about this development is that all these approaches to therapy appear without the benefit of research, and certainly without the benefit of being reviewed in some comparative context. It thus appears evident that this is still another indication of research having no impact upon clinical practice. A question worth exploring is: What factors influence the appearance and degree of acceptance of new therapies? If research is not the source of new therapies, what is?

## Need for a New Paradigm

We should now like to consider a fundamental issue, and that is: Can laboratory-type research solve the problem of assessing the effectiveness of psychotherapy? Consider some of the problems. Let us assume that we have decided to systematically compare each type of therapy with every other type. If we believe that there are 140 types of therapy as Parloff (1975) tells us, then it will take 9,730 experiments to make all such comparisons. Even if we ignore most of the labels that masquerade as psychotherapies and assume that there are only twenty-five types of therapy, comparative research of each type against every other type would involve 300 experiments. But that is just the beginning.

Obviously, there are many parameters that influence outcome. Some examples are frequency of therapy, types of patients studied, selection criteria, outcome measures, and therapist personality or style. In order for research to resolve the issue of comparative effectiveness, all of these parameters must also be manipulated. Further, since duration of therapy is likely to be a relevant parameter, the whole series of experiments should be repeated using different durations of treatment (for example, three months, six months, one year, two years). Therefore, as we increase the number of parameters to be considered in our research, the total number of experiments needed to investigate them all becomes astronomical. This is true even if we assume that there is only a relatively small number of basic types of psychotherapy. Such a decision would still require us to provide a convincing rationale for excluding most current therapies.

There are three other brief but important points that should be made about significant problems in the methodology of research as applied to psychotherapy. One concerns the "ecological validity" (Brunswick 1956) of the manipulations that are carried out. The concept of "ecological validity" refers to the degree to which the conditions of an experiment are similar to, or are an appropriate sample of, the conditions found in the "real world." For example, if one wished to compare short-term with long-term therapy (Luborsky, Singer, and Luborsky 1975), there would be little ecological validity to assume that "long-term" therapy was defined by treatment periods of six to eight months of once-a-week treatment. Similarly, if we wished to compare experienced with inexperienced therapists, it would not be sufficient to use one or two "experienced" therapists and assume that they are an adequate sample of all experienced therapists (Karon and Vandenbos 1972). A similar point about the lack of generality and limited meaningfulness of outcome studies has been made by Carpenter, Heinrichs, and Hanlon (1981).

The second point concerns the idea that researchers have unambiguous ways to determine, by means of some sort of box-score method, which experiments are "good" and which are "poor." The evidence is now accumulating that those experiments judged "good" produce essentially the same conclusions as those judged "poor" (Luborsky, Singer, and Luborsky 1975) and that effect sizes determined on the basis of "good" experiments are of about the same magnitude as those obtained from "poor" experiments (Smith, Glass, and Miller 1980). Smith et al. (1980) also point out that "open" experiments, in contrast to "double-blind" experiments, tend also to produce comparable effect sizes. A similar point has been made by Klein et al. (1980) in relation to drug studies.

These observations raise questions either about the adequacy of any rating scheme for experiments, or about the degree of importance of experiments for psychotherapy research. It may turn out that just as there have been various patient and therapist "uniformity myths" (Kiesler 1966), there may also be a "controlled-experiment" myth as well.

Finally, there is one other general research problem that has not been given sufficient attention, and that concerns the necessity for keeping most conditions constant while carrying out any given experiment. Examples of this would be the use of RDC criteria for selecting patients, the use of psychometric tests for defining levels of pathology by means of cut-off scores, the use of fixed numbers of therapy sessions, the use of therapists with certain levels of training, and so on.

What is often not appreciated is the fact that the more variables are held constant, the less able we are to generalize to other conditions. Quite simply this means that if you apply your therapy to carefully selected depressed patients, then there is no way to judge the extent to which the therapy applies to patients with other diagnostic labels. If you select only those patients who get a score of 15 on the Beck Depression Inventory, then there is no way to determine if your therapy would apply to those who get a 14 on the Beck. If you provide patients with only sixteen sessions, you have no way of knowing what twenty or forty or sixty sessions would accomplish.

We may state this in a more general way. Just as physics has the Heisenberg Uncertainty Principle, psychotherapy research has a parallel principle and that is: *The more narrowly one defines and limits the parameters of an experiment, the less generalization is possible.* The very process of applying the laboratory model of research to psychotherapy creates impossible problems of implementation and generalization. This apparent impasse calls for new ways of conceptualizing the problem of evaluating the outcome of psychotherapy. What may be needed is a "paradigm shift," just as physics underwent a "paradigm shift" when moving from a Newtonian, absolutistic philosophy to an Einsteinian, relativistic one (Kuhn 1962).

The most important issue for the future of psychotherapy concerns the question of whether or not the model of psychotherapy research currently considered the appropriate paradigm is in fact appropriate. Much of the current literature approves the idea of strict control of independent variables and affirms the absolute necessity for utilization of a control group. This model is based on the laboratory research that is typical of certain aspects of psychology, such as animal learning, memory and psychophysiology, and in turn is based on a model of research that was developed for the physical and biological sciences. In other branches of medicine, and in drug research, it is known as the controlled clinical trial. One can raise the question of whether this model is in fact appropriate to all forms of psychotherapy research at this time.

## Controlled Experiments in Psychotherapy Research

Interestingly, the adequacy of this model has been questioned for some time, particularly as it is applied to educational and personality research. Campbell and Stanley (1963) cite earlier sources indicating that the direct contributions from controlled experimentation have been disappointing.

The disillusionment about formal experiments is related to the fact that "claims [were] made [about] the rate and degree of progress which would result from experiments [that] were grandiosely overoptimistic and were accompanied by an unjustified depreciation of nonexperimental wisdom . . ." (Campbell and Stanley 1963). A related point was made many years before by the physicist Campbell (1921). He wrote, "The uniformly certain and completely universal laws of science can be realized only in the carefully guarded conditions of the laboratory and are never found in the world outside."

In more recent years, a number of criticisms have been raised about the experimental group/control group model of experimentation as applied to psychotherapy research. Some of the criticisms are concerned with the practical problems of applying the model to psychotherapy. For example, Frank (1979) points out that criteria for selecting patient samples are often vague or inadequate; that therapies are so defined that large and unrecognized variations in style of application by different therapists occur; that measures of outcome are not comparable from one investigation to the next; that outcome measures are sometimes trivial; and that independent variables are too often demographic measures such as age, sex, and social class, which are, at best, indirectly related to therapeutic outcome.

Another way to look at the practical side of controlled experimentation is to consider the cost and the time involved in examining all the possibly relevant variables in psychotherapy research. In one five-year period a multicenter comparison of two psychotherapies for depressions might be carried out for a cost of several million dollars. In the next five-year period patients with another diagnostic label might be studied using two other psychotherapies. At this rate it could take several thousand years and untold wealth to examine any large number of potentially efficacious treatments for patients in the various diagnostic categories.

A specific illustration of the limitations of current psychotherapy research is given by O'Leary and Borkovec (1978). They surveyed the *Journal of Consulting and Clinical Psychology* for the year 1976 and discovered that thirty-four psychotherapy studies had been published. The average number of therapy sessions for these studies was *five,* a number hardly representative of psychotherapy as typically carried out in clinical settings.

This finding is also pertinent to the meta-analyses reported by Smith, Glass, and Miller (1980). Their results are based on the research as it is actually reported in the literature, and the restricted conditions and limitations of the published research are reflected in the meta-analysis.

From a theoretical point of view other types of criticisms have been offered although they do not apply equally to all research studies. Argyris (1975) has provided a critique of what he calls Model I research designs of which psychotherapy research is simply one instance. In this kind of research the subjects are willing to allow themselves to be placed in a setting in which their behavior is controlled to a considerable degree. This means that the interactions are manipulated by the experimenter, no public confrontation between subject and experimenter is permitted, and the subject accepts a dependent and submissive role. In a sense, the individual is converted to a passive subject who changes stimulus inputs into correlated responses. In the supposed interests of science, subjects are told little about the nature of the experiment, the methods to be used, or the theory behind the methods. This appears to be founded on the idea that the experimenter cannot trust the subjects to act in a "real" way if the subject knows what the experimenter is up to. Secrecy (and sometimes overt deception) is thus based on a fundamental distrust of subjects by experimenters.

One of the results of the asymmetrical relation between passive subject and controlling experimenter is that some subjects rebel against the implicit rules of the game. This rebellion may take the form of fight (negative reactions?), flight (withdrawal?), or attempts to change the rules of the interaction (seduction, acting out?).

Still another critique of the experimental model has been proposed by Scheibe (1978). He points out that psychology has two major historical roots, biology and biography, and that the modes of thinking are different in the two contexts. The biological source has emphasized the belief that human behavior is understandable, predictable, controllable, and subject to the same experimental methods as are used in the study of animal physiology. The biographic view sees all individuals as unique and as constantly involved in interactions with others in such complex systems that prediction is possible only under the most restrictive conditions.

The conclusion that Scheibe draws from his analysis is that it is always possible, in principle, for a human being to avoid being predicted in any interaction. The implication of this point is that the pursuit of predictability in psychotherapy research may be the pursuit of an illusion.

This same idea is elaborated by Koch (1981), a philosopher of science. He points out that the current view of science assumes that anything should be accepted if it has been established by the "correct" methodology even if the findings are inconsistent with traditional wisdom or individual experience. He points out, however, that there are many problems in the human condition that are meaningful yet undecidable in scientific terms. For example: Is it better to do good deeds or sinful ones? How does one distinguish between guilt and innocence? When is a person telling the truth or lying? When is a person being treated as an object or a person? Do I really understand my patient or is it an illusion that I do? The same idea is echoed in the words of the philosopher, Bertrand Russell (1945): "Science

**199**

tells us what we can know, but what we can know is little, and if we forget how much we cannot know, we become insensitive to many things of great importance" (p. XIII).

Koch (1981) concludes that "psychological events are multiply determined, ambiguous in their human meaning, polymorphous, contextually environed or embedded in complex and vaguely bounded ways, evanescent and labile in the extreme" (p. 268). As a result he assumes that there are important areas of psychological study that require methods of inquiry more like those of the humanities than the sciences. Such areas include motivation, personality, and psychopathology.

## Other Limitations of Controlled Clinical Trials

Frank (1979) has pointed out several problems with experimental/control group designs that have not been given sufficient attention. Although one of the criticisms of contemporary psychotherapy research is that different therapists do not do the same things, Frank believes that uniformity is not only an impossible criterion to meet, but an undesirable one as well. He believes that standard measures of outcome, and manuals on how to do each particular brand of therapy, are largely irrelevant to long-term, open-ended therapies. "To the extent that the spontaneity of the therapist's actions is considered crucial, and the patient's improvement is defined solely by changes in his or her subjective state, it is hard to see how either the therapy or the measures of benefit could ever be standardized" (p. 312). Any therapeutic encounter is necessarily characterized by therapeutic improvisations.

Frank also notes that since therapy occurs in the midst of complex social and family systems, many of the determinants of outcome lie outside the specific interaction between patient and therapist. This implies that causal statements about the relation between therapy modality and outcome cannot be made unequivocably. Finally, Frank states that the types of symptoms and signs of distress that patients exhibit often shift in idiosyncratic ways during the course of long-term psychotherapy. This creates problems both for standard outcome measures as well as for systems of diagnostic classification.

Another analysis of methodological problems associated with the experimental group/control group design has been presented by O'Leary and Borkovec (1978). They pay particular attention to the concept of a placebo and the often expressed idea that placebo control groups are necessary for psychotherapy research. Placebos in drug research are well known and consist of a pharmacologically inert substance. In psychotherapy it is unclear as to what an "inert" condition could be. If one finds a "placebo effect" as a result of casual conversation between a therapist and a patient, then one tends to relabel the placebo effect as the result of "demand stimuli," "expectation effects," "desire to please the therapist," and so on. Any reliable placebo will not remain theoretically inert very long but will be incorporated into some body of theory. Therefore, O'Leary and Borkovec recommend that the term *placebo* be abandoned in psychotherapy research.

They suggest several other reasons for abandoning the placebo concept. First, they believe that few therapists would accept the task of implementing a true placebo condition for more than a few sessions. Second, if the placebo condition was applied for a long time, the patients would probably become disenchanted with their lack of progress, and might even feel that they were harmed by the treatment. Third, placebo conditions are by definition theoretically inert, and are yet presented to the patients as potentially effective treatment. This is ethically questionable deception and has been criticized as a research tool. Fourth, patients in a placebo condition may postpone seeking treatment elsewhere. Finally, if patients suffer deterioration when in a placebo condition, not only does this harm them, but it acts to reduce the confidence of the public-at-large in the therapeutic endeavor.

All the issues that have been discussed so far converge to raise serious questions about the appropriateness of the experimental group/control group design as commonly used. These ideas and several new ones can be summarized by means of Table 9. In this table, differences are presented between the ideal experimental-laboratory-research design, which compares a control group with an experimental group, and the realities of psychotherapy research. Perusal of this list strongly suggests that the differences between these two models of understanding are so different that we must approach the problem of the effectiveness of psychotherapy by as many methods as possible, which may include controlled clinical trials, but are not limited to them.

As an extension of this point, Glass' meta-analysis attempted to relate certain aspects of the experimental design such as the use of double- or single-blind controls to outcome. He reported that comparisons of such features as randomization versus matching and double versus single versus no-blinding had

**Table 9.** Differences Between the Ideal Experimental-Laboratory-Research Design Model and the Realities of Psychotherapy Research

| *Classical Model* | *Psychotherapy* |
|---|---|
| 1. The independent variable is a discrete stimulus or a bounded set of discrete stimuli. | 1. The independent variable is a complex strategy or interaction with constantly changing tactics. |
| 2. The pattern of presentation of the independent variable is standardized. | 2. Variation of therapist behavior from moment to moment and patient to patient is the rule. |
| 3. There is a provable causal relation between the independent variable and the dependent variable. | 3. There is no provable causal relation between what the therapist does and the behavior of the patient. |
| 4. The dependent variables are discrete responses. | 4. The dependent variables are a complex set of responses and attitudes that change over time. |
| 5. There is a small number of important variables that influence the dependent variable. | 5. There is a large number of variables that influence therapy outcome; each exerts only a small influence. |
| 6. Each relevant variable can be held constant if desired. | 6. Few relevant variables can be held constant, even if desired. |
| 7. The direction of causation is one way from stimulus to response, from independent variable to dependent variable. | 7. The direction of influence is two-way, from therapist to patient and from patient to therapist. |
| 8. Stimulus and response tend to be contiguous. | 8. There is no point in time at which the therapist's behavior or strategy can be said to have produced a therapeutic response. |
| 9. The system is isolated from all others as much as possible in an effort to produce a closed system. | 9. The therapist-patient system constantly interacts with other systems. Uncontrolled and unmeasured inputs constantly occur. |
| 10. This system is concerned with the regularity and predictability of events. | 10. This system is concerned with the meaning and logical structure of events. |

**Table 9** *continued*

| | |
|---|---|
| **11.** Experiments are temporally linear; that is, *A* follows *B* follows *C*. | **11.** The meanings of an event are conditional; that is, the meaning of *A* is determined by the meanings of *B* and *C*. |
| **12.** There is an experimenter, who manipulates conditions that affect the subject, who is treated as an object. | **12.** Manipulation, to the extent that it occurs, works both ways. The patient is not treated as an object. |
| **13.** The possible range of responses of the subject are restricted to a few simple responses such as "yes," "no," or "sometimes." | **13.** The range of responses of the patient is large and encouraged to become larger (as, for example, in free association). |
| **14.** The experimenter is unconcerned with the circumstances of the subject's life. | **14.** The therapist is vitally interested in the circumstances of the patient's life. |

virtually no correlation with outcome. Similarly, whether a study was defined as "good," "bad," or "indifferent" had no correlation with psychotherapy outcome (Glass et al. 1980).

The causes of certain outcomes, which controlled trials attempt to establish, is an issue that has had a long and controversial history in philosophy as well as science. Psychotherapy research also deals with a balanced set of social, psychological, economic, and biological factors whose interactions are not known and that may be so complex that they may never be known to any significant degree.

The philosopher John Stuart Mill described *four* methods for experimentally identifying causes, and demonstrated that each had its limitations (Plutchik 1974). For example, the Method of Agreement attempts to identify a common event associated with a type of outcome (for example, successful therapy). Although this method provides clues to the existence of possibly relevant variables, the observer is seldom able to recognize all the events that might be connected with a given outcome. Mills' second method, or Method of Difference, states that if two conditions or two groups are equal except for one different element, then that element is the cause of any obtained difference in outcome. This method is what is today referred to as the controlled clinical trial. It is based on the assumption that the two groups being compared are equal at the start of the experiment, an assumption that can never be unequivocally proved. It is also based on the assumption that only one factor has been manipulated, another dubious assumption.

Controlled clinical trials are not the source of new ideas; they do not generate creative innovations in any science. All the many psychotherapies in current use did not result from experimental research; they are the outcome of clinical observation, insight, wisdom, and serendipity. At best, controlled clinical trials are useful only for *hypothesis testing*, after a new therapy has been created.

Other methods for demonstrating causes are the Method of Artificial Variation and the Method of Stabilization. In the former case, if one suspects the existence of a certain cause, the experimenter should try to vary its magnitude by an amount greater than normal to see what effects are associated with the variations. This is somewhat like analogue research in which suspected variables are manipulated in ways that are perhaps more extreme than may occur in "natural" therapeutic interactions. The Method of Stabilization attempts to infer the existence of a cause by decreasing the magnitude of the variable's action, in other words, by keeping the variable constant. The important point to be made is that each method of identifying causes has its limitations and each provides only some partial insight into the "truth." Other criteria of "truth" must also be considered, such as the breadth of a theory, its coherence, its relevance to a variety of contexts, and its ability to suggest novel ideas.

It is also important to emphasize that certain of the natural sciences are not experimental (for example, geology and astronomy). They flourish nevertheless. The desire of some to shackle psychotherapy research with a purely experimental model may be a major mistake.

There is one other theoretical point to be made about the presumed necessity for controlled clinical trials in psychotherapy outcome research. Kaswan (1981) has argued that psychotherapy has both a manifest and a latent function in society. The manifest functions are to identify, correct, and prevent failures of psychological adaptation. The extent to which these functions are satisfied can be evaluated, in part, by experimental studies that look at outcome measures under controlled conditions.

The latent functions of psychotherapy according to Kaswan are to take care of the sick in a humane way. "The profession should note that though there are environmental and other limits to the effectiveness of many interventions, society demands professional caring and control. These demands and functions therefore constitute the socially responsive basis of the field. Accordingly, mental health services should be evaluated not so much on their general effectiveness in helping people solve problems but on how accessible they are and to what extent they provide care and control in an ethical, humane, and economical manner" (p. 295).

## Alternatives to Controlled Clinical Trials

There are a number of alternatives to the experimental group/control group traditional research design that may usefully contribute to research in psychotherapy. Some of these alternatives are: (1) the use of special groups; (2) the use of scaled comparison groups; (3) the use of analogue research; and (4) the use of computer simulation. Although each may have its own pitfalls, or drawbacks, they provide us with a new range of possibilities that need to be explored.

### The Use of Special Control Groups

Imber et al. (1957) have described an alternative to the use of no-treatment controls in psychotherapy research, an alternative that allows the existence of a long-term group. This approach is based on the idea that all patients receive therapeutic contact, but that the control patients receive therapy with an assumed "essential ingredient" missing. This procedure allows predictions to be made concerning patient change as a function of some specific element or technique that is normally considered an essential aspect of the given therapy. The therapists will typically be informed of the element that is eliminated, since in most cases they will have to implement the experimental protocol. The patients, however, are blind to the experimental manipulation, and are therefore in a single-blind design. Kazdin and Wilson (1978) have discussed this alternative as a "dismantling strategy."

An illustration of this technique is given by Imber et al. (1957). They assumed that an essential ingredient effective in psychotherapy is repeated, long-term contact between therapist and patient. Based on this hypothesis they compared a group of patients who received once-a-week, one-hour-per-session individual therapy with a randomly selected group of patients who received half an hour of therapy every two weeks. The results showed that the minimal contact group showed less of an improvement than did the experimental group over a six-month period. Other hypothesized essential ingredients can be studied in a similar way over long periods of therapy.

*Component Control Comparisons.* The design described above dealing with an essential ingredient of psychotherapy is one aspect of what Stuart (1973) has called a component control strategy. This approach involves either the omission of an active ingredient of therapy for the control group, or the use of *only* one element of therapy for the control group (for example, relaxation training without biofeedback). Using these procedures, both experimental and control groups have expectations of improvement; Borkovec and Nau (1972) have demonstrated that each treatment component is likely to generate an improvement expectation that is comparable to that generated by the whole treatment package.

*Alternative Treatment Controls.* Given the fact that hundreds of studies have by now demonstrated that psychotherapy produces better results than doing nothing, it seems reasonable to conclude that each new study is not required to document this point. Instead, and in view of the difficulties of long-term research, therapies should now be compared against each other. In this way every patient is treated for an equivalent period of time and therapy may continue for long periods.

In addition, research of this type may help deal with one of the limitations of meta-analysis; namely, that in the effort to standardize effect sizes, the actual outcome variables are not standardized so that different therapies are really not comparable. For example, the statement that behavioral therapies have greater effect sizes than gestalt therapies is largely meaningless. Behavioral therapies may be concerned with reducing anxiety as the primary (or only) focus of therapy, while gestalt therapies may be concerned with restructuring personality and reducing defensiveness. A meta-analysis of different therapies will be meaningful only when equivalent outcome measures are used.

*Community Controls.* In medical research it is often possible to obtain data, through epidemiological surveys, on the degree to which a disease or condition exists in the community. The same idea can be applied to psychotherapy research. Over the years a number of surveys (Hollingshead and Redlich 1957,

Srole et al. 1962) have attempted to determine the extent to which various psychiatric conditions exist in the general population. As an extension of these findings it should be possible to identify and follow people who have a defined illness or diagnosis, but who have not sought psychotherapeutic treatment. To the extent that this can be done, norms will become available on the natural course of untreated mental illnesses. For example, suppose a community survey identified five percent of the population as moderately to severely depressed. These identified persons could be re-interviewed each year for several years to determine what happens to the depression over time for those individuals who do not seek formal psychiatric treatment.

Such data can be used as base-rate information for future studies of psychotherapy without requiring that each investigator provide untreated controls of his or her own. Such community controls can also provide base-rates for long-term as well as short-term therapy. Although it is unlikely that such epidemiological surveys can provide base-rates for all diagnostic entities (for example, schizophrenia), they can probably provide data on many conditions usually treated by psychotherapy (for example, anxiety states, phobias, depressions, adjustment reactions, and character disorders). In England, a community survey has established the levels of measured hopelessness in the general population (Greene 1981).

*Use of Scaled Control Groups.* Many critics have noted that the concept of an untreated control group is probably an illusion. What it means at most is that an identified potential patient has not sought out treatment by the more formal sources (for example, psychiatrists, psychologists, social workers, hospitals). But it certainly does not imply that this potential patient has not discussed his or her problems with family members, friends, teachers, pastors, or others. What this implies is that a *zero* level of treatment is unattainable.

A similar situation exists in physics and chemistry. There are certain conditions that cannot be studied directly because these conditions cannot be obtained in the real world. These include such conditions as absolute zero degrees on the Kelvin scale, zero levels of friction, or extremely high temperatures or pressures. Despite these limitations physicists can describe a great many of the properties of these extreme conditions. They do this, in part, by a method of successive approximations and by extrapolation based on the use of scaled variables.

For example, in order to determine the properties of substances at the absolute zero of temperature, the objects are studied at progressively lower temperatures, e.g. $-100°K$, $-200°K$, $-250°K$, and so on. One may use regression equations to *extrapolate* the measures obtained to the lowest level of the scale.

The same idea can be used in psychotherapy research. This can be illustrated by a hypothetical extension of the Imber et al. study (1957). One group of patients (randomly selected) could see their therapist three times a week for one year. Another group could see their therapists once a week for one year. A third group could see their therapists once every two weeks, and a fourth group could see their therapists once a month. If we measure (for example) decreases in level of depression, we might find a gradual decrease in the amount of change as a mathematical function of the frequency of therapeutic contacts. From the curve we could then estimate (extrapolate) the change in depression to be expected if the potential patient did not see the therapist at all.

In such a situation one might ask which group is the control group and which is the experimental group. The answer is that the distinction between experimental and control groups is invalid and that each group represents a point of comparison for every other group. The measures of outcome that are obtained take on meaning only in relation to the results obtained from all the comparison groups. This procedure treats each group as a kind of control group. But each group is also scaled on a variable of interest. The variable of interest that is chosen depends on the theoretical concerns of the investigator.

Two examples of the use of scaled comparison groups in connection with certain areas of psychosocial research are given by Plutchik (1973). Examples that are somewhat similar in the psychotherapy research literature may also be found. In a study of the effectiveness of psychotherapy with physically ill elderly patients, three conditions were established: (1) brief supportive psychotherapy; (2) brief cognitive-interactions; and (3) two evaluation interviews (Godbole and Verinis 1974). Results showed a decreasing proportion of beneficial effects.

Another study with the aged used four conditions: (1) elderly men and women in a retirement home were visited on a regular schedule by college student "therapists"; (2) residents were allowed to control the duration and frequency of the visits; (3) residents were visited on a random schedule; and (4) a group of residents were not visited (Schulz 1976). Self-regard and measures of happiness, boredom, health, and so on showed certain trends related to the scaling of the various control groups.

A final set of illustrations comes from the literature on the psychotherapy of depression. A major review of the literature on the psychological treatment of depression (Weissman 1979) demonstrated that a variety of control conditions have been used. One is a waiting-list control, which is a temporary approximation to a no-treatment group. A second is a low-contact treatment group where therapy is scheduled once every two weeks or once every month. A third comparison is a non-scheduled condition in which therapy is given only at the patient's request. These various illustrations may be thought of as approximations to the strategy of using scaled comparison (or experimental) groups.

## Use of Analogue Research

The concept of analogue research has already been discussed in an earlier section, but there are some additional points that need to be made. Analogue research refers to research carried out under more restricted, simplified conditions than are found in the natural clinical setting, and may even involve the use of college-student volunteers to take the role of patients. Such restricted research is said to have certain advantages, for example, to enable a greater degree of control over the selection of "patients" and "therapists" and what they do and say. Other advantages include the opportunity to manipulate variables systematically, to introduce unusual control groups, and to test specific, if limited, hypotheses. These advantages must be considered in the light of the limited generalizability of results to the clinical situation.

There are, however, a number of important issues that need to be considered. The most important, perhaps, is the concept of an analogue experiment itself. One can argue that all research in psychotherapy represents an analogue of the "real" clinical situation, and all represent the result of various restrictions and simplifications. There is little doubt that "real" psychotherapeutic interactions are carried out in a looser, more improvizational style than experimental protocols would permit. Finally, therapists in practice are undoubtedly older and more experienced than the graduate students, interns, and residents who typically act as therapists in most psychotherapy research.

Several other points may be made about analogue research. Basically, many experiments may be thought of as expressions of the Method of Artificial Variation described earlier. If the investigator suspects the operation of a particular variable, that variable may then be exaggerated in order to determine more readily whether it has an effect and how large the relative effect is. In such situations, an appropriate control group is not doing nothing, but is rather undergoing the usual therapy without the exaggerated values of a particular variable. Good analogue research helps to establish the relative importance of each major variable that is hypothesized to operate.

Analogue research has sometimes been criticized on the grounds that it often uses college-student volunteers as patients. This criticism is not necessarily valid until someone demonstrates that such volunteers do not, in fact, behave in the same way as do bona fide patients. In order to demonstrate this the method of multiple, scaled, comparison groups could be used. One could carry out brief psychotherapy with: (1) college-student volunteers; (2) college-counseling-center patients; and (3) outpatients in a hospital clinic. If the same outcome variables are measured in each case, it should be possible to determine the validity of a generalization that is made. It should always be kept in mind that all research begins with estimates of relevant variables which are suspected on the basis of knowledge gained by methods that are not experimental.

### Computer Simulation

At one time computers were used almost exclusively as high-speed automatic calculators. They made it possible to do statistical computations of great complexity in a very brief period, and this use of computers remains an important one. However, over the years many additional functions have been added to the repertoire of the computer. These include: natural language translation, pattern recognition, content analyses of verbal interactions, interactive teaching, and simulation, among others. Although all of these roles of the computer have a place in psychotherapy research, the most potentially important is probably the computer as a simulator of personality and as a simulator of the therapy interaction.

The basic idea of simulation is simple; that is, a model is made to represent a device, an environment, or a process. Model airplanes are simulations of real airplanes, just as wind tunnels are simulations of the environment of high-velocity, high-altitude flights. The process that a physician uses when making a diagnosis can also be simulated by a complex program in a computer. Computers have been programmed to solve problems in ways that are comparable to the way a human being solves problems. Chess-playing computers have reached the point that they rank among the top 300 players in the United States. Computer models have been built to simulate long-term memory and language acquisition (Simon 1979). Several simulation models of personality have also been developed.

Loehlin (1968) has presented details of four computer models of personality. The simplest is called "Aldous" in honor of Aldous Huxley. Aldous is able to evaluate stimuli (written inputs to the computer), "feel" anger, fear, or attraction, and report behaviors of attack, withdrawal, or approach. If several emotions are aroused by an event (input), then conflict occurs according to certain defined rules. Aldous is able to store the results of interaction in short- or long-term memory so that they may influence, to some degree, the results of new encounters.

The personality of Aldous can be changed by modifying certain aspects of the program; for example, the weight given to immediate experiences relative to permanent memory; or the readiness to react as a function of the intensity of the emotions evaluated by the action subroutine. Several such versions of Aldous have been tested: Decisive Aldous, who acts strongly on slight emotion; Hesitant Aldous, who acts only weakly on strong emotion; Radical Aldous, who is highly reactive to current conditions; and Conservative Aldous, who is more governed by his past. These different personalities have been exposed to different types of environments, including other models of Aldous, some benign and some hostile, and the results compared.

Another model of personality that has particular relevance to psychotherapy research is the one developed by the psychiatrist Kenneth Colby (1964). In his model, Colby has attempted to simulate a number of well-known clinical concepts such as: ideas and wishes having varying amounts of affect associated with them; conflicts between superego standards and wishes leading to anxiety; and the presence of conflicts leading to the expression of ideas or wishes in disguised forms through the operation of defense mechanisms.

The model assumes that there are five basic modes of internal operation. These are: feelings of danger, excitation, pleasure, esteem, and well-being. Also in the model is a matrix of beliefs, a dictionary of terms, and various rules of interaction. Colby assumes that individuality resides in the data specific to each person that is entered into the model, but the processes are assumed to be general to all individuals.

Colby has also developed a model of the paranoid patient (Colby, Weber, and Hief 1971). In this simulation, the "patient" can have different levels of anger, fear, or mistrust. The responses of the model (PERRY) to statements or questions by the interviewer depend on two factors: (1) current levels of these emotional states; and (2) the connections between the "therapist's" words and special "sensitive" words in PERRY's memory (for example, related to the delusion or personal references). The level of emotion determines PERRY's sensitivity to symbols that are capable of triggering defenses or evoking his delusions. When the thresholds are high (anger and fear are low), PERRY is capable of relatively "normal" conversation. When anger and fear are high, PERRY will defend himself by a verbal attack or by withdrawal. Emotions once evoked, subside gradually, even if not aroused again. It has been demonstrated that records obtained of PERRY interacting with a psychiatrist cannot be reliably distinguished by other psychiatrists from interactions produced by "real" paranoid patients.

These few examples of computer simulation in psychiatry are only a small subset of the research and theory that has evolved in the past two decades. In 1970, the National Institute of Mental Health published a booklet entitled *Computer Applications in Psychotherapy: Bibliograpy and Abstracts* that contained 176 references. The bibliography did not include reports on medical record keeping and diagnosis, but was primarily limited to theoretical issues related to computer simulation of patients, therapists, and their interactions.

Development of computer simulation models of the kind described has several important implications. First, since personality and psychotherapy theories are often wordy and ambiguous, and sometimes contain unstated assumptions, the computer model will bring some of these weaknesses to light. Second, the fact that the assumptions of the model are made explicit (in the form of explicit programs and subroutines) means that the rules of interaction can be changed in systematic ways in order to explore the consequences of such changes. Thus, for example, changes in the assumptions of the model created the different versions of Aldous that were tried out. Third, it should be possible to simulate patients of any diagnostic type and allow these "patients" to interact with "therapists" of any defined school of psychotherapy. The computer may be particularly important in distinguishing the "technical" aspect of psychotherapy from the "relationship" aspect. In psychotherapy practice both are linked. The parameters of the interaction can be manipulated easily and standard output measures can be obtained (for example, affect, behavior, defenses, and so on). Fourth, the process of interaction can be speeded up as fast as one might wish, so that a major compression of time could occur. This would enable long-term psychotherapy to be modeled or simulated over a relatively brief real-time period. Last, but not least, the computer models will allow students to receive training in interpersonal skills and in particular modes of psychotherapy. This will allow greater consistency of strategies to be developed among practitioners of any given therapy.

In conclusion, computer simulation may represent an additional new tool for dealing with the many problems of psychotherapy research.

# CHAPTER 18

# Summary and Conclusions

From its modest beginnings in the 1940s, research in psychotherapy has grown impressively in terms of the scope of the issues investigated and in the sophistication of the techniques and research designs employed. However, despite the increasing sophistication and number of investigations, results of psychotherapy researches have been inconsistent. It has been the purpose of the early sections of this report to describe in detail the major methodological issues and problems that arise in research on psychotherapy and to propose guidelines and recommendations that represent the views of the most knowledgeable methodologists writing at the present time. In later sections, the major reviews in the literature that deal with the outcomes of psychotherapy have been examined and their conclusions critically evaluated. Finally, a series of suggestions have been made for conceptualizing psychotherapy research within a wider framework.

## General Issues in Psychotherapy Research

Since therapy outcomes depend on the characteristics of the patients and therapists as well as on the characteristics of the therapy provided, the necessity for precise definitions and descriptions of these various elements that enter into the process of psychotherapy is evident. In addition to the use of traditional diagnostic categories, many other measures need to be employed to characterize the patients. We are still clearly in need of better methods of assessing the totality of a patient's functioning, both in terms of strengths and weaknesses.

Therapist and therapy variables cannot be completely separated, and specified therapist variables are always in danger of being confounded with other uncontrolled variables, including the therapist's idiosyncratic interpretation of treatment techniques. Nevertheless, it is incumbent upon any researcher to characterize his or her sample of therapists with the greatest possible accuracy in terms of theoretical orientation, training, and experience, as well as in terms of the specific methods and techniques used by them to achieve their goals. There is also the need for supplementary assessment techniques such as audio- and videotapes and independent ratings of process and outcome.

Once the patients, the therapists, and the therapy under investigation have been described, it is then necessary to specify what control or comparison groups are appropriate for ruling out plausible alternative hypotheses to account for experimental findings. There are advantages and disadvantages in the use of untreated controls, dropout and waiting-list controls, attention/placebo controls, alternative treatment controls, crossover controls, and patients-as-their-own controls. There is no single approach that would be appropriate for the testing of all hypotheses, and what type is best in any given situation will be determined by both theoretical and empirical considerations. When more than one hypothesis is being tested, more than one type of control group should be used.

There are five general ways of selecting and assigning individuals to treatment and control groups: random sampling; stratified random sampling; cluster sampling; matching of pairs of subjects; and matching of group means. The best method of attaining equivalent groups when a sufficiently large pool of patients is available is through the use of randomization techniques. This method of assignment assumes that, in the long run, all significant variables will be equally distributed among the groups so that any differences found at the end of the study can be attributed, within statistically definable probability limits, to treatment effects rather than to extraneous patient or other variables.

Research designs for investigating the effectiveness of a particular mode of psychotherapy or for studying the comparative efficacy of two or more therapeutic modalities may be characterized along a great many dimensions. These include levels of inference permitted, time period under consideration, type of sampling procedures used, number of variables considered, and number of levels of each variable. The present report conceptualized research designs as existing on five different and increasingly complex levels. At each succeeding level, control is increased, the possible confounding of variables is reduced, the number of alternative explanations to account for findings is reduced, and the investigator's confidence that results are due to the specified intervention is increased.

The five design levels are as follows: the one-shot case study (Level I); the one-group pretest/posttest design (Level II); the extended baseline $A-B$ design (Level III), which also includes the single case, $N=1$ type design; the pretest/posttest control group design (Level IV); and multivariate designs (Level V), which include factorial designs.

There are advantages and limitations of each type of design and not all good research need be conducted at Level V. Because of the tremendous investment in terms of personnel, time, money, and number of patients required by Level V designs, investigations at a lower level should probably be conducted prior to the conduct of these more complex designs. Their use is more properly reserved for the investigations of the differential effects of treatments whose parameters are well specified and that are known to be effective for specific types of patients.

In addition to the above relatively standard research designs, there are advantages and limitations of other design strategies. "Constructive" and "dismantling" strategies refer, respectively, to the adding of components designed to enhance the effects of therapy or to the elimination of certain treatment components from treatment in order to determine how crucial they are for behavior change. These strategies are recommended when the investigator is still in the process of trying to understand what the effective components of his or her treatment are. The lack of consistency in the findings of studies using these various strategies implies the need for alternative models for the conduct of research in this area.

Another general issue in psychotherapy research is how best to study process, or the *how* of therapeutic change. Process research may be divided into two broad areas: in vivo studies that focus on the naturally occurring events in actual therapy sessions; and analogue studies in which variables are systematically manipulated under controlled conditions outside the therapy setting. There are serious methodological problems in the coding of observations that are usually recorded via film and/or sound recording for in vivo studies. While reliability and validity of observations made during in vivo studies pose a problem, generalizability to "real-life" situations is often problematical for analogue findings. Therefore, controlled experimentation needs to be complemented by replication studies in naturalistic settings; ideally research should be conducted over the whole range, from the virtually unmodified clinical setting to the most abstracted laboratory conditions.

The last general issue concerns the ethics of psychotherapy research. There are three areas in which ethical issues lead to pragmatic difficulties and pragmatic issues lead to ethical problems. The invasion of privacy for the purpose of collecting the objective data necessary to evaluate psychotherapy systematically is one area. The long tradition in medicine of reporting clinical findings that may benefit others may serve as a rationale for this practice. A second area concerns the ethical issues involved in assigning patients with distressing problems to no-treatment or placebo conditions in order to provide baselines for evaluation of experimental treatments. The third area relates to the possible refusal to participate in a study or to the differential attrition that may result from our ethical responsibility to obtain informed consent. Nevertheless, informed consent still represents the best way of reconciling the conflict between our ethical responsibility to protect the rights of human subjects, and our ethical responsibility to society to evaluate the efficacy of treatment.

## Assessment Issues in Psychotherapy

Among the methodological issues concerned with the assessment of change in psychotherapy are: the reliability and validity of techniques for measuring change, the measurement of therapeutic outcome, issues related to follow-up procedures, the measurement of cost-effectiveness and cost-benefit, and statistical issues.

There are controversies over outcome criteria, for example, what type of measuring instruments to use, who or what is to be the source of information upon which to base evaluation, and the generality or specificity of assessment. Research on the effectiveness of psychotherapy would benefit from an expanded set of outcome criteria, and changes should be evaluated in many dimensions obtained from as many sources as possible.

"Batteries" of instruments may be used to assess different types of psychotherapy, but it is doubtful that a single core battery can be appropriately applied to all cases. There are advantages and disadvantages to measures designed to elicit information from different viewpoints (that is, the patient, the therapist, independent clinical evaluators, and community members). Although the collection of information from all these sources can be both time consuming and expensive, each vantage point provides a unique perspective and each has some degree of validity.

A discussion of issues related to follow-up, and particularly to long-term follow-up procedures, centered on two main questions: how long should patients be followed; and what is the ultimate criterion of the success of therapy. With regard to the first question, six months seems to be the most frequently utilized time period. However, systematic investigation of follow-up patterns at varying times after treatment is needed. Regarding the criteria for a treatment's success, efficacy of a therapy should be evaluated not only in terms of its immediate results but in terms of its long-term effectiveness as well.

## Measuring Cost-Effectiveness and Cost-Benefit

There is a variety of methods to assess the costs and benefits of psychotherapy and to compare results generated by different studies. They are extremely complex procedures and, in general, have not been used for a comparison of different psychotherapy treatments. Rather, they have most often been applied when policy decisions about large-scale programs or projects are needed; thus a major emphasis has been upon differences among treatment settings. Also, because of the difficulties associated with measuring psychotherapy's benefits in monetary terms, the literature tends to be concerned primarily with the assessment of low-cost treatments. In all cases, the usefulness of such analyses hinges on the availability and quality of outcome data, and it appears that greater methodological sophistication is needed before these techniques are fully applicable for psychotherapy assessments. Nevertheless, in spite of these methodological problems, cost-effectiveness analyses add an important new dimension to the assessment of the outcome of psychotherapy.

## Statistical Issues

The major problem associated with a method frequently used to assess outcome, pretreatment/posttreatment raw change scores, is that there are likely to be important pretreatment differences between groups, and a simple comparison of raw change scores could reflect not only treatment effects, but these groups' pretreatment differences as well. The use of analysis of covariance and the use of final adjustment status alone to reduce the effect of initial differences are limited in their usefulness. These and additional considerations have led

**219**

to the recommendation of "residual" change scores, which represent the difference between actual outcome and that which could be predicted from initial scores. This approach reduces but does not totally eliminate initial group differences. It does, however, appear to be the most reliable and most frequently recommended method of assessing change.

Another statistical issue concerns the distinction between interrater agreement and interrater reliability. The importance of presenting both types of data, where appropriate, was emphasized, and various procedures that have been suggested for determining these parameters were described and evaluated. Recommendations were made concerning what are considered to be the best measures to use for data having different types of characteristics and properties. In spite of advances that have been made in the development of statistical techniques, all existing coefficients provide somewhat ambiguous solutions.

An additional problem in the use of statistics concerns the issue of statistical versus clinical significance. The level at which an investigator is willing to declare findings significant says nothing about the relative magnitude or clinical importance of the effect that has been observed. Of equal importance is the fact that the units in which we measure our outcome variables are not only arbitrary, but also without absolute meaning. These and other considerations underlined the need for a concept of magnitude, or effect size, that is sufficiently general to be useful in all situations where a variable under consideration is scaled or dichotomized, that is not dependent on sample size, that yields a number that is independent of the units used to measure that variable, and that can be meaningfully interpreted by the clinician. Such a measure, discussed in detail in the present report, represents a tremendous advance in the methodology of psychotherapy research in that it makes possible direct comparisons of the effectiveness of a large number of studies.

An issue closely related to that of effect size concerns statistical power analysis, which may be viewed as the formal study of the complex relations that exist among four parameters: sample size; the magnitude of the phenomenon in the population, or effect size; significance level criterion; and power, that is, the probability of correctly rejecting the null hypothesis. There are potentially four ways of investigating the interrelations among these parameters. However, the major practical application of power analysis has been to make rationally based decisions as to sample sizes in the planning of research. It was cautioned that the utilization of very large samples can make even the most clinically trivial results statistically significant, and that a large *n* can never replace good planning, reliable and valid measures, random sampling procedures, and all the other factors that have been explored at length earlier in this report.

## Combinatory Techniques for Assessing Studies of the Efficacy of Psychotherapy

Due to the rapid expansion of research dealing with the efficacy of psychotherapy over the past thirty years, investigators who have attempted to review segments of the literature have had to develop schemas for deciding on methodological grounds which studies to include in their reviews and also for deciding on how to combine the results of large numbers of investigations whose results are often conflicting.

The first comprehensive attempt to categorize and review controlled outcome studies was conducted in 1970 by Meltzoff and Kornreich, who reviewed 101 studies and divided them into adequate and questionable categories on the basis of five criteria. A second subdivision, based on results, was then made that divided them into *positive, null,* and *negative.*

Since 1970, a number of investigators have attempted to develop more detailed methods and criteria for comparing the results of outcome studies. With the exception of the more recent "meta-analysis" approach, all have basically been variations on the "box-score" method developed by Luborsky and his colleagues. The box-score method is essentially a way of evaluating, in terms of a number of criteria, the quality of a study, and comparing, in terms of outcome, studies using different modalities or techniques of treatment. Studies that have assessed the effect of a specific modality of treatment on a specific outcome variable are examined. Studies showing positive, negative, or no effects in either direction are simply tallied. If a majority of the studies fall into one of these three categories, that category is assumed to give the best estimate of the true effect of that particular mode of treatment. A number of criticisms of this approach were noted, including the fact that it provides no rational or statistical basis for combining results of different investigations and that it ignores considerations of sample size in the studies integrated.

Meta-analysis, as developed by Smith, Glass, and Miller, attempts to overcome the deficiencies of past techniques. To be included in a meta-analysis, a study must have at least one therapy treatment group that is compared to an untreated or waiting-list control group or to a different therapy group. It also must survive a number of exclusionary criteria. For each study included, information is collected on a large number of characteristics.

Since the most important feature of an outcome is the magnitude of the effect of the therapy employed, it is effect size with which meta-analysis is primarily concerned. Effect size may be calculated on any outcome variable, and in many cases a study may yield more than one effect size. The effect sizes of the separate studies that meet the inclusion criteria become the "dependent variables." The "independent variables" consist of the characteristics of the study.

Meta-analysis as a methodological and statistical approach for integrating and analyzing large numbers of psychotherapy outcome studies is impressive in that it enables the researcher to extract information that would not be available from analysis of the individual studies. The approach is, however, not without its critics. One major criticism that has been made concerns the fact that the psychotherapies, the patients, and the therapists included in the meta-analysis are not representative of psychotherapy as it is practiced in the "real" world. Therefore, generalizations from the data are limited. Also, it has been questioned whether or not the hundreds of small, often poorly controlled studies may somehow be added up to produce one overall conclusion. Nevertheless, meta-analysis is an important new statistical advance and deserves continued use and evaluation.

## Results of Effectiveness Studies

Since 1952, many individuals have attempted to summarize the literature on the effectiveness of psychotherapy. Depending on who was doing the review and the number and types of studies reviewed, the conclusions have varied from deep pessimism to enthusiastic optimism about the effectiveness of psychotherapy. However, over the years, the general trend has been for the more recent and more comprehensive reviews to conclude that psychotherapy is effective for a variety of symptomatic and behavioral problems; these include chronic moderate anxiety states, simple phobias, depressive symptoms, sexual dysfunctions, adjustment disorders, family conflicts, and communication difficulties.

A large number of studies have been concerned with combined treatment for various diagnostic conditions. Research on schizophrenia has demonstrated that traditional psychotherapies contribute little additional benefit to pharmacotherapy. However, token economy therapies and psychosocial rehabilitation are valuable as adjunct treatments for schizophrenics.

Studies of drug/psychotherapy interactions for major affective disorders reveal that the effects of psychotherapy plus drugs are basically additive in treatment of depression. Combining drugs with psychotherapy for personality disorders and some neuroses may have limited additional benefits. Research data suggest, however, that effectiveness of pharmacotherapy alone is increasingly effective for the treatment of certain neurotic disorders.

Studies of psychotherapy for medically ill patients suggest that psychotherapy plus medical regimen is more effective in certain medical illnesses than is medical treatment alone. Psychotherapy is especially useful for post-illness psychosocial rehabilitation.

A general conclusion about interaction effects is that drugs affect symptoms relatively early whereas psychotherapy has an influence on interpersonal relations and social adjustment, especially at a later stage of treatment.

Relatively little research has been directed at the question of the effectiveness of psychotherapy with patients of different ages. The limited findings suggest that children show both higher "spontaneous remission" rates and higher rates of improvement due to psychotherapy. Variables such as parent levels of motivation, child symptoms and diagnoses, and types of therapy are probably important, but have not been systematically studied. Only about fifteen investigations of adolescents have been reported that compare a treated group with a control group. Results indicate that about two out of three adolescents benefit from psychotherapy, while about one out of three improve in the control conditions. The data available strongly support the role of psychotherapy for adolescents. Unfortunately, the literature on psychotherapy for the aged is largely anecdotal and greatly in need of expansion.

Although a number of papers have proposed the possibility of deterioration effects due to psychotherapy, and anecdotes on this topic have been reported by clinicians, research data on the subject is very limited. In addition, the idea of negative effects is fraught with conceptual as well as research problems. The most extensive review of this literature comes to the conclusion that about 5 percent of patients in psychotherapy get worse.

A few investigations have dealt with the cost-effectiveness or cost-benefits of psychotherapy. These studies have examined variables related to the delivery of care, have compared alternative treatment programs, and have determined the effects of psychotherapy on medical utilization. The results support the conclusion that community-based programs are more cost-effective than institutional treatment. Several studies have shown that the provision of minimal amounts of psychotherapeutic contact tends to decrease the use of medical services over a short time period. Overall, it appears that the economics of delivering psychotherapy, including salary and rent costs, determine cost-effectiveness more than the techniques used.

Controversy still reigns over the question of whether certain types of therapy are more effective than other types for certain kinds of problems. What has also not been adequately studied is what aspects or elements of the complex therapeutic interaction are relatively the most effective. Another question at issue is spontaneous remission, which may be high in certain conditions.

In addition, the comparability of therapies bearing the same generic labels has been challenged, and many investigators have noted that relatively little is known about the actual process of psychotherapy and about the degree of variation that exists in the way that it is carried out. Attempts are now being made to create manuals designed to provide guidelines for the therapist on the conduct of different modes of therapy. Such guidelines may be useful in controlled research settings, but are believed by many clinicians to be largely inappropriate to the operation of their day-to-day practice. Currently it is unclear whether this apparent conflict between the research demands of reproducibility and standardization will ever be reconciled with the clinicians' need for flexibility, creativity, and sensitivity to the uniqueness of their individual patients.

Among the important conclusions of the various reviews of psychotherapy outcome is the fact that better-controlled studies do not show that therapy is more (or less) effective than do the less-well-controlled studies. The use of double-blind techniques also does not appear to change the conclusions reached about therapy's effectiveness as compared to open studies. The relative effectiveness of psychotherapy appears to depend, at least in part, on the type of outcome measure used.

## Alternatives to Traditional Controlled Trials

The point made that laboratory-type research applied to psychotherapy tends to be of very limited generality raises the question of whether the laboratory model is the "best" or most appropriate paradigm for carrying out psychotherapy research. Although it is too early to say what a new paradigm for psychotherapy research should be, one may identify several relatively unexplored alternatives that may be helpful.

First, it is evident that one cannot justify untreated control groups for longer than very brief periods. One approach that has been suggested for dealing with this problem is to provide all patients with therapy, but to omit some "essential ingredient" for the control or comparison group. This procedure has sometimes been called a component control comparison and it deserves more attention.

A second alternative is to use community controls on a much larger scale than has hitherto been done. This would involve community surveys to identify one or more patient populations such as depressed, anxious, or phobic individuals, and to follow them over long periods of time, particularly if they do not seek formal psychiatric treatment. This procedure would establish reasonable base rates of spontaneous remission and deterioration against which the data of psychotherapy studies may be compared. A few preliminary investigations of this sort have been carried out, but much more research of this sort is needed. Obviously, this may only be applicable to certain conditions.

A third alternative is to use scaled comparison groups in which patients are exposed to different degrees of psychotherapeutic interventions. From such data it should be possible to *extrapolate* the results to the hypothetical limits of zero intervention. This procedure thus creates data for a hypothetical control condition that is not obtainable in a direct way in the real world.

A fourth alternative is the use of computer simulation of patients, therapists, and therapy. A number of computer simulation models have been described and tested, and the limited evidence that exists suggests that the behavior of real patients and therapists can be very effectively simulated by computer. Such research has many implications. It requires the assumptions underlying personality and psychotherapy theories to be made explicit. It allows rules of interaction to be changed in systematic ways to explore the consequences of such changes. It allows modeling of different schools of psychotherapy as well as an examination of different therapist variables. It allows the modeling of long-term psychotherapy through a compression of time. In addition, it may help to differentiate the "technique" aspect of psychotherapy from the "relationship" aspect of psychotherapy.

We should also continue and expand analogue studies, and not neglect $N = 1$ descriptive studies. Such designs are a useful form of research for developing hypotheses and as a source of new ideas. Most of the many psychotherapies in current use did not result from experimental research; they are the outcome of clinical observation, insight, wisdom, and serendipity.

However, it should be emphasized that the various innovations and alternatives that have been described do not rule out the utility of traditional controlled trials, but that such trials may be more appropriate at a later stage of inquiry.

## Conclusions

Although research in psychotherapy is still plagued by many problems connected with assignment of patients, use of statistics, outcome measures, and experimental designs, the data have shown empirically that psychotherapy is effective with some populations and some problems. There are, though, a number of other important issues that need to be considered.

A first issue concerns the considerable and continuing need for careful, systematic research on the effects of psychotherapy for various conditions. The present diagnostic system is not adequate for psychotherapy research. In addition to the necessity for precisely establishing diagnoses for patient populations, attention should be directed toward developing a psychotherapy-related diagnostic and evaluation system. These should take account of factors such as conflicts, ego functions, defenses, coping styles and degree and quality of motivation, the quality of the relationship between patient and therapist, and psychosocial supports that are available.

The second concerns the way in which psychotherapy is to be defined. For example, for purposes of research it is not productive to define psychotherapy in terms of simple labels that refer to widely varying concepts ranging from specific procedures to broad-ranging global strategies. The therapies, therefore, must be more precisely defined. This may in some cases be done in terms of manuals describing specific tools and techniques, applicable to specific disorders. In other cases, it might be preferable to delineate the therapy in terms of goals, strategies, and the nature of the relationship between patient and therapist, as well as in terms of more specific factors. There is a need to understand in precise ways what the essential ingredients of psychotherapy are and also to define more precisely the different (and overlapping) strategies of psychotherapy. However, this operational approach to the definition of the practice of psychotherapy must be flexible enough to permit the practitioner both spontaneity and necessary therapeutic improvisation.

The third issue is that psychotherapy as the sole therapeutic modality seems to be most useful in such conditions as some psychoneuroses, personality disorders, and maladjustments. Psychotherapy alone has been shown to be less effective for the major affective disorders and much less so for schizophrenia. The prototypic relationship between psychotherapy and pharmacotherapy seems reciprocal, favoring psychotherapy for personality disorders and favoring pharmacotherapy for psychotic disorders. For many conditions the interrelationship seems to be additive. Therefore, for most of the disorders, an evaluation of psychotherapy's efficacy may be more relevant if it is confined to the relative contribution it plays under that broader umbrella of combined psychopharmacological treatment.

Fourth, controlled clinical trials are not necessarily the only suitable method for evaluating the efficacy of psychotherapy. There is a need to seek other approaches that may be useful in the development of a new paradigm. It is to be hoped that such a paradigm will also bring into greater harmony the methods and goals of the clinician and those of the researchers.

A final issue that should be emphasized is that most research data available do not adequately reflect the work of clinicians as actually practiced. It is especially true that long-term psychotherapy and psychoanalysis have not been adequately evaluated. This lack of evidence for the efficacy of long-term psychotherapy should not be interpreted as an indication of its lack of effectiveness. There is a large body of clinical experience and knowledge, accumulated by practitioners over many decades, that must be considered in the overall evaluation of psychotherapy.

Even if all the above issues could be adequately resolved, unequivocal conclusions about causal connections between treatment and outcome may never be possible in psychotherapy research. Psychotherapy is a highly complex set of interactions that take place between individuals over an often indeterminate period of time. It is an open-ended, interactive feedback process in contrast to the closed, one-way causation that is typical of most laboratory research. Research has not as yet been able to fully document these complex sets of interactions. However, our objective should not be the impossible one of seeking the ultimate truth—no other field is near to it—but rather of creating a framework that can provide at least successive approximations to it.

# References

Adams, M. How should we measure outcome in psychotherapy? *British Journal of Psychiatry*, 1978, *132*, 595–597.

American Psychiatric Association Task Force on Nomenclature and Statistics. *Diagnostic and Statistical Manual of Mental Disorders* (3rd ed.). Washington, D.C.: American Psychiatric Association, 1980.

American Psychological Association (APA). *Ethical Principles in the Conduct of Research with Human Participants*. Washington, D.C.: APA, 1973.

Angel, C., Leach, B.E., Martens, S., Cohen, M., and Heath, R. Serum oxidation tests in schizophrenic and normal subjects. *Archives of Neurology and Psychiatry*, 1957, *78*, 500–504.

Anthony, R.N. *Management Accounting*. Homewood, Ill.: Irwin, 1964.

Argyris, C. Dangers in applying results from experimental social psychology. *American Psychologist*, 1975, *30*, 469–485.

Attkisson, C.C., Hargreaves, W.A., Horowitz, M.J., and Sorenson, J.E. Evaluation: Current strengths and future directions. In C.C. Attkisson, W.A. Hargreaves, M.J. Horowitz, and J.E. Sorenson (Eds.), *Evaluation of Human Service Programs*. New York: Academic Press, 1978.

Auld, F., Jr. and Murray, E.J. Content-analysis studies of psychotherapy. *Psychological Bulletin*, 1955, *52*, 377–395.

Baekeland, F. and Lundwall, L. Dropping out of treatment: A critical review. *Psychological Bulletin*, 1975, *82*, 738–783.

Bales, R.F. *Interaction Process Analysis: A Method for the Study of Small Groups*. Cambridge, Mass.: Addison-Wesley, 1950.

Bandura, A. Psychotherapy based upon modeling principles. In A.E. Bergin and S.L. Garfield (Eds.), *Handbook of Psychotherapy and Behavior Change.* New York: John Wiley & Sons, 1971, pp. 653–708.

Barrett, C.L., Hampe, I.E., and Miller, L. Research on psychotherapy with children. In S.L. Garfield and A.E. Bergin (Eds.), *Handbook of Psychotherapy and Behavior Change: An Empirical Analysis* (2nd ed.). New York: John Wiley & Sons, 1978, pp. 411–436.

Bartko, J.J. and Carpenter, W.T. On the methods and theory of reliability. *Journal of Nervous and Mental Disease,* 1976, *163,* 307–317.

Battle, C.C., Imber, S.D., Hoehn-Saric, R., Stone, A.R., Nash, C., and Frank, J.D. Target complaints as criteria of improvement. *American Journal of Psychotherapy,* 1966, *20,* 184–192.

Bednar, R.L. and Lawles, G.F. Empirical research in group psychotherapy. In A.E. Bergin and S.L. Garfield (Eds.), *Handbook of Psychotherapy and Behavior Change.* New York: John Wiley & Sons, 1971.

Bellak, L. and Smith, M.B. An experimental exploration of the psychoanalytic process: Exemplification of a method. *Psychoanalytic Quarterly,* 1956, *25,* 385–414.

Bergin, A.E. The effects of psychotherapy: Negative results revisited. *Journal of Counseling Psychology,* 1963, *10,* 244–250.

Bergin, A.E. Some implications of psychotherapy research for therapeutic practice. *Journal of Abnormal Psychology,* 1966, *71,* 235–246.

Bergin, A.E. Further comments on psychotherapy research for therapeutic practice. *International Journal of Psychiatry,* 1967, *3,* 317–323.

Bergin, A.E. The evaluation of therapeutic outcomes. In A.E. Bergin and S.L. Garfield (Eds.), *Handbook of Psychotherapy and Behavior Change.* New York: John Wiley & Sons, 1971.

Bergin, A.E. and Lambert, M.J. The evaluation of therapeutic outcomes. In S.L. Garfield and A.E. Bergin (Eds.), *Handbook of Psychotherapy and Behavior Change: An Empirical Analysis* (2nd ed.). New York: John Wiley & Sons, 1978, pp. 139–190.

Bergin, A.E. and Strupp, H.H. New directions in psychotherapy research. *Journal of Abnormal Psychology*, 1970, *76*, 13–26.

Bergin, A.E. and Strupp, H.H. *Changing Frontiers in the Science of Psychotherapy*. Chicago: Aldine-Atherton, 1972.

Bernstein, D.A. and Paul, G.L. Some comments on therapy analogue research with small animal "phobias." *Journal of Behavior Therapy and Experimental Psychiatry*, 1971, *2*, 225–237.

Binner, P.R., Halpern, J., and Potter, A. Patients, programs, and results in a comprehensive mental health center. *Journal of Consulting and Clinical Psychology*, 1973, *41*, 148–156.

Bordin, E.S. Simplification as a strategy for research in psychotherapy. *Journal of Consulting Psychology*, 1965, *29*, 493–503.

Bordin, E.S. Free association: An experimental analogue of the psychoanalytic situation. In L.A. Gottschalk and A.H. Auerbach (Eds.), *Methods of Research in Psychotherapy*. New York: Appleton-Century Crofts, 1966, pp. 189–208.

Bordin, E.S. Outcome or process? In E.S. Bordin (Ed.), *Research Strategies in Psychotherapy*, New York: John Wiley & Sons, 1974a.

Bordin, E.S. Tactics in process studies. In E.S. Bordin (Ed.), *Research Strategies in Psychotherapy*. New York: John Wiley & Sons, 1974b.

Brunswik, E. *Perception and the Representative Design of Psychological Experiments*. Berkeley: University of California Press, 1956.

Bryk, A.S. and Weisberg, H.I. Use of the nonequivalent control group design when subjects are growing. *Psychological Bulletin*, 1977, *84*, 950–962.

Buros, O.K. (Ed.), *Personality Tests and Reviews*. Highland Park, N.J.: Gryphon, 1970.

Butcher, J.N. and Koss, M.P. Research on brief and crisis oriented therapies. In S.L. Garfield and A.E. Bergin (Eds.), *Handbook of Psychotherapy and Behavior Change: An Empirical Analysis* (2nd ed.). New York: John Wiley & Sons, 1978, pp. 725–767.

Butler, J. and Haigh, G. Changes in the relation between self-concepts and ideal concepts consequent upon client-centered counseling. In C.R. Rogers and R. Dymond (Eds.), *Psychotherapy and Personality Change*. Chicago: University of Chicago Press, 1954, pp. 55–75.

Campbell, D.T. and Stanley, J.C. *Experimental and Quasi-Experimental Designs for Research*. Chicago: Rand McNally & Company, 1963.

Campbell, N. *What Is Science?* New York: Dover, 1952.

Carpenter, W.T., Heinrichs, D.W., and Hanlon, T.E. Methodologic standards for treatment outcome research in schizophrenia. *American Journal of Psychiatry*, 1981, *138*, 465–471.

Carter, D.E. and Newman, F.L. *A Client-Oriented System of Mental Health Service Delivery and Program Management: A Workbook and Guide*. DHEW Publ. No. (ADM) 76–307. Rockville, Md.: National Institute of Mental Health, 1976.

Cartwright, D.S. Patient self-report measures. In I.E. Waskow and M.B. Parloff (Eds.), DHEW Publ. No. (ADM) 74-120. Washington, D.C., 1975, pp. 48–64.

Chartier, G.M. A–B therapist variable: Real or imagined. *Psychological Bulletin*, 1971, *75*, 22–33.

Chassan, J.B. *Research Design in Clinical Psychology and Psychiatry*. New York: Appleton-Century Crofts, 1967.

Cochrane, R. and Sobol, M.P. Myth and methodology in behaviour therapy research. In M.P. Feldman and A. Broadhurst (Eds.), *Theoretical and Empirical Bases of the Behaviour Therapies.* London: John Wiley & Sons, 1976.

Cohen, J. A coefficient of agreement for nominal scales. *Educational and Psychological Measurement,* 1960, *20,* 37–46.

Cohen, J. The statistical power of abnormal-social psychological research: A review. *Journal of Abnormal and Social Psychology,* 1962, *65,* 145–153.

Cohen, J. Some statistical issues in psychological research. In B. Wolman (Ed.), *Handbook of Clinical Psychology.* New York: McGraw-Hill, 1965, pp. 95–121.

Cohen, J. Nominal scale agreement with provision for scaled disagreement or partial credit. *Psychological Bulletin,* 1968, *70,* 213–220.

Cohen, J. *Statistical Power Analysis for the Behavioral Sciences.* New York: Academic Press, 1969.

Cohen, J. and Cohen, P. *Applied Multiple Regression/Correlation Analysis for the Behavioral Sciences.* Hillsdale, N.J.: Lawrence Erbaum Associates, 1975.

Colby, K.M. Experimental treatment of neurotic computer programs. *Archives of General Psychiatry,* 1964, *10,* 220–227.

Colby, K.M., Weber, S., and Hilf, F.D. Artificial paranoia. *Artificial Intelligence,* 1971, *2,* 1–25.

*Computer Applications in Psychotherapy: Bibliography and Abstracts.* National Institute of Mental Health. PHS Publ. No. 1981, 1970.

Cook. T.D. and Campbell, D.T. The design and conduct of quasi-experiments and true experiments in field settings. In M.D. Dunnette (Ed.), *Handbook of Industrial and Organizational Psychology.* Chicago: Rand McNally College Publishing Company, 1976, pp. 223–326.

Cooper, J.E. A study of behavior therapy in 30 psychiatric patients. *Lancet,* 1963, *i,* 411.

Cooper, J.E., Gelder, M.G., and Marks, I.M. Results of behavior therapy in 77 psychiatric patients. *British Medical Journal,* 1965, *1,* 1222–1225.

*Cost-Effectiveness Analysis of Medical Technology.* Background paper no. 3: The efficacy and cost effectiveness of psychotherapy. Washington, D.C.: Office of Technology Assessment, U.S. Congress, October 1980.

Covi, L., Lipman, R.S., Deragotis, L.R., Smith, J.E., and Pattison, J.H. Drugs and group psychotherapy in neurotic depression. *American Journal of Psychiatry,* 1974, *131,* 191–198.

Cristol, A.H. Studies of outcome of psychotherapy. *Comprehensive Psychiatry,* 1972, *13,* 189–200.

Cronbach, L.J. Beyond the two disciplines of scientific psychology. *American Psychologist,* 1975, *30,* 116–127.

Cronbach, L.J. Validity. In C.W. Harris (Ed.), *Encyclopedia of Educational Research.* New York: The Macmillan Company, 1960.

Cronbach, L.J. *Designing Evaluations.* Stanford, CA.: Stanford Evaluation Consortium, 1978.

Cronbach, L.J. and Furby, L. How we should measure "change"—or should we? *Psychological Bulletin,* 1970, *74,* 68–80.

Cronbach, L.J., Gleser, C.C., Nanda, H., and Rajaratnam, N. *The Dependability of Behavioral Measurements: Theory of Generalizability for Scores and Profiles.* New York: John Wiley & Sons, 1972.

Cummings, N.A. and Follette, W.T. Brief psychotherapy and medical utilization: An eight-year follow-up. In H. Dorken and Associates (Eds.), *The Professional Psychologist Today: New Developments in Law, Health Insurance, and Health Practice.* San Francisco, CA.: Jossey-Bass, 1976.

Dahlstrom, W.G., Welsh, G.A., and Dahlstrom, L.E. *An MMPI Handbook. Volume 1: Clinical Applications* (rev. ed.). Minneapolis: University of Minnesota Press, 1972.

Daneman, E.A. Imipramine in office management of depressive reactions (a double-blind study). *Diseases of the Nervous System*, 1961, *22*, 213–217.

Davenport, Y.B., Ebert, M.H., Adland, M.L., and Goodwin, F.K. Lithium prophylaxis: The married couples group. Unpublished manuscript, 1975.

Davis, J.M., Schaffer, C.B., Killian, G.A., Kinard, C., and Chan, C. Important issues in the drug treatment of schizophrenia. In *Schizophrenia 1980. U.S.* Government Printing Office, 1980.

Dittman, A.T. Psychotherapeutic processes. In P. Farnsworth et al. (Eds.), *Annual Review of Psychology*. Palo Alto, CA.: Annual Reviews, 1966.

Derogatis, L.R., Lipman, R.S., and Covi, L. SCL-90: An outpatient psychiatric rating scale (preliminary report). *Psychopharmacology Bulletin*, 1973, *9*, 13–27.

Derogatis, L.R., Lipman, R.S., Rickels, K., Uhlenhuth, E.H., and Covi, L. The Hopkins Symptom Checklist (HSCL): A measure of primary symptom dimensions. In P. Pichot (Ed.), *Psychological Measurements in Psychopharmacology: Modern Problems in Pharmacopsychiatry, Vol. 7.* Basel, Switzerland: S. Karger, 1974, 79–110.

Diagnosis: The reliability barrier. *Drug Therapy (Hosp.)*, August 1977, 48–50.

Dittes, J.E. Previous studies bearing on content analysis of psychotherapy. In J.F. Dollard and F.J. Auld (Eds.), *Scoring Human Motives*. New Haven, Conn.: Yale University Press, 1959, pp. 325–351.

Edwards, A.L. and Cronbach, L.J. Experimental design for research in psychotherapy. In G.E. Stollak, G. Bernard, and M. Rothberg (Eds.), *Psychotherapy Research: Selected Readings*. Chicago: Rand McNally & Company, 1966, pp. 56–66.

Ellsworth, R.B. Consumer feedback in measuring the effectiveness of mental health programs. In E.L. Struening and M. Guttentag (Eds.), *Handbook of Evaluation Research.* Beverly Hills, CA.: Sage Publications, 1975.

Endicott, J., Spitzer, R.L., Fleiss, J.L., and Cohen, J. The Global Assessment Scale. *Archives of General Psychiatry,* 1976, *33,* 766–771.

Endicott, N.A. Standard methods needed. *International Journal of Psychiatry,* 1969, *7,* 118–121.

Endicott, N.A. and Endicott, J. Assessment of outcome by projective tests. In I.E. Waskow and M.B. Parloff (Eds.), DHEW Publ. No. (ADM) 74–120. Washington, D.C., 1975, pp. 143–150.

Erickson, R.C. Outcome studies in mental hospitals: A review. *Psychological Bulletin,* 1975, *82,* 519–540.

Erwin, E. Psychoanalytic therapy: The Eysenck agreement. *American Psychologist,* 1980, *35,* 435–443.

Eysenck, H.J. The effects of psychotherapy: An evaluation. *Journal of Consulting Psychology,* 1952, *16,* 319–324.

Eysenck, H.J. *The Effects of Psychotherapy.* New York: International Science Press, 1966.

Eysenck, H.J. An exercise in mega-silliness. *American Psychologist,* 1978, *33,* 517.

Farkas, G.M. An ontological analysis of behavior therapy. *American Psychologist,* 1980, *35,* 364–374.

Feighner, J.P., Robins, E., Guze, S.B., Woodruff, R.A., Winokur, G., and Munoz, R. Diagnostic criteria for use in psychiatric research. *Archives of General Psychiatry,* 1972, *26,* 57–63.

Feinsilver, D.B. and Gunderson, J.G. Psychotherapy for schizophrenics—is it indicated? A review of the relevant literature. *Schizophrenia Bulletin,* Fall 1972.

Finn, R.H. A note on estimating the reliability of categorical data. *Educational and Psychological Measurement*, 1970, *30*, 71–76.

Fishman, D.B. Development of a generic cost-effectiveness methodology for evaluating the patient services of a community mental health center. In J. Zusman and C.R. Wurster (Eds.), *Evaluation in Alcohol, Drug Abuse, and Mental Health Service Programs.* Lexington, Mass.: D.C. Heath and Co., 1975.

Fiske, D.W. A source of data is not a measuring instrument. *Journal of Abnormal Psychology*, 1975a, *84*, 20–23.

Fiske, D.W. The use of significant others in assessing the outcome of psychotherapy. In I.E. Waskow and M.B. Parloff (Eds.), DHEW Publ. No. (ADM) 74–120, Washington, D.C., 1975b, pp. 189–201.

Fiske, D.W. Methodological issues in research on the psychotherapist. In A.S. Gurman and A.M. Razin (Eds.), *Effective Psycotherapy: A Handbook of Research*. New York: Pergamon Press, 1977, pp. 27–43.

Fiske, D.W., Hunt, H.F., Luborsky, L., Orne, M.T., Parloff, M.B., Reiser, M.F., and Tuma, A.H. Planning of research on effectiveness of psychotherapy. *Archives of General Psychiatry*, 1970, *22*, 22–32.

Fleiss, J.L. Measuring nominal scale agreement among many raters. *Psychological Bulletin*, 1971, *76*, 378–382.

Fleiss, J.L. and Cohen, J. The equivalence of weighted kappa and the intraclass coefficient as measures of reliability. *Educational and Psychological Measurement*, 1973, *33*, 613–619.

Fleiss, J.L., Cohen, J., and Everitt, B.S. Large sample standard errors of kappa and weighted kappa. *Psychological Bulletin*, 1969, *72*, 323–327.

Ford, D.H. and Urban, H.B. Psychotherapy. *Annual Review of Psychology*, 1967, *18*, 333–372.

Frank, J.D. Problems of controls in psychotherapy as exemplified by the psychotherapy research project of the Phipps Psychiatric Clinic. In G.E. Stollak, B.C. Guerney, and M. Rothberg (Eds.), *Psychotherapy Research: Selected Readings.* Chicago: Rand McNally & Company, 1966, pp. 79–95.

Frank, J.D. Common features account for effectiveness. *International Journal of Psychiatry,* 1969, *7,* 122–127.

Frank, J. Common features of psychotherapies and their patients. *Psychotherapy and Psychosomatics,* 1974, *24,* 368–371.

Frank, J.D. The present status of outcome studies. *Journal of Consulting and Clinical Psychology,* 1979, *47,* 310–316.

Frank, J.D., Gliedman, L.H., Imber, S.D., Stone, A.R., and Nash, E.H. Patients' expectancies and relearning as factors determining improvement in psychotherapy. *American Journal of Psychiatry,* 1959, *115,* 961–968.

Friedman, A.S. Interaction of drug therapy with marital therapy in depressive patients. *Archives of General Psychiatry,* 1975, *32,* 619–637.

Gardner, R.A. On box score methodology as illustrated by three reviews of overtraining reversal effects. *Psychological Bulletin,* 1966, *66,* 416–418.

Garfield, S.L. What are the therapeutic variables in psychotherapy. *Psychotherapy and Psychosomatics,* 1974, *24,* 372–378.

Garfield, S.L. Research on client variables in psychotherapy. In S.L. Garfield and A.E. Bergin (Eds.), *Handbook of Psychotherapy and Behavior Change: An Empirical Analysis* (2nd ed.). New York: John Wiley & Sons, 1978a, pp. 191–232.

Garfield, S.L. Research problems in clinical diagnosis. *Journal of Consulting and Clinical Psychology,* 1978b, *46,* 596–607.

Garfield, S.L. *Psychotherapy: An Eclectic Approach.* New York: John Wiley & Sons, 1980.

Garfield, S.L. Psychotherapy: A 40-year appraisal. *American Psychologist,* 1981, *36,* 174–183.

Garfield, S.L. and Kurtz, R. Clinical psychologists in the 1970's. *American Psychologist,* 1976, *31,* 1–9.

Garfield, S.L., Prager, R.A., and Bergin, A.E. Evaluation of outcome in psychotherapy. *Journal of Consulting and Clinical Psychology,* 1971, *37,* 307–315.

Gelder, M.G., Marks, I.M., Wolff, H.H., and Clarke, M. Desensitization and psychotherapy in the treatment of phobic states: A controlled inquiry. *British Journal of Psychiatry,* 1967, *113,* 53–73.

Gibbs, J.J., Wilkins, B., and Lauterbach, C.G. A controlled clinical psychiatric study of chlorpromazine. *Journal of Clinical and Experimental Psychopathology,* 1957, *18,* 269–283.

Glass, G.V. Primary, secondary, and meta-analysis of research. *The Educational Researcher,* 1976, *10,* 3–8.

Glass, G.V., Willson, V.L., and Gottman, J.M. *Design and Analysis of Time-Series Experiments.* Boulder, CO.: Laboratory of Educational Research Press, 1973.

Gleser, G.C. Evaluation of psychotherapy outcome by psychological tests. In I.E. Waskow and M.B. Parloff (Eds)., DHEW Publ. No. (ADM) 74–120, Washington, D.C., 1975, pp. 32–39.

Godbole, A. and Verinis, J.S. Brief psychotherapy in the treatment of emotional disorders in physically ill geriatric patients. *Gerontologist,* 1974, *14,* 143–148.

Goldstein, M.J., Rodnick, E.H., Evans, J.R., May, P.R.A., and Steinberg, M.R. Drug and family therapy in the aftercare of acute schizophrenics. *Archives of General Psychiatry,* 1978, *35,* 1169–1177.

Gorham, D.R., Pokorny, A.D., and Moseley, E.C. Effects of a phenothiazine and/or group psychotherapy with schizophrenics. *Diseases of the Nervous System,* 1964, *25,* 77–86.

**239**

Gottman, J.M. N-of-one and N-of-two research in psychotherapy. *Psychological Bulletin,* 1973, *80,* 93–105.

Gottman, J.M. and Markman, H.J. Experimental designs in psychotherapy research. In S.L. Garfield and A.E. Bergin (Eds.), *Handbook of Psychotherapy and Behavior Change: An Empirical Analysis* (2nd ed.). New York: John Wiley & Sons, 1978, pp. 23–62.

Green, B.L., Gleser, G.C., Stone, W.N., and Seifert, R.F. Relationships among diverse measures of psychotherapy outcome. *Journal of Consulting and Clinical Psychology,* 1975, *43,* 689–699.

Greene, S.M. Levels of measured hopelessness in the general population. *British Journal of Clinical Psychology,* 1981, *20,* 11–14.

Grinspoon, L., Ewalt, J.R., and Shader, R.I. *Schizophrenia: Pharmacotherapy and Psychotherapy.* Springfield, Ill.: C.C. Thomas, 1972.

Grove, W.M., Andreasen, N.C., McDonald-Scott, P., Keller, M.B., and Shapiro, R.W. Reliability studies of psychiatric diagnosis: Theory and practice. *Archives of General Psychiatry,* 1981, *38,* 408–413.

Guilford, J.P. *Fundamental Statistics in Psychology and Education.* New York: McGraw-Hill Book Company, 1965.

Gunderson, J.G. Patient-therapist matching: A research evaluation. *American Journal of Psychiatry,* 1978, *135,* 1193–1197.

Gurman, A.S. and Kniskern, D.P. Research on marital and family therapy: Progress, perspective and prospect. In S.L. Garfield and A.E. Bergin (Eds.), *Handbook of Psychotherapy and Behavior Change: An Empirical Analysis* (2nd ed.). New York: John Wiley & Sons, 1978, pp. 817–902.

Halpern, J. and Binner, J.R. A model for an output value analysis of mental health programs. *Administration in Mental Health,* Winter 1972, 40–52.

Hampton, P. Placebo treatment techniques in behavior therapy. *Behavior Therapy*, 1973, *4*, 481–482.

Harris, C.W. (Ed.). *Problems in Measuring Change*. Madison, Wis.: The University of Wisconsin Press, 1967.

Hays, W.L. *Statistics*. New York: Holt, Rinehart and Winston, 1963.

Heller, K., Davis, J.D., and Myers, R.A. The effects of interviewer style in a standardized interview. *Journal of Consulting Psychology*, 1966, *30*, 501–508.

Hogarty, G.E. Informant ratings of community adjustment. In I.E. Waskow and M.B. Parloff (Eds.), DHEW Publ. No. (ADM) 74-120, Washington, D.C., 1975, pp. 202–221.

Hogarty, G.E. and Katz, M.M. Norms of adjustment and social behavior. *Archives of General Psychiatry*, 1971, *25*, 470–480.

Hogarty, G.E., Schooler, N.R., Ulrich, R., Mussare, F., Ferro, P., and Herron, E. Fluphenazine and social therapy in the aftercare of schizophrenic patients. *Archives of General Psychiatry*, 1979, *36*, 1283–1294.

Hollon, S.D. and Beck, A.T. Psychotherapy and drug therapy: Comparisons and combinations. In S.L. Garfield and A.E. Bergin (Eds.), *Handbook of Psychotherapy and Behavior Change: An Empirical Analysis* (2nd ed.). New York: John Wiley & Sons, 1978, pp. 437–489.

Holt, R.R. Experimental methods in clinical psychology. In B.B. Wolman (Ed.), *Handbook of Clinical Psychology*. New York: McGraw Hill Book Company, 1965, pp. 40–77.

Holt, R.R. and Luborsky, L. *Personality Patterns of Psychiatrists: A Study in Selection Techniques*. Vol. 1. New York: Basic Books, 1958.

Holzman, P.S. Cognitive and perceptual tests for evaluating psychotherapy outcome. In I.E. Waskow and M.B. Parloff (Eds.), DHEW Publ. No. (ADM) 74-120, Washington, D.C., 1975, pp. 129–142.

Horngren, C.T. *Cost Accounting.* Englewood Cliffs, N.J.: Prentice-Hall, 1967.

Horowitz, M.J. *Stress Response Syndromes.* New York: Aronson, 1976.

Horowitz, M.J. Strategic dilemmas and the socialization of psychotherapy researchers. Presidential address delivered at the meeting of the Society for Psychotherapy in Aspen, Colorado, June 1981.

Howard, K.I. and Orlinsky, D.E. Psychotherapeutic processes. *Annual Review of Psychology,* 1972, *23,* 615–668.

Hunt, J. McV. Toward an integrated program of research on psychotherapy. In G.E. Stollak, G. Bernard, and M. Rothberg (Eds.), *Psychotherapy Research: Selected Readings.* Chicago: Rand McNally & Company, 1966, pp. 67–68.

Hyman, R. and Breger, L.: Discussion of H.J. Eysenck, The effects of psychotherapy. *International Journal of Psychiatry,* 1965, *1,* 317–322.

Imber, S.D. Patient self-report measures. In I.E. Waskow and M.B. Parloff (Eds.), DHEW Publ. No. (ADM) 74-120, Washington, D.C., 1975, pp. 40–47.

Imber, S.D. Some research issues in psychotherapy. In J.D. Frank, R. Hoehn-Saric, S.D. Imber, B.L. Liberman, and A.R. Stone (Eds.), *Effective Ingredients of Successful Psychotherapy.* New York: Brunner/Mazel, 1978, pp. 130–154.

Imber, S.D., Frank, J.D., Nash, E.H., Stone, A.R., and Gliedman, L.H. Improvement and amount of therapeutic contact: An alternative to the use of no-treatment controls in psychotherapy. In G.E. Stollak, B.G. Guerney, and M. Rothberg (Eds.), *Psychotherapy Research: Selected Readings.* Chicago: Rand McNally & Company, 1966.

Isaac, S. and Michael, W.B. *Handbook in Research and Evaluation.* San Diego, CA: Robert R. Knapp, 1971.

Jones, K. and Vischi, R. *The ADAMHA Impact Report*. Supplement to *Medical Care*, December 1979.

Karasu, T.B. Psychotherapies: An overview. *American Journal of Psychiatry*, 1977, *134*, 851–863.

Karasu, T.B. The ethics of psychotherapy. *American Journal of Psychiatry*, 1980, *137*, 1502–1512.

Karasu, T.B. Psychotherapy and pharmacotherapy: Towards an integrative model. *American Journal of Psychiatry*, In press.

Karasu, T.B. and Skodol, A.E. *DSM-III:* Psychodynamic evaluation. *American Journal of Psychiatry*, 1980, *137*, 607–610.

Karen, B.P. and Vandenbos, G.R. Experience, medication and the effectiveness of psychotherapy with schizophrenics. *British Journal of Psychiatry*, 1970, *116*, 427–428.

Karen, B.P. and Vandenbos, G.R. The consequences of psychotherapy for schizophrenic patients. *Psychotherapy: Theory, Research, and Practice*, 1972, *9*, 111–119.

Kaswan, J. Manifest and latent functions of psychological services. *American Psychologist*, 1981, *36*, 290–299.

Katz, M.M. and Lycrly, S.B. Methods of measuring adjustment and social behavior in the community: I. Rationale, description, discriminative validity and scale development. *Psychological Reports*, 1963, *13*, 503–535.

Kazdin, A.E. and Wilcoxon, L.A. Systematic desensitization and nonspecific treatment effects: A methodological evaluation. *Psychological Bulletin*, 1976, *83*, 729–758.

Kazdin, A.E. and Wilson, G.T. *Evaluation of Behavior Therapy: Issues, Evidence, and Research Strategies*. Cambridge, Mass.: Ballinger Publishing Company, 1978.

Kerlinger, F.N. *Foundations of Behavioral Research*. New York: Holt, Rinehart and Winston, Inc., 1967.

Kernberg, O., Burskin, E., Coyne, L., Appelbaum, A., Horowitz, L., and Voth, H. Psychotherapy and psychoanalysis: Final report of the Menninger Foundation's Psychotherapy Research Project. *Bulletin of the Menninger Clinic*, 1972, *36*, 1–275.

Kiesler, D.J. Some myths of psychotherapy research and the search for a paradigm. *Psychological Bulletin*, 1966, *65*, 110–136.

Kiesler, D.J. Experimental designs in psychotherapy research. In A.E. Bergin and S.L. Garfield (Eds.), *Handbook of Psychotherapy and Behavior Change*. New York: John Wiley & Sons, 1971, pp. 36–74.

Kiesler, D.J. *The Process of Psychotherapy*. Chicago: Aldine Publishing Company, 1973.

Klein, D.F., Gittelman, R., Quitkin, F., and Rifkin, A. *Diagnosis and Drug Treatment of Psychiatric Disorders: Adults and Children* (2nd ed.). Baltimore: Williams & Wilkins, 1980.

Klerman, G.L., DiMascio, A., Weissman, M., Prusoff, B., and Paykel, E.S. Treatment of depression by drugs and psychotherapy. *American Journal of Psychiatry*, 1974, *131*, 186–191.

Koch, S. The nature and limits of psychological knowledge: Lessons of a century qua "Science." *American Psychologist*, 1981, *36*, 257–269.

Koran, L.M. The reliability of clinical methods, data and judgments (Part I). *New England Journal of Medicine*, 1975a, *293*, 642–646.

Koran, L.M. The reliability of clinical methods, data and judgments (Part II). *New England Journal of Medicine*, 1975b, *293*, 695–701.

Krasner, L. Techniques of assessment in behavior therapy. In I.E. Waskow and M.B. Parloff (Eds.), DHEW Publ. No. (ADM) 74-120, Washington, D.C., 1975, pp. 65–74.

Kuhn, T. *The Structure of Scientific Revolutions.* Chicago: University of Chicago Press, 1962.

Lambert, M.J. Spontaneous remission in adult neurotic disorders: A revision and summary. *Psychological Bulletin,* 1976, *83,* 107–119.

Lambert, M.J., Bergin, A.E., and Collins, J.L. Therapist-induced deterioration in psychotherapy. In A.S. Gurman and A.M. Razin (Eds.), *Effective Psychotherapy: A Handbook of Research.* New York: Pergamon Press, 1977.

Lang, P.J. The mechanics of desensitization and the laboratory study of fear. In C.M. Franks (Ed.), *Behavior Therapy: Appraisal and Status.* New York: McGraw-Hill, 1969.

Langsley, D.G., Kaplan, D.M., Pittman, F.S., Machotka, P., Flomenhaft, K., and DeYoung, C.D. *The Treatment of Families in Crisis.* New York: Grune and Stratton, 1968.

Lawlis, G.F. and Lu, E. Judgment of counseling process: Reliability, agreement and error. *Psychological Bulletin,* 1972, *78,* 17–20.

Levin, H.M. Cost-effectiveness analysis in evaluation research. In M. Guttentag and E.L. Struening (Eds.), *Handbook of Evaluation Research* (Vol. 2). Beverly Hills, CA.: Sage Publications, 1975, pp. 89–122.

Levitt, E.E. The results of psychotherapy with children: An evaluation. *Journal of Consulting Psychology,* 1957, *21,* 186–189.

Levitt, E.E. Psychotherapy with children: A further evaluation. *Behavior Research and Therapy,* 1963, *60,* 326–329.

Liberman, B.L. The maintenance and persistence of change: Long-term follow-up of investigations of psychotherapy. In J.D. Frank, R. Hoehn-Saric, S.D. Imber, B.L. Liberman, and A.R. Stone (Eds.), *Effective Ingredients of Successful Psychotherapy.* New York: Brunner/Mazel Publishers, 1978, pp. 107–129.

Lieberman, M. *Survey and Evaluation of the Literature on Verbal Psychotherapy of Depressive Disorders.* Clinical Research Branch, NIMH, March 7, 1975.

Light, R.J. and Smith, P.V. Accumulating evidence: Procedures for resolving contradictions among different research studies. *Harvard Educational Review,* 1971, *41,* 429–471.

Lipsedge, M.S., Hajioff, J., Huggins, P., Napier, L., Pearce, J., Pike, D.J., and Rich, M. The management of severe agorophobia: A comparison of iproniazid and systematic desensitization. *Psychopharmacologia,* 1973, *32,* 67–80.

London, P. *Behavior Control.* New York: Harper & Row, 1969.

Lord, F.M. A paradox in the interpretation of group comparisons. *Psychological Bulletin,* 1967, *68,* 304–305.

Lorr, M. Therapist measures of outcome. In I.E. Waskow and M.B. Parloff (Eds.), DHEW Publ. No. (ADM) 74–120, Washington, D.C., 1975, pp. 181–188.

Lorr, M., McNair, D.M., and Weinstein, G.J. Early effects of chlordiazepoxide (Librium) used with psychotherapy. *Journal of Psychiatric Research,* 1962, *1,* 257–270.

Lorr, M., McNair, D.M., Weinstein, G.J., Michaux, W.W., and Raskin, A. Meprobamate and chlorpromazine in psychotherapy: Some effects on anxiety and hostility of outpatients. *Archives of General Psychiatry,* 1961, *4,* 381–389.

Luborsky, L. A note on Eysenck's article "The Effects of Psychotherapy: An Evaluation." *British Journal of Psychology,* 1954, *45,* 129–131.

Luborsky, L. Clinicians' judgments of mental health. *Archives of General Psychiatry,* 1962, *7,* 407–417.

Luborsky, L. Research cannot yet influence clinical practice. An evaluation of Strupp and Bergin's study, "Some empirical and conceptual bases for coordinated research in psychotherapy: A critical review of issues, trends, and evidence." *International Journal of Psychiatry,* 1969, *7,* 135–140.

Luborsky, L. Another reply to Eysenck. *Psychological Bulletin,* 1972, *78,* 406–408.

Luborsky, L. Assessment of outcome of psychotherapy by independent clinical evaluators: A review of the most highly recommended research measures. In I.E. Waskow and M.B. Parloff (Eds.), DHEW Publ. No. (ADM) 74-120, Washington, D.C., 1975, pp. 233–242.

Luborsky, L. and Bachrach, H. Factors influencing clinical judgment of mental health. *Archives of General Psychiatry,* 1974, *31,* 292–297.

Luborsky, L., Chandler, M., Auerbach, A.H., and Cohen, J. Factors influencing the outcome of psychotherapy: A review of quantitative research. *Psychological Bulletin,* 1971, *75,* 145–185.

Luborsky, L., Mintz, J., Auerbach, A., Christoph, P., Bachrach, H., Todd, T., Johnson, M., Cohen, M., and O'Brien, C.P. Predicting the outcome of psychotherapy: Findings of the Penn Psychotherapy Project. *Archives of General Psychiatry,* 1980, *37,* 471–481.

Luborsky, L., Singer, B., and Luborsky, Lise. Comparative studies of psychotherapies. Is it true that "Everyone has won and all must have prizes"? *Archives of General Psychiatry,* 1975, *32,* 995–1008.

Luborsky, L., and Spence, D.P. Quantitative research on psychoanalytic therapy. In A.E. Bergin and S.L. Garfield (Eds.), *Handbook of Psychotherapy and Behavior Change.* New York: John Wiley & Sons, 1971, pp. 331–368.

Luborsky, L., Woody, G.E., McLellan, A.T., O'Brien, C.P., and Rosenzweig, J. Can independent judges recognize different psychotherapies? An experience with manual-guided therapies. *Journal of Consulting and Clinical Psychology,* 1981, In press.

Malen, D.H. The outcome problem in psychotherapy research: A historical review. *Archives of General Psychiatry,* 1973, *29,* 719–729.

Manning, W.H. and DuBois, P.H. Correlational methods in research on human learning. *Perceptual and Motor Skills*, 1962, *15*, 287–321.

Marks, I.M. Empiricism is accepted. *International Journal of Psychiatry*, 1969, *7*, 141–148.

Marks, I.M. Behavioral psychotherapy of adult neurosis. In A.E. Bergin and S.L. Garfield (Eds.), *Handbook of Psychotherapy and Behavior Change*. New York: John Wiley & Sons, 1971, pp. 493–548.

Marks, I.M. and Gelder, M. Transvestism and fetishism: Clinical and psychological changes during faradic aversion. *British Journal of Psychiatry*, 1967, *113*, 711–739.

Marmor, J. Psychoanalytic therapy as an educational process: Common denominators in the therapeutic approaches of different psychoanalytic "schools." In *Psychiatry in Transition: Selected Papers*. New York: Brunner/Mazel, 1974, pp. 105–209.

Marmor, J. The nature of the psychotherapeutic process. In *Psychiatry in Transition: Selected Papers*. New York: Brunner/Mazel, 1974, pp. 296–309.

Marsden, G. Content-analysis studies of therapeutic interviews: 1954–1964. *Psychological Bulletin*, 1965, *63*, 298–321.

Marsden, G. Content-analysis studies of psychotherapy: 1954 through 1968. In A.E. Bergin and S.L. Garfield (Eds.), *Handbook of Psychotherapy and Behavior Change*. New York: John Wiley & Sons, 1971, pp. 345–407.

Masserman, J. Threescore and thirteen tangential therapies— A review and integration. 1978 (unpublished manuscript).

May, P.R.A. *Treatment of Schizophrenia*. New York: Science House, 1968.

May, P.R.A. For better or for worse? Psychotherapy and variance change: A critical review of the literature. *Journal of Nervous and Mental Disease*, 1971, *152*, 184–192.

May, P.R.A. Psychotherapy research in schizophrenia—another view of present reality. *Schizophrenia Bulletin,* Summer 1974, 126–132.

May, P.R.A. Schizophrenia: Evaluation of treatment methods. In A.M. Freedman, H.I. Kaplan, and B.J. Sadock (Eds.), *Comprehensive Textbook of Psychiatry—II.* Volume I. Baltimore: The Williams & Wilkins Company, 1975, pp. 955–982.

May, P.R.A. Pharmacotherapy of schizophrenia in relation to alternative treatment methods. In G. Sedvall, B. Uvnas, and Y. Zotterman (Eds.), *Antipsychotic Drugs: Pharmacodynamics and Pharmacokinetics.* New York: Pergamon Press, 1976, pp. 375–387.

May, P.R.A. and Tuma, A.H. Methodological problems in psychotherapy research: Observations on the Karon-Vanderbos study of psychotherapy and drugs in schizophrenia. *British Journal of Psychiatry,* 1970, *117,* 569–570.

May, P.R.A., Tuma, A.H., and Dixon, W.J. Schizophrenia—A followup study of results of treatments. I and II. *Archives of General Psychiatry.* 1976, *33,* 474–480; 481–506.

May, P.R.A. and Van Putten, T. Treatment of schizophrenia: II. A proposed rating scale of design and outcome for use in literature surveys. *Comprehensive Psychiatry,* 1974, *15,* 267–275.

McFall, R.M. and Marston, A.R. An experimental investigation of behavior rehearsal in assertive training. *Journal of Abnormal Psychology,* 1970, *76,* 295–303.

McFall, R.M. and Twentyman, C.T. Four experiments on the relative contributions of rehearsal, modeling, and coachings to assertion training. *Journal of Abnormal Psychology,* 1973, *81,* 199–218.

McNair, D.M. and Lorr, M. An analysis of professed psychotherapeutic techniques. *Journal of Consulting Psychology,* 1964, *28,* 265–271.

Meltzoff, J. and Kornreich, M. *Research in Psychotherapy*. New York: Atherton Press, 1970.

Miller, L.C., Barrett, C.L., Hampe, E., and Noble, H. Comparison of reciprocal inhibition, psychotherapy and waiting list control for phobic children. *Journal of Abnormal Psychology*, 1972, *79*, 269–279.

Mintz, J. The role of the therapist in assessing psychotherapy outcome. In A.S. Gurman and A.M. Razin (Eds.), *Effective Psychotherapy: A Handbook of Research*. New York: Pergamon Press, 1977, pp. 590–602.

Mintz, J., Luborsky, L., and Christoph, P. Measuring the outcomes of psychotherapy: Findings of the Penn Psychotherapy Project. *Journal of Consulting and Clinical Psychology*, 1979, *47*, 319–334.

Mintz, J., O'Brien, C.P., and Luborsky, L. Predicting the outcome of psychotherapy for schizophrenics. *Archives of General Psychiatry*, 1976, *33*, 1183–1186.

Mischel, W. *Introduction to Personality*. New York: Holt, Rinehart and Winston, 1971.

Mitchell, S.K. Interobserver agreement, reliability, and generalizability of data collected in observational studies. *Psychological Bulletin*, 1979, *86*, 376–390.

Moore, C.L. and Jaedicke, R.K. *Managerial Accounting*. Cincinnati: South-Western Publishing, 1967.

Mosher, L.R. and Keith, S.J. Psychosocial treatment: Individual, group, family, and community support approaches. *Schizophrenia 1980*. U.S. Government Printing Office, 1980.

Nunnally, J.C. *Psychometric Theory*. New York: McGraw-Hill Book Company, 1967.

Nunnally, J.C. and Wilson, W.H. Method and theory for developing measures in evaluation research. In E.L. Streuning and M. Guttenberg (Eds.), *Handbook of Evaluation Research*, Vol. 1. Beverly Hills, CA.: Sage Publications, 1975.

O'Leary, K.D. and Borkovec, T.D. Conceptual, methodological, and ethical problems of placebo groups in psychotherapy research. *American Psychologist,* 1978, *9,* 821–830.

Orlinsky, D.E. and Howard, K.I. *Varieties of Psychotherapeutic Experience.* New York: Teachers College Press, 1975.

Orlinsky, D.E. and Howard K.I. The relation of process to outcome in psychotherapy. In S.L. Garfield and A.E. Bergin (Eds.), *Handbook of Psychotherapy and Behavior Change: An Empirical Analysis* (2nd ed.). New York: John Wiley & Sons, 1978, pp. 283–329.

Panzetta, A.F. Cost-benefit studies in psychiatry. *Comprehensive Psychiatry,* 1973, *14,* 451–455.

Parloff, M.B. Some factors affecting the quality of therapeutic relationships. *Journal of Abnormal and Social Psychology,* 1956, *52,* 5–10.

Parloff, M.B. Twenty-five years of research in psychotherapy. New York: Paper presented at the Albert Einstein College of Medicine, Dept. of Psychiatry, 17 Oct. 1975.

Parloff, M.B. Psychotherapy evidence and reimbursement decisions: Bambi meets Godzilla. Paper presented at the meeting of the Society for Psychotherapy Research, Aspen, Colorado, June 1981.

Parloff, M.B. and Dies, R.R. Group psychotherapy outcome research 1966–1975. *International Journal of Group Psychotherapy,* 1977, *27,* 281–319.

Parloff, M.B., Wolfe, B., Hadley, S., and Waskow, I.E. *Assessment of Psychosocial Treatment of Mental Disorders: Current Status and Prospects.* National Technical Information Service PB 287 640, February 1978.

Parloff, M.B., Waskow, I.E., and Wolfe, B.E. Research on therapist variables in relation to process and outcome. In S.L. Garfield and A.E. Bergin (Eds.), *Handbook of Psychotherapy and Behavior Change: An Empirical Analysis* (2nd ed.). New York: John Wiley & Sons, 1978, 233–329.

Paul, G.L. Insight versus desensitization in psychotherapy two years after termination. *Journal of Consulting Psychology*, 1967, *31*, 333–348.

Paul, G.L. Strategy of outcome research in psychotherapy. In A.P. Goldstein and N. Stein (Eds.), *Prescriptive Psychotherapy*. New York: Pergamon Press Inc., 1976, pp. 141–154.

Paul, G.L. and Lentz, R.J. *Psychosocial Treatment of Chronic Mental Patients: Milieu Versus Social-Learning Programs*. Cambridge: Harvard University Press, 1977.

Perloff, E. and Perloff, R. Selected processes for evaluation of service delivery programs: Overview. *Professional Psychology*, 1977, *8*, 389.

Pierce, W.D. and Mosher, D.L. Perceived empathy, interviewer behavior, and interviewee anxiety. *Journal of Consulting Psychology*, 1967, *31*, 101.

Plutchik, R. Problems of multidimensional evaluation. *Annals of the New York Academy of Sciences*, 1973, *218*, 78–86.

Plutchik, R. *Foundations of Experimental Research*. New York: Harper & Row, 1968.

Plutchik, R. *Foundations of Experimental Research* (2nd ed.). New York: Harper & Row, 1974.

Plutchik, R. and Conte, H.R. Methodological considerations in evaluating therapeutic interventions with the elderly. Paper presented at the workshop "Preventive and prosthetic therapies with the elderly and their families: Theory, practice and research," American Orthopsychiatric Association, Toronto, 7–8 April 1980.

Plutchik, R., Karasu, T.B., Conte, H.R., and Buckley, P. Sequential psychodiagnostic evaluation. Presented at the 11th Annual Meeting of the Society for Psychotherapy Research, Pacific Grove, CA., 17–20 June 1980.

Pokorny, A.D. and Klett, C.J. Comparison of psychiatric treatments: Problems and pitfalls. In A.P. Goldstein and N. Stein (Eds.), *Prescriptive Psychotherapies*. New York: Pergamon Press Inc., 1976, pp. 155–161.

Rachman, S. *The Effects of Psychotherapy*. Oxford, England: Pergamon Press, 1971.

Razin, A.M. The A–B variable: Still promising after twenty years? In A.S. Gurman and A.M. Razin (Eds.), *Effective Psychotherapy: A Handbook of Research*. New York: Pergamon Press, 1977, 291–324.

Rogers, C.R., Gendlin, E.T., Keisler, D.J., and Truax, C.B. *The Therapeutic Relationship and Its Impact: A Study of Psychotherapy with Schizophrenics*. Madison: University of Wisconsin Press, 1967.

Rosen, J.N. Psychotherapy and schizophrenia. *International Journal of Psychiatry*, 1969, *8*, 748–752.

Rosenthal, D. and Frank, J.D. Psychotherapy and the placebo effect. *Psychological Bulletin*, 1956, *53*, 294–302.

Rosenzweig, S. A transevaluation of psychotherapy—a reply to Hans Eysenck. *Journal of Abnormal and Social Psychology*, 1954, *49*, 298–304.

Rothenberg, J. Cost-benefit analysis: A methodological exposition. In M. Guttentag and E.L. Struening (Eds.) *Handbook of Evaluation Research* (Vol. 2). Beverly Hills, CA.: Sage Publications, pp. 55–88.

Ro-Trock, G.K., Wellisch, D.K., and Schoolar, J.C. A family therapy outcome study in an inpatient setting. *American Journal of Orthopsychiatry*, 1977, *47*, 514–522.

Rounsaville, B.J., Klerman, G.L., and Weissman, M.M. Do psychotherapy and pharmacotherapy for depression conflict? Empirical evidence from a clinical trial. *Archives of General Psychiatry*, 1981, *38*, 24–29.

Rush, A.J., Beck, A.T., Kovacs, M., and Hollon, S.D. Comparative efficacy of cognitive therapy and pharmacotherapy in the treatment of depressed outpatients. *Cognitive Therapy and Research*, 1977, *1*, 17–37.

Russell, B. *A History of Western Philosophy*. New York: Simon and Schuster, 1945.

Sanford, R.N. Clinical methods: Psychotherapy. *Annual Review of Psychology*, 1953, *4*, 317-342.

Sargent, H.D. Intrapsychic change: Methodological problems in psychotherapy research. *Psychiatry*, 1961, *24*, 93–108.

Scheibe, K.E. The psychologists' advantage and its nullification: Limits of human predictability. *American Psychologist*, 1978, *33*, 869–881.

Schlesinger, H.J., Mumford, E., and Glass, G.V. Mental health services and medical utilization. In G.R. Vandenbos (Ed.), *Psychotherapy: Practice, Research, Policy*. Beverly Hills, CA.: Sage Publications, 1980.

Schlessinger, N., Pollock, G.H., Sabshin, M., Sadow, L., and Gedo, J.E. Psychoanalytic contributions to psychotherapy research. In L.A. Gottschalk and A.H. Auerbach (Eds.), *Methods of Research in Psychotherapy*. New York: Appleton-Century-Crofts, 1966, pp. 334–360.

Schulz, R. The effects of control and predictability on the physical and psychological well-being of the institutionalized aged. *Journal of Personality and Social Psychology*, 1976, *33*, 563–573.

Shader, R.I., Grinspoon, L., Ewalt, J.R., and Zahn, D.A. Drug responses in schizophrenia. In D.V.S. Sankar (Ed.), *Schizophrenia: Current Concepts and Research*. Hicksville, N.Y.: P.J.D. Publications, 1969.

Sharfstein, S.S. Third-party payers: To pay or not to pay. *American Journal of Psychiatry*, 1978, *135*, 1185–1188.

Showstack, J.A., Hargreaves, W.A., Glick, I.D., and O'Brien, R.S. Psychiatric follow-up studies: Practical procedures and ethical concerns. *Journal of Nervous and Mental Disease,* 1978, *166,* 34–43.

Shrout, P.E. and Fleiss, J.L. Intraclass correlations: Uses in assessing rater reliability. *Psychological Bulletin,* 1979, *86,* 420–428.

Simon, H.A. Information processing models of cognition. *Annual Review of Psychology,* 1979, *30,* 363–396.

Sloane, R.B., Staples, F.R., Cristol, A.H., Yorkston, N.J., and Whipple, K. *Psychotherapy Versus Behavior Therapy.* Cambridge, Mass.: Harvard University Press, 1975.

Smith, M.L. and Glass, G.V. Meta-analysis of psychotherapy outcome studies. *American Psychologist,* 1977, *32,* 752–760.

Smith, M.L., Glass, G.V., and Miller, T.I. *The Benefits of Psychotherapy.* Baltimore: The Johns Hopkins University Press, 1980.

Solyon, L., Heseltine, G.F.D., McClure, D.J., Solyon, C., Ledridge, B., and Steinberg, G. Behavior therapy versus drug therapy in the treatment of phobic neurosis. *Canadian Psychiatric Association Journal,* 1973, *18,* 25–31.

Sparacino, J. Individual psychotherapy with the aged: A selective review. *International Journal of Aging and Human Development.* 1978–79, *9,* 197–217.

Spitzer, R.L., Endicott, J., and Cohen, J. *The Psychiatric Status Schedule: Technique for Evaluating Social and Role Functioning and Mental Status.* New York: New York State Psychiatric Institute and Biometrics Research, 1967.

Spitzer, R.L., Endicott, J., Fleiss, J.L., and Cohen, J. The psychiatric status schedule: A technique for evaluating psychopathology and impairment in role functioning. *Archives of General Psychiatry,* 1970, *23,* 41–55.

Spitzer, R.L., Endicott, J.E., and Robins, E. *Research Diagnostic Criteria (RDC) for a Selected Group of Functional Disorders.* (3rd ed.). NIMH Clinical Research Branch Collaborative Program on the Psychobiology of Depression, 1978.

Spitzer, R.L. and Endicott, J. Assessment of outcome by independent clinical evaluators. In I.E. Waskow and M.B. Parloff (Eds.), DHEW Publ. No. (ADM) 74-120, Washington, D.C., 1975. pp. 222–232.

Spitzer, R.L. and Cohen, J. Common errors in quantitative psychiatric research. *International Journal of Psychiatry,* 1968, *6,* 109–118.

Spitzer, R.L., Cohen, J., Fleiss, J.L., and Endicott, J. Quantification of agreement in psychiatric diagnosis. *Archives of General Psychiatry,* 1967, *17,* 83–87.

Spohn, H.E., Lacoursiere, R., Thompson, K., and Coyne, L. Phenothiazine effects on psychological and psychophysiological dysfunction in chronic schizophrenia. *Archives of General Psychiatry,* 1977, *34,* 633–644.

Srole, L., Langner, T.S., Michael, S.T., Opler, M.K., and Rennie, T.A.C. *Mental Health in the Metropolis: The Midtown Manhattan Study.* Vol. 1. New York: McGraw-Hill, 1962.

Sterling, T.D. Publication decisions and their possible effects on inferences drawn from tests of significance—or vice versa. *Journal of The American Statistical Association,* 199, *54,* 30–34.

Stern, R. and Marks, I.M. Brief and prolonged flooding. *Archives of General Psychiatry,* 1973, *28,* 270–276.

Stollak, E., Guerney, G., and Rotheberg, M. (Eds.). *Psychotherapy Research: Selected Readings.* Chicago: Rand McNally & Company, 1966, pp. 313–317.

Stone, A.R., Frank, J.D., Nash, E.H., and Imber, S.D. An intensive five-year follow-up study of treated psychiatric outpatients. *Journal of Nervous and Mental Disease,* 1961, *133,* 410–422.

Stotsky, B. A., and Zolik, E.S. Group psychotherapy with psychotics: 1921–1963—A review. *International Journal of Group Psychotherapy*, 1965, *15*, 321–344.

Strupp, H.H. The performance of psychiatrists and psychologists in a therapeutic interview. *Journal of Clinical Psychology*, 1958, *14*, 219–226.

Strupp, H.H. Patient-doctor relationships: Psychotherapists in the therapeutic process. In A.H. Bachrach (Ed.), *Experimental Foundations of Clinical Psychology*. New York: Basic Books, 1962a, pp. 576–615.

Strupp, H.H. The therapist's contribution to the treatment process: Beginnings and vagaries of a research program. In H.H. Strupp and L. Luborsky (Eds.), *Research in Psychotherapy*. Washington, D.C.: American Psychological Association, 1962b, pp. 25–40.

Strupp, H.H. The outcome problem in psychotherapy revisited. *Psychotherapy*, 1963, *1*, 1–13.

Strupp, H.H. *Psychotherapy: Clinical, Research, and Theoretical Issues*. New York: Aronson, 1973.

Strupp, H.H. Psychotherapy research and practice: An overview. In S.L. Garfield and A.E. Bergin (Eds.), *Handbook of Psychotherapy and Behavior Change: An Empirical Analysis*. (2nd ed.). New York: John Wiley & Sons, 1978, pp. 3–22.

Strupp, H.H. and Bergin, A.E. Some empirical and conceptual bases for coordinated research in psychotherapy: A critical review of issues, trends, and evidence. *International Journal of Psychiatry*, 1969, *7*, 18–90.

Strupp, H.H. and Bloxom, A.L. Therapists' assessments of outcome. In I.E. Waskow and M.B. Parloff (Eds.), DHEW Publ. No. (ADM) 74-120, Washington, D.C., 1975, pp. 170–180.

Strupp, H.H. and Hadley, S.W. A tripartite model of mental health and therapeutic outcomes with special reference to negative effects in psychotherapy. *American Psychologist*, 1977, *32*, 187–196.

Strupp, H.H., Hadley, S.W., and Gomes-Schwartz, B. *Psychotherapy: For Better or For Worse.* New York: Aronson, 1977.

Strupp, H.H., Hadley, S.W., Gomes, B., and Armstrong, S.H. *Negative Effects in Psychotherapy: A Review of Clinical and Theoretical Issues Together with Recommendations for a Program of Research.* (unpublished report) May 1976.

Strupp, H.H. and Luborsky, L. (Eds.). *Research in Psychotherapy.* Vol. 2. Washington, D.C.: American Psychological Association, 1962.

Stuart, R.B. Notes on the ethics of behavior research and intervention. In L.A. Hamerlynck, L.C. Handy, and E.J. Mash (Eds.), *Behavior Change: Metholodogy, Concepts and Practice.* Champaign, Ill.: Research Press, 1973.

Sundland, D.M. Theoretical orientations of psychotherapists. In A.S. Gurman and A.M. Razin, *Effective Psychotherapy: A Handbook of Research.* New York: Pergamon Press, 1977, pp. 189–219.

Tinsley, H.E.A. and Weiss, D.J. Interrater reliability and agreement of subjective judgments. *Journal of Counseling Psychology,* 1975, *22,* 358–376.

Tramontana, M.G. Critical review of research on psychotherapy outcome with adolescents: 1967–1977. *Psychological Bulletin,* 1980, *88,* 429–450.

Truax, C.B. and Mitchell, K.M. Research on certain therapist interpersonal skills in relation to process and outcome. In A.E. Bergin and S.L. Garfield (Eds.), *Handbook of Psychotherapy and Behavior Change.* New York: John Wiley & Sons, 1971, pp. 299–344.

Truax, C.B. and Wargo, D.G. Effects of vicarious therapy pretraining and alternate sessions on outcome in group psychotherapy with outpatients. *Journal of Consulting and Clinical Psychology,* 1969, *33,* 440–447.

Truax, C.B., Wargo, D.G., and Silber, L.D. Effects of group psychotherapy with high accurate empathy and nonpossessive warmth upon female institutionalized delinquents. *Journal of Abnormal Psychology,* 1966, *71,* 267–274.

Truax, C.B., Wargo, D.G., and Volksdorf, N.R. Antecedents to outcome in group counseling with institutionalized juvenile delinquents: Effects of therapeutic conditions, patient self-exploration, alternate sessions, and vicarious therapy pretraining. *Journal of Abnormal Psychology,* 1970, *76,* 235–242.

Uhlenhuth, E.H., Lipman, R.S., and Covi, L. Combined pharmacotherapy and psychotherapy: Controlled studies. *Journal of Nervous and Mental Disease,* 1969, *148,* 52–64.

Van Dalen, D.B. and Meyer, W.J. *Understanding Educational Research: An Introduction.* New York: McGraw-Hill Book Company, 1962.

Vandenbos, G.R. and Pino, C.D. Research on the outcome of psychotherapy. In G.R. Vandenbos (Ed.), *Psychotherapy: Practice, Research, Policy.* Beverly Hills, CA.: 1980, pp. 23–69.

Voth, H.M. and Orth, M.H. *Psychotherapy and the Role of the Environment.* New York: Behavioral Publications, 1973.

Waskow, I.E. Selection of a core battery. In I.E. Waskow and M.B. Parloff (Eds.), DHEW Publ. No. (ADM) 74–120, Washington, D.C., 1975, pp. 245–269.

Weisbrod, B.A. A guide to benefit-cost analysis, as seen through a controlled experiment in treating the mentally ill. Madison: Institute for Research on Poverty, University of Wisconsin, discussion pages 559–579, 1979.

Weissman, M., Klerman, G.L., Paykel, E.S., Prusoff, B., and Hanson, B. Treatment effects on the social adjustment of depressed patients. *Archives of General Psychiatry,* 1974, *30,* 771–778.

Weissman, M.M. The psychological treatment of depression: Evidence for the efficacy of psychotherapy alone, in comparison with, and in combination with pharmacotherapy. *Archives of General Psychiatry*, 1979, *36*, 1261–1269.

Whitehorn, J.C. and Betz, B.A. A study of psychotherapeutic relationships between physicians and schizophrenic patients. *American Journal of Psychiatry*, 1954, *111*, 321–331.

Whitehorn, J.C. and Betz, B.A. A comparison of psychotherapeutic relationships between physicians and schizophrenic patients when insulin is combined with psychotherapy and when insulin is used alone. *American Journal of Psychiatry*, 1957, *113*, 901–910.

Whitehorn, J.C. and Betz, B. Further studies of the doctor as a crucial variable in the outcome of treatment of schizophrenic patients. *American Journal of Psychiatry*, 1960, *117*, 215–223.

Wolpe, J. Behavior therapy versus psychoanalysis: Therapeutic and social implications. *American Psychologist*, 1981, *36*, 159–164.

Yates, B.T. The theory and practice of cost-utility, cost-effectiveness, and cost-benefit analysis in behavioral medicine: Toward delivering more health care for less money. In J. Ferguson and C.B. Taylor (Eds.), *A Comprehensive Handbook of Behavioral Medicine*, Vol. 3. Englewood Cliffs, N.J.: Spectrum, 1980.

Yates, B.T. and Newman, F.L. Findings of cost-effectiveness and cost-benefit analyses of psychotherapy. In G.R. Vandenbos (Ed.), *Psychotherapy: Practice, Research, Policy*. Beverly Hills, CA.: Sage Publications, 1980.

Yates, B.T., Haven, W.G., and Thorensen, C.E. Cost-effectiveness analysis of Learning House: How much change for how much money? In J.S. Stumphauzer (Ed.), *Progress in Behavior Therapy with Delinquents*. Springfield, Ill.: Thomas, 1979.

Zax, M. and Klein, A. Measurement of personality and behavior change following psychotherapy. In G.E. Stollak, B.G. Guerney, and M. Rothbert (Eds.), *Psychotherapy Research: Selected Readings*. Chicago: Rand McNally & Company, 1966, pp. 177–189.

Zitrin, C.M., Klein, D.F., Lindemann, C., Tobak, P., Rock, M., Kaplan, J.H., and Ganz, V.H. Comparisons of short-term treatment regimens in phobic patients. In R.L. Spitzer and D.F. Klein (Eds.), *Evaluation of Psychological Therapies*. Baltimore: Johns Hopkins University Press, 1976.

Zitrin, C.M., Klein, D.F., and Woerner, M.G. Behavior therapy, supportive psychotherapy, imipramine, and phobias. *Archives of General Psychiatry*, 1978, *35*, 307–316.